# Maple 9 Advanced Programming Guide

M. B. Monagan K. O. Geddes K. M. Heal
G. Labahn S. M. Vorkoetter J. McCarron
P. DeMarco

This document was produced using a special version of Maple that reads and updates LaTeX files.

Printed in Canada

ISBN 1-894511-44-1

# Contents

**Preface** 1

Audience . . . 1
Worksheet Graphical Interface . . . 2
Manual Set . . . 2
Conventions . . . 3
Customer Feedback . . . 3

**1 Procedures, Variables, and Extending Maple** 5

Prerequisite Knowledge . . . 5
In This Chapter . . . 5
1.1 Nested Procedures . . . 5
Scoping Rules . . . 6
Local Versus Global Variables . . . 6
The Quick-Sort Algorithm . . . 8
Example . . . 8
Creating a Uniform Random Number Generator . . . 11
1.2 Procedures That Return Procedures . . . 14
Conveying Values . . . 14
Creating a Newton Iteration . . . 14
Example 1 . . . 15
Example 2 . . . 16
A Shift Operator . . . 17
1.3 Local Variables and Invoking Procedures . . . 19
Example 1 . . . 19
Example 2 . . . 20
Procedure as a Returned Object . . . 22
Example 3 . . . 22
Example 4 . . . 24
Exercises . . . 26
1.4 Interactive Input . . . 27

Reading Strings from the Terminal . . . . . . . . . . . 27
Example 1 . . . . . . . . . . . . . . . . . . . . . . . 28
Reading Expressions from the Terminal . . . . . . . . . 28
Example 2 . . . . . . . . . . . . . . . . . . . . . . . 29
Converting Strings to Expressions . . . . . . . . . . . 30
1.5 Extending Maple . . . . . . . . . . . . . . . . . . . 31
Defining New Types . . . . . . . . . . . . . . . . . . 31
Exercises . . . . . . . . . . . . . . . . . . . . . . . 33
Neutral Operators . . . . . . . . . . . . . . . . . . . 33
Example 1 . . . . . . . . . . . . . . . . . . . . . . . 34
Exercise . . . . . . . . . . . . . . . . . . . . . . . . 37
Extending Commands . . . . . . . . . . . . . . . . . . 39
1.6 Conclusion . . . . . . . . . . . . . . . . . . . . . . 42

**2 Programming with Modules 43**
Modules . . . . . . . . . . . . . . . . . . . . . . . . 43
Examples . . . . . . . . . . . . . . . . . . . . . . . . 44
Module Versus Procedure . . . . . . . . . . . . . . . . 45
Accessing Module Exports . . . . . . . . . . . . . . . 46
In This Chapter . . . . . . . . . . . . . . . . . . . . 46
2.1 Syntax and Semantics . . . . . . . . . . . . . . . . . 47
The Module Definition . . . . . . . . . . . . . . . . . 47
The Module Body . . . . . . . . . . . . . . . . . . . . 48
Module Parameters . . . . . . . . . . . . . . . . . . . 48
Named Modules . . . . . . . . . . . . . . . . . . . . . 48
Declarations . . . . . . . . . . . . . . . . . . . . . . 50
Exported Local Variables . . . . . . . . . . . . . . . . 52
Module Options . . . . . . . . . . . . . . . . . . . . . 57
Implicit Scoping Rules . . . . . . . . . . . . . . . . . 58
Lexical Scoping Rules . . . . . . . . . . . . . . . . . 58
Modules and Types . . . . . . . . . . . . . . . . . . . 60
Example: A Symbolic Differentiator . . . . . . . . . . 61
2.2 Records . . . . . . . . . . . . . . . . . . . . . . . . 72
2.3 Packages . . . . . . . . . . . . . . . . . . . . . . . . 78
What Is a Package . . . . . . . . . . . . . . . . . . . 78
Writing Maple Packages by Using Modules . . . . . . . 80
The `LinkedList` Package . . . . . . . . . . . . . . . . 80
Code Coverage Profiling Package . . . . . . . . . . . . 87
The Shapes Package . . . . . . . . . . . . . . . . . . 94
2.4 The `use` Statement . . . . . . . . . . . . . . . . . . 103
Operator Rebinding . . . . . . . . . . . . . . . . . . 106

2.5 Modeling Objects . . . . . . . . . . . . . . . . . . . . . . . . . 108
Priority Queues . . . . . . . . . . . . . . . . . . . . . . . . . 111
An Object-oriented Shapes Package . . . . . . . . . . . . . 115
2.6 Interfaces and Implementations . . . . . . . . . . . . . . . . 117
Interfaces . . . . . . . . . . . . . . . . . . . . . . . . . . . . 118
Generic Graph Algorithms . . . . . . . . . . . . . . . . . . 124
Quotient Fields . . . . . . . . . . . . . . . . . . . . . . . . . 129
A Generic Group Implementation . . . . . . . . . . . . . . 138
2.7 Extended Example: A Search Engine . . . . . . . . . . . . . 159
Introduction to Searching . . . . . . . . . . . . . . . . . . . 159
Inverted Term Occurrence Indexing . . . . . . . . . . . . . 161
The Vector Space Model . . . . . . . . . . . . . . . . . . . 164
Term Weighting . . . . . . . . . . . . . . . . . . . . . . . . 167
Building a Search Engine Package . . . . . . . . . . . . . . 168
Latent Semantic Analysis . . . . . . . . . . . . . . . . . . . 172
The Search Engine Package . . . . . . . . . . . . . . . . . . 173
Using the Package . . . . . . . . . . . . . . . . . . . . . . . 180
2.8 Conclusion . . . . . . . . . . . . . . . . . . . . . . . . . . . . 184

**3 Input and Output** **185**
In This Chapter . . . . . . . . . . . . . . . . . . . . . . . . 185
3.1 A Tutorial Example . . . . . . . . . . . . . . . . . . . . . . . 186
3.2 File Types and Modes . . . . . . . . . . . . . . . . . . . . . . 190
Buffered Files versus Unbuffered Files . . . . . . . . . . . . 190
Text Files versus Binary Files . . . . . . . . . . . . . . . . . 190
Read Mode versus Write Mode . . . . . . . . . . . . . . . . 191
The `default` and `terminal` Files . . . . . . . . . . . . . . 191
3.3 File Descriptors versus File Names . . . . . . . . . . . . . . . 192
3.4 File Manipulation Commands . . . . . . . . . . . . . . . . . . 193
Opening and Closing Files . . . . . . . . . . . . . . . . . . . 193
Position Determination and Adjustment . . . . . . . . . . . 194
Detecting the End of a File . . . . . . . . . . . . . . . . . . 195
Determining File Status . . . . . . . . . . . . . . . . . . . . 195
Removing Files . . . . . . . . . . . . . . . . . . . . . . . . . 196
3.5 Input Commands . . . . . . . . . . . . . . . . . . . . . . . . . 197
Reading Text Lines from a File . . . . . . . . . . . . . . . . 197
Reading Arbitrary Bytes from a File . . . . . . . . . . . . . 197
Formatted Input . . . . . . . . . . . . . . . . . . . . . . . . 198
Reading Maple Statements . . . . . . . . . . . . . . . . . . 204
Reading Tabular Data . . . . . . . . . . . . . . . . . . . . . 204
3.6 Output Commands . . . . . . . . . . . . . . . . . . . . . . . . 205

Configuring Output Parameters Using the `interface` Command . . . 205
One-Dimensional Expression Output . . . 206
Two-Dimensional Expression Output . . . 207
Writing Maple Strings to a File . . . 210
Writing Bytes to a File . . . 210
Formatted Output . . . 210
Writing Tabular Data . . . 214
Flushing a Buffered File . . . 216
Redirecting the `default` Output Stream . . . 217
3.7 Conversion Commands . . . 217
Conversion between Strings and Lists of Integers . . . 217
Parsing Maple Expressions and Statements . . . 218
Formatted Conversion to and from Strings . . . 219
3.8 Notes to C Programmers . . . 220
3.9 Conclusion . . . 221

**4 Numerical Programming in Maple 223**
Floating-Point Calculations . . . 223
In This Chapter . . . 223
Why Use Numerical Computations . . . 223
4.1 The Basics of `evalf` . . . 224
4.2 Hardware Floating-Point Numbers . . . 227
Newton's Method . . . 230
Computing with Arrays of Numbers . . . 232
4.3 Floating-Point Models in Maple . . . 235
Software Floats . . . 235
Roundoff Error . . . 236
4.4 Extending the `evalf` Command . . . 238
Defining New Constants . . . 238
Defining New Functions . . . 240
4.5 Using the Matlab Package . . . 243
4.6 Conclusion . . . 244

**5 Programming with Maple Graphics 245**
Maple Plots . . . 245
Creating Plotting Procedures . . . 245
In This Chapter . . . 245
5.1 Basic Plotting Procedures . . . 246
Altering a Plot . . . 248
5.2 Programming with Plotting Library Procedures . . . 249

Plotting a Loop . . . . . . . . . . . . . . . . . . . . . . . . . 249
Exercise . . . . . . . . . . . . . . . . . . . . . . . . . . . . 251
A Ribbon Plot Procedure . . . . . . . . . . . . . . . . . . . 251
5.3 Maple Plot Data Structures . . . . . . . . . . . . . . . . . . 254
The PLOT Data Structure . . . . . . . . . . . . . . . . . . . 256
Arguments Inside a PLOT Structure . . . . . . . . . . . . . . 257
A Sum Plot . . . . . . . . . . . . . . . . . . . . . . . . . . 259
The PLOT3D Data Structure . . . . . . . . . . . . . . . . . . 262
Objects Inside a PLOT3D Data Structure . . . . . . . . . . . 264
5.4 Programming with Plot Data Structures . . . . . . . . . . . . 266
Writing Graphic Primitives . . . . . . . . . . . . . . . . . . 266
Plotting Gears . . . . . . . . . . . . . . . . . . . . . . . . 268
Polygon Meshes . . . . . . . . . . . . . . . . . . . . . . . . 272
5.5 Programming with the plottools Package . . . . . . . . . . . 273
A Pie Chart . . . . . . . . . . . . . . . . . . . . . . . . . . 275
A Dropshadow Procedure . . . . . . . . . . . . . . . . . . . 276
Creating a Tiling . . . . . . . . . . . . . . . . . . . . . . . 278
A Smith Chart . . . . . . . . . . . . . . . . . . . . . . . . 280
Exercise . . . . . . . . . . . . . . . . . . . . . . . . . . . . 281
Modifying Polygon Meshes . . . . . . . . . . . . . . . . . . 281
5.6 Vector Field Plots . . . . . . . . . . . . . . . . . . . . . . . 286
Drawing a Vector . . . . . . . . . . . . . . . . . . . . . . . 286
Generating a Vector Plot Field . . . . . . . . . . . . . . . . 288
5.7 Generating Grids of Points . . . . . . . . . . . . . . . . . . 296
5.8 Animation . . . . . . . . . . . . . . . . . . . . . . . . . . . 301
Animation in Static Form . . . . . . . . . . . . . . . . . . . 302
Graphical Object as Input . . . . . . . . . . . . . . . . . . . 302
Methods for Creating Animations . . . . . . . . . . . . . . . 303
Two and Three Dimensions . . . . . . . . . . . . . . . . . . 305
Demonstrating Physical Objects in Motion . . . . . . . . . . 306
5.9 Programming with Color . . . . . . . . . . . . . . . . . . . . 308
Generating Color Tables . . . . . . . . . . . . . . . . . . . . 309
Using Animation . . . . . . . . . . . . . . . . . . . . . . . . 310
Adding Color Information to Plots . . . . . . . . . . . . . . 312
Creating A Chess Board Plot . . . . . . . . . . . . . . . . . 315
5.10 Conclusion . . . . . . . . . . . . . . . . . . . . . . . . . . 316

**6 Advanced Connectivity** **319**
In This Chapter . . . . . . . . . . . . . . . . . . . . . . . . 319
Code Generation . . . . . . . . . . . . . . . . . . . . . . . . 319
External Calling: Using Compiled Code in Maple . . . . . . . 319

OpenMaple: Using Maple in Compiled Code . . . . . . . . 319
6.1 Code Generation . . . . . . . . . . . . . . . . . . . . . . . . 319
The CodeGeneration Package . . . . . . . . . . . . . . . 319
Calling `CodeGeneration` Functions . . . . . . . . . . . . 320
Translation Process . . . . . . . . . . . . . . . . . . . . . 321
Extending the CodeGeneration Translation Facilities . . . 324
Defining a Custom Translator . . . . . . . . . . . . . . . 325
6.2 External Calling: Using Compiled Code in Maple . . . . . 330
Method 1: Calling External Functions . . . . . . . . . . 332
External Definition . . . . . . . . . . . . . . . . . . . . . 334
Type Specification . . . . . . . . . . . . . . . . . . . . . 335
Scalar Data Formats . . . . . . . . . . . . . . . . . . . . 336
Structured Data Formats . . . . . . . . . . . . . . . . . . 336
Specifying Argument Passing Conventions . . . . . . . . 338
Method 2: Generating Wrappers . . . . . . . . . . . . . . 338
Additional Types and Options . . . . . . . . . . . . . . . 339
Structured Data Formats . . . . . . . . . . . . . . . . . . 339
Enumerated Types . . . . . . . . . . . . . . . . . . . . . 339
Procedure Call Formats . . . . . . . . . . . . . . . . . . 340
Call by Reference . . . . . . . . . . . . . . . . . . . . . . 340
Array Options . . . . . . . . . . . . . . . . . . . . . . . . 340
Non-passed Arguments . . . . . . . . . . . . . . . . . . . 341
Argument Checking and Efficiency Considerations . . . . 342
Conversions . . . . . . . . . . . . . . . . . . . . . . . . . 342
Compiler Options . . . . . . . . . . . . . . . . . . . . . . 344
Evaluation Rules . . . . . . . . . . . . . . . . . . . . . . 348
Method 3: Customizing Wrappers . . . . . . . . . . . . . 350
External Function Entry Point . . . . . . . . . . . . . . . 350
Inspecting Automatically Generated Wrappers . . . . . . 352
External API . . . . . . . . . . . . . . . . . . . . . . . . 356
System Integrity . . . . . . . . . . . . . . . . . . . . . . 374
6.3 OpenMaple: Using Maple in Compiled Code . . . . . . . . 374
Interface Overview . . . . . . . . . . . . . . . . . . . . . 375
Call-back Functions . . . . . . . . . . . . . . . . . . . . . 380
Maple Online Help Database . . . . . . . . . . . . . . . . 386
Technical Issues . . . . . . . . . . . . . . . . . . . . . . . 389
File Structure . . . . . . . . . . . . . . . . . . . . . . . . 389
Building the Sample Program . . . . . . . . . . . . . . . 390
6.4 Conclusion . . . . . . . . . . . . . . . . . . . . . . . . . . 392

**A Internal Representation and Manipulation 397**

A.1 Internal Organization . . . 397
Components . . . 398
Internal Functions . . . 398
Flow of Control . . . 399
A.2 Internal Representations of Data Types . . . 400
Logical AND . . . 401
Assignment Statement . . . 401
Binary Object . . . 401
Break Statement . . . 401
Name Concatenation . . . 402
Complex Value . . . 402
Communications Control Structure . . . 402
Type Specification or Test . . . 403
Debug . . . 403
Equation or Test for Equality . . . 403
Error Statement . . . 403
Expression Sequence . . . 404
Floating-Point Number . . . 404
For/While Loop Statement . . . 404
Foreign Data . . . 405
Function Call . . . 406
Garbage . . . 406
Hardware Float . . . 406
If Statement . . . 407
Logical IMPLIES . . . 407
Not Equal or Test for Inequality . . . 407
Negative Integer . . . 407
Positive Integer . . . 408
Less Than or Equal . . . 409
Less Than . . . 409
Lexically Scoped Variable within an Expression . . . 409
List . . . 410
Local Variable within an Expression . . . 410
Member . . . 410
Module Definition . . . 410
Module Instance . . . 412
Identifier . . . 412
Next Statement . . . 413
Logical NOT . . . 413
Logical OR . . . 413
Procedure Parameter within an Expression . . . 413

Power . . . 414
Procedure Definition . . . 414
Product, Quotient, Power . . . 416
Range . . . 416
Rational . . . 416
Read Statement . . . 417
Return Statement . . . 417
Rectangular Table . . . 417
Save Statement . . . 419
Series . . . 419
Set . . . 419
Statement Sequence . . . 420
Stop Maple . . . 420
String . . . 420
Sum, Difference . . . 421
Table . . . 421
Table Reference . . . 421
Try Statement . . . 422
Unevaluated Expression . . . 422
Use Statement . . . 422
Logical XOR . . . 423
Polynomials with Integer Coefficients modulo $n$ . . . 423
A.3 The Use of Hashing in Maple . . . 424
Basic Hash Tables . . . 424
Dynamic Hash Tables . . . 425
The Simplification Table . . . 426
The Name Table . . . 427
Remember Tables . . . 427
Maple Language Arrays and Tables . . . 428
Maple Language Rectangular Tables . . . 428
A.4 Portability . . . 429

**Index** **431**

# Preface

This manual describes advanced Maple$^{TM}$ programming concepts, including:

- Variable scope, procedures, modules, and packages
- Advanced input and output
- Numerical programming
- Programming with Maple plots
- Connectivity: translating Maple code to other programming languages, calling external libraries from Maple, and calling Maple code from external libraries
- Internal representation and manipulation

## Audience

This manual provides information for experienced Maple programmers. You should be familiar with the following.

- Maple Online Help Introduction
- Example worksheets
- How to use Maple interactively
- The *Introductory Programming Guide*

## Worksheet Graphical Interface

You can access the power of the Maple computation engine through a variety of user interfaces: the standard worksheet, the command-line[1] version, the classic worksheet (not available on Macintosh®), and custom-built Maplet™ applications. The full Maple system is available through all of these interfaces. In this manual, any references to the graphical Maple interface refer to the standard worksheet interface. For more information on the various interface options, refer to the `?versions` help page.

## Manual Set

There are three other manuals available for Maple users, the *Maple Getting Started Guide*, the *Maple Learning Guide*, and the *Maple Introductory Programming Guide*.[2]

- The *Maple Getting Started Guide* contains an introduction to the graphical user interface and a tutorial that outlines using Maple to solve mathematical problems and create technical documents. It also includes information for new users about the online help system, New User's Tour, example worksheets, and the Maplesoft Web site.
- The *Maple Learning Guide* explains how Maple and the Maple language work. It describes the most important commands and uses them to solve technical problems. User hints for Maplet applications are also described in this guide.
- The *Maple Introductory Programming Guide* introduces the basic Maple programming concepts, such as expressions, data structures, looping and decision mechanisms, procedures, input and output, debugging, and the Maplet User Interface Customization System.

The Maple software also has an online help system. The Maple help system allows you to search in many ways and is always available. There are also examples that you can copy, paste, and execute immediately.

---

[1]The command-line version provides optimum performance. However, the worksheet interface is easier to use and renders typeset, editable math output and higher quality plots.

[2]The Student Edition does not include the *Maple Introductory Programming Guide* and the *Maple Advanced Programming Guide*. These programming guides can be purchased from school and specialty bookstores or directly from Maplesoft.

## Conventions

This manual uses the following typographical conventions.

- `courier` font - Maple command, package name, and option name
- **bold roman** font - dialog, menu, and text field
- *italics* - new or important concept, option name in a list, and manual titles
- **Note** - additional information relevant to the section
- **Important** - information that must be read and followed

## Customer Feedback

Maplesoft welcomes your feedback. For suggestions and comments related to this and other manuals, email doc@maplesoft.com.

# 1 Procedures, Variables, and Extending Maple

### Prerequisite Knowledge

Before reading this chapter, you must have an understanding of Maple evaluation rules for variables and parameters as described in chapter 6 of the *Introductory Programming Guide*.

### In This Chapter

**Nested Procedures** You can define a Maple procedure within another Maple procedure.

**Procedures That Return Procedures** You can create procedures that return procedures by using Maple evaluation rules.

**Local Variables** Local variables can exist after the procedure which created them has exited. This feature allows a procedure to return a procedure. The new procedure requires a unique place to store information.

**Interactive Input** You can write interactive procedures, querying the user for missing information or creating an interactive tutorial or a test.

**Extending Maple** The Maple software includes useful mechanisms for extending Maple functionality, which reduce the need to write special-purpose procedures. Several Maple commands can be extended.

## 1.1 Nested Procedures

You can define a Maple procedure inside another Maple procedure. Some Maple commands are very useful inside a procedure. In the worksheet environment, the `map` command is used to apply an operation to the elements of a structure. For example, you can divide each element of a list by a number, such as 8.

```
> lst := [8, 4, 2, 16]:
> map( x->x/8, lst);
```

$$[1, \frac{1}{2}, \frac{1}{4}, 2]$$

Consider a variation on the `map` command, which appears in the following procedure.

**Example** This new procedure divides each element of a list by the first element of that list.

```
> nest := proc(x::list)
>     local v;
>     v := x[1];
>     map( y -> y/v, x );
> end proc:
> nest(lst);
```

$$[1, \frac{1}{2}, \frac{1}{4}, 2]$$

The procedure `nest` contains a second procedure, `map`, which in this case is the Maple command `map`. Maple applies its lexical scoping rules, which declare the `v` within the call to `map` as the same `v` as in the outer procedure, `nest`.

## Scoping Rules

This section explains Maple scoping rules. You will learn how Maple determines which variables are local to a procedure and which are global. You must have a basic understanding of Maple evaluation rules for parameters, and for local and global variables. For more information, refer to chapter 6 of the *Introductory Programming Guide*.

## Local Versus Global Variables

In general, when writing a procedure, you should explicitly declare which variables are global and which are local. Declaring the scope of the variables makes your procedure easier to read and debug. However, sometimes declaring the variables is not the best method. In the previous `nest` procedure, the variable in the `map` command is defined by the surrounding procedure. What happens if you define this variable, v, as local to the invocation of the procedure within map?

```
> nest2 := proc(x::list)
>     local v;
>     v := x[1];
>     map( proc(y) local v; y/v; end, x );
> end proc:
> nest2(lst);
```

$$[\frac{8}{v}, \frac{4}{v}, \frac{2}{v}, \frac{16}{v}]$$

The nest2 procedure produces different results. When the variables are declared in the inner procedure, the proper values from the enclosing procedure are not used. Either a variable is local to a procedure and certain procedures that are completely within it, or it is global to the entire Maple session.

**Rule** Maple determines whether a variable is local or global, from the inside procedure to the outside procedure. The name of the variable is searched for among:

1. Parameters of the inner procedure
2. Local declarations and global declarations of the inner procedure
3. Parameters of the outside procedure
4. Local and global declarations of the outside procedure
5. Implicitly declared local variables of any surrounding procedure(s)

If found, that specifies the binding of the variable.

If, using the above rule, Maple cannot determine whether a variable is global or local, the following default decisions are made.

- If a variable appears on the *left* side of an *explicit* assignment or as the controlling variable of a for loop, Maple regards the variable as local.
- Otherwise, Maple regards the variable as global to the whole session. In particular, Maple assumes by default that the variables you pass as arguments to other procedures, which may set their values, are global.

## The Quick-Sort Algorithm

Sorting a few numbers is quick using any method, but sorting large amounts of data can be very time consuming; thus, finding efficient methods is important.

The following quick-sort algorithm is a classic algorithm. The key to understanding this algorithm is to understand the operation of partitioning. This involves choosing any one number from the array that you are about to sort. Then, you reposition the numbers in the array that are less than the number that you chose to one end of the array and reposition numbers that are greater to the other end. Lastly, you insert the chosen number between these two groups.

At the end of the partitioning, you have not yet entirely sorted the array, because the numbers less than or greater than the one you chose may still be in their original order. This procedure divides the array into two smaller arrays which are easier to sort than the original larger one. The partitioning operation has thus made the work of sorting much easier. You can bring the array one step closer in the sorting process by partitioning each of the two smaller arrays. This operation produces four smaller arrays. You sort the entire array by repeatedly partitioning the smaller arrays.

## Example

The `partition` procedure uses an array to store the list because you can change the elements of an array directly. Thus, you can sort the array in place and not waste any space generating extra copies.

The `quicksort` procedure is easier to understand if you look at the procedure `partition` in isolation first. This procedure accepts an array of numbers and two integers. The two integers are element numbers of the array, indicating the portion of the array to partition. While you could possibly choose any of the numbers in the array to partition around, this procedure chooses the last element of the section of the array for that purpose, namely `A[n]`. The intentional omission of `global` and `local` statements shows which variables Maple recognizes as local and which are global by default. It is recommended, however, that you not make this omission in your procedures.

```
> partition := proc(A::array(1, numeric),
>                   m::posint, n::posint)
>    i := m;
>    j := n;
>    x := A[j];
>    while i<j do
>       if A[i]>x then
```

```
>             A[j] := A[i];
>             j := j-1;
>             A[i] := A[j];
>         else
>             i := i+1;
>         end if;
>     end do;
>     A[j] := x;
>     eval(A);
> end proc:
```

```
Warning, `i` is implicitly declared local to procedure
`partition`
Warning, `j` is implicitly declared local to procedure
`partition`
Warning, `x` is implicitly declared local to procedure
`partition`
```

Maple declares `i`, `j`, and `x` local because the `partition` procedure contains explicit assignments to those variables. The `partition` procedure also assigns explicitly to `A`, but `A` is a parameter, not a local variable. Because you do not assign to the name `eval`, Maple makes it the global name which refers to the `eval` command.

After partitioning the array `a` in the following, all the elements less than 3 precede 3 but they are in no particular order; similarly, the elements larger than 3 come after 3.

```
> a := array( [2,4,1,5,3] );
```

$$a := [2, 4, 1, 5, 3]$$

```
> partition( a, 1, 5);
```

$$[2, 1, 3, 5, 4]$$

The `partition` procedure modifies its first argument, changing `a`.

```
> eval(a);
```

$$[2, 1, 3, 5, 4]$$

The final step in assembling the `quicksort` procedure is to insert the `partition` procedure within an outer procedure. The outer procedure first defines the `partition` subprocedure, then partitions the array. In general, avoid inserting one procedure in another. However, you will encounter situations in following sections of this chapter in which it is necessary to nest procedures. Since the next step is to partition each of the two subarrays by calling `quicksort` recursively, `partition` must return the location of the element which divides the partition.

**Example** This example illustrates the role of nested procedures. The outer procedure, `quicksort`, contains the inner procedure, `partition`.

```
> quicksort := proc(A::array(1, numeric),
>                   m::integer, n::integer)
>    local partition, p;
>
>    partition := proc(m,n)
>       i := m;
>       j := n;
>       x := A[j];
>       while i<j do
>          if A[i]>x then
>             A[j] := A[i];
>             j := j-1;
>             A[i] := A[j];
>          else
>             i := i+1;
>          end if;
>       end do;
>       A[j] := x;
>       p := j;
>    end proc:
>
>    if m<n then    # if m>=n there is nothing to do
>       p:=partition(m, n);
>       quicksort(A, m, p-1);
>       quicksort(A, p+1, n);
>    end if;
>
>    eval(A);
> end proc:
```

```
Warning, `i` is implicitly declared local to procedure
`partition`
Warning, `j` is implicitly declared local to procedure
`partition`
Warning, `x` is implicitly declared local to procedure
`partition`
```

```
> a := array( [2,4,1,5,3] );
```

$$a := [2, 4, 1, 5, 3]$$

```
> quicksort( a, 1, 5);
```

$$[1, 2, 3, 4, 5]$$

```
> eval(a);
```

$$[1, 2, 3, 4, 5]$$

Maple determines that the `A` and `p` variables in the `partition` subprocedure are defined by the parameter and local variable (respectively) from the outer `quicksort` procedure and everything works as planned. The variable `A` can be passed as a parameter to the `partition` subprocedure (as in the stand-alone `partition` procedure). However, `A` does not need to be passed because, by using Maple scoping rules, it is available to the inner procedure.

## Creating a Uniform Random Number Generator

If you want to use Maple to simulate physical experiments, you likely need a random number generator. The uniform distribution is particularly simple: any real number in a given range is equally likely. Thus, a *uniform random number generator* is a procedure that returns a random floating-point number within a certain range. This section develops the procedure, `uniform`, which creates uniform random number generators.

The `rand` command generates a procedure which returns random *integers*. For example, `rand(4..7)` generates a procedure that returns random integers between 4 and 7, inclusive.

```
> f := rand(4..7):
> seq( f(), i=1..20 );
```

$$5, 6, 5, 7, 4, 6, 5, 4, 5, 5, 7, 7, 5, 4, 6, 5, 4, 5, 7, 5$$

The `uniform` procedure is similar to `rand` but returns floating-point numbers rather than integers. You can use `rand` to generate random floating-point numbers between 4 and 7 by multiplying and dividing by `10^Digits`.

```
> f := rand( 4*10^Digits..7*10^Digits ) / 10^Digits:
> f();
```

$$\frac{12210706011}{2000000000}$$

The procedure f returns fractions rather than floating-point numbers so you must compose it with evalf; that is, use evalf(f()). Alternatively, you can perform this operation by using the Maple composition operator, @.

```
> (evalf @ f)();
```

$$6.648630719$$

The following uniform procedure uses evalf to evaluate the constants in the range specification, r, to floating-point numbers, the map command to multiply both endpoints of the range by 10^Digits, and round to round the results to integers.

```
> uniform := proc( r::constant..constant )
>     local intrange, f;
>     intrange := map( x -> round(x*10^Digits), evalf(r) );
>     f := rand( intrange );
>     (evalf @ eval(f)) / 10^Digits;
> end proc:
```

You can now generate random floating-point numbers between 4 and 7.

```
> U := uniform(4..7):
> seq( U(), i=1..20 );
```

4.559076346, 4.939267370, 5.542851096, 4.260060897,
4.976009937, 5.598293374, 4.547350944,
5.647078832, 5.133877918, 5.249590037,
4.120953928, 6.836344299, 5.374608653,
4.586266491, 5.481365622, 5.384244382,
5.190575456, 5.207535837, 5.553710879,
4.163815544

The uniform procedure has a serious flaw: uniform uses the current value of Digits to construct intrange; thus, U depends on the value of Digits when uniform creates it. On the other hand, the evalf command within U uses the value of Digits that is current when you invoke U. These two values are not always identical.

```
> U := uniform( cos(2)..sin(1) ):
> Digits := 15:
> seq( U(), i=1..8 );
```

$$0.828316845400000, -0.328875163100000,$$
$$0.790988967100000, 0.624953401700000,$$
$$0.362773633800000, 0.679519822000000,$$
$$-0.0465278542000000, -0.291055180800000$$

The proper design choice here is that `U` should depend only on the value of `Digits` when you invoke `U`. The following version of `uniform` accomplishes this by placing the entire computation inside the procedure that `uniform` returns.

```
> uniform := proc( r::constant..constant )
>
>    proc()
>       local intrange, f;
>       intrange := map( x -> round(x*10^Digits),
>                        evalf(r) );
>       f := rand( intrange );
>       evalf( f()/10^Digits );
>    end proc;
> end proc:
```

The `r` within the inner `proc` is not declared as local or global, so it becomes the same `r` as the parameter to the outer `proc`.

The procedure that `uniform` generates is now independent of the value of `Digits` at the time you invoke `uniform`.

```
> U := uniform( cos(2)..sin(1) ):
> Digits := 15:
> seq( U(), i=1..8 );
```

$$0.476383408581006, 0.554836962987261,$$
$$0.147655743361511, 0.273247304736175,$$
$$0.148172828708797, -0.258115633420094,$$
$$0.558246581434993, 0.518084711267009$$

**Note:** The interface variable `displayprecision` controls the number of decimal places to be displayed. The default value is $-1$, representing full precision as determined by the `Digits` environment variable. This simplifies display without introducing round-off error. For more information, refer to `?interface`.

**Summary** This section introduced:

- Rules Maple uses to distinguish global and local variables
- Principal implications of these rules
- Tools available for writing nested procedures

## 1.2 Procedures That Return Procedures

Some of the standard Maple commands return procedures. For example, `rand` returns a procedure which in turn produces randomly chosen integers from a specified range. The `dsolve` function with the `type=numeric` option returns a procedure which supplies a numeric estimate of the solution to a differential equation.

You can write procedures that return procedures. This section discusses how values are passed from the outer procedure to the inner procedure.

### Conveying Values

The following example demonstrates how locating the roots of a function by using Newton's method can be implemented in a procedure.

### Creating a Newton Iteration

Use Newton's method to find the roots of a function.

1. Choose a point on the $x$-axis that you think might be close to a root.
2. Find the slope of the curve at the point you chose.
3. Draw the tangent to the curve at that point and observe where the tangent intersects the $x$-axis. For most functions, this second point is closer to the real root than your initial guess. To find the root, use the new point as a new guess and keep drawing tangents and finding new points.

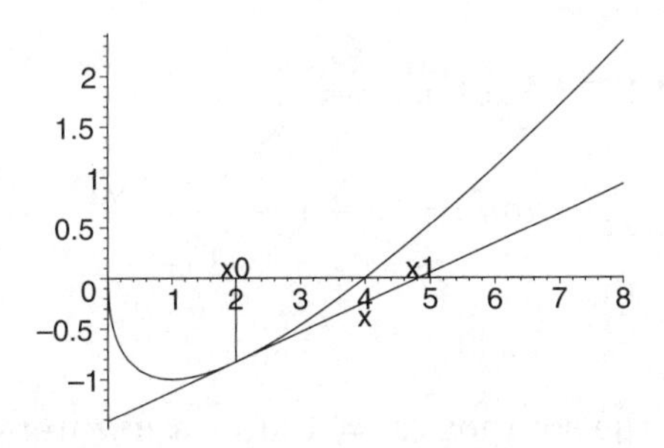


To find a numerical solution to the equation $f(x) = 0$, guess an approximate solution, $x_0$, and then generate a sequence of approximations using:

1. Newton's method
2. The following formulation of the previous process

$$x_{k+1} = x_k - \frac{f(x_k)}{f'(x_k)}$$

You can implement this algorithm on a computer in a number of ways.

## Example 1

The following procedure takes a function and creates a new procedure, which takes an initial guess and, for that particular function, generates the next guess. The new procedure does not work for other functions. To find the roots of a new function, use `MakeIteration` to generate a new guess-generating procedure. The `unapply` command turns an expression into a procedure.

```
> MakeIteration := proc( expr::algebraic, x::name )
>     local iteration;
>     iteration := x - expr/diff(expr, x);
>     unapply(iteration, x);
> end proc:
```

The procedure returned by the `MakeIteration` procedure maps the name `x` to the expression assigned to the iteration.
Test the procedure on the expression $x - 2\sqrt{x}$.

```
> expr := x - 2*sqrt(x);
```

$$expr := x - 2\sqrt{x}$$

```
> Newton := MakeIteration( expr, x);
```

$$Newton := x \to x - \frac{x - 2\sqrt{x}}{1 - \frac{1}{\sqrt{x}}}$$

Newton returns the solution, $x = 4$ after a few iterations.

```
> x0 := 2.0;
```

$$x0 := 2.0$$

```
> to 4 do x0 := Newton(x0);  end do;
```

$$x0 := 4.828427124$$

$$x0 := 4.032533198$$

$$x0 := 4.000065353$$

$$x0 := 4.000000000$$

## Example 2

The MakeIteration procedure requires its first argument to be an algebraic expression. You can also write a version of MakeIteration that works on functions. Since the following MakeIteration procedure recognizes the parameter $f$ as a procedure, you must use the eval command to evaluate it fully.

```
> MakeIteration := proc( f::procedure )
>     (x->x) - eval(f) / D(eval(f));
> end proc:
> g := x -> x - cos(x);
```

$$g := x \to x - \cos(x)$$

```
> SirIsaac := MakeIteration( g );
```

$$SirIsaac := (x \to x) - \frac{x \to x - \cos(x)}{x \to 1 + \sin(x)}$$

Note that SirIsaac is independent of the name g. Thus, you can change g without breaking SirIsaac. You can find a good approximate solution to $x - \cos(x) = 0$ in a few iterations.

```
> x0 := 1.0;
```

$$x0 := 1.0$$

```
> to 4 do x0 := SirIsaac(x0) end do;
```

$$x0 := 0.7503638679$$

$$x0 := 0.7391128909$$

$$x0 := 0.7390851334$$

$$x0 := 0.7390851332$$

## A Shift Operator

Consider the problem of writing a procedure that takes a function, $f$, as input and returns a function, $g$, such that $g(x) = f(x+1)$. You can write such a procedure in the following manner.

```
> shift := (f::procedure) -> ( x->f(x+1) ):
```

Try performing a shift on $\sin(x)$.

```
> shift(sin);
```

$$x \to \sin(x+1)$$

Maple lexical scoping rules declare the f within the inner procedure to be the same f as the parameter within the outer procedure. Therefore, the shift command works as written.

The previous example of shift works with univariate functions but it does not work with functions of two or more variables.

```
> h := (x,y) -> x*y;
```

$$h := (x, y) \to x\, y$$

```
> hh := shift(h);
```

$$hh := x \rightarrow h(x+1)$$

```
> hh(x,y);
```

```
Error, (in h) h uses a 2nd argument, y, which is
missing
```

**Multivariate Functions** To modify `shift` to work with multivariate functions, rewrite it to accept the additional parameters.

In a procedure, `args` is the sequence of actual parameters, and `args[2..-1]` is the sequence of actual parameters except the first one. For more information on the selection operation (`[ ]`), refer to chapter 4 of the *Introductory Programming Guide*. It follows that the procedure `x->f(x+1,args[2..-1])` passes all its arguments except the first directly to $f$.

```
> shift := (f::procedure) -> ( x->f(x+1, args[2..-1]) ):
```

```
> hh := shift(h);
```

$$hh := x \rightarrow h(x+1,\, \mathrm{args}_{2..-1})$$

```
> hh(x,y);
```

$$(x+1)\, y$$

The function `hh` depends on `h`; if you change `h`, you implicitly change `hh`;

```
> h := (x,y,z) -> y*z^2/x;
```

$$h := (x,\, y,\, z) \rightarrow \frac{y\, z^2}{x}$$

```
> hh(x,y,z);
```

$$\frac{y\, z^2}{x+1}$$

## 1.3 Local Variables and Invoking Procedures

Local variables are local to a procedure and to an invocation of that procedure. Calling a procedure creates and uses new local variables each time. If you invoke the same procedure twice, the local variables it uses the second time are distinct from those it used the first time.

Local variables do not necessarily disappear when the procedure exits. You can write procedures which return a local variable, either explicitly or implicitly, to the interactive session, where it can exist indefinitely. These variables are called escaped local variables. This concept can be confusing, particularly since they can have the same name as global variables, or local variables which another procedure or a different call to the same procedure created. You can create many distinct variables with the same name.

### Example 1

The following procedure creates a new local variable, a, and then returns this new variable.

```
> make_a := proc()
>         local a;
>         a;
> end proc;
```

$$make\_a := \textbf{proc}()\, \textbf{local}\, a;\, a\, \textbf{end proc}$$

By using local variables, you can produce displays that Maple would otherwise simplify. For example, in Maple, a set contains *unique* elements. The following demonstrates that each variable a that make_a returns is unique.

```
> test := { a, a, a };
```

$$test := \{a\}$$

```
> test := test union { make_a() };
```

$$test := \{a,\, a\}$$

```
> test := test union { 'make_a'()$5 };
```

$$test := \{a,\, a,\, a,\, a,\, a,\, a,\, a\}$$

This demonstrates that Maple identities consist of more than names.

**Important:** Independent of the number of variables you create with the same name, when you type a name in an interactive session, Maple interprets that name to be a *global* variable . You can easily find the global a in the previous set test.

```
> seq( evalb(i=a), i=test);
```

$$true, false, false, false, false, false, false$$

## Example 2

You can display expressions that Maple would ordinarily simplify automatically. For example, Maple automatically simplifies the expression $a + a$ to $2a$. It is difficult to display the equation $a + a = 2a$. To display such an equation, use the procedure make_a from Example 1.

```
> a + make_a() = 2*a;
```

$$a + a = 2\,a$$

When you type a name in an interactive session, the Maple program interprets it as the global variable. While this prevents you from using the assignment *statement* to directly assign a value to an escaped local variable, it does not prevent you from using the assign command. You must write a Maple expression which extracts the variable. For example, in the previous equation, you can extract the local variable a by removing the global a from the left side of the equation.

```
> eqn := %;
```

$$eqn := a + a = 2\,a$$

```
> another_a := remove( x->evalb(x=a), lhs(eqn) );
```

$$another\_a := a$$

You can then assign the global name a to this extracted variable and verify the equation.

```
> assign(another_a = a);
> eqn;
```

$$2\,a = 2\,a$$

```
> evalb(%);
```

$$true$$

**Assume Facility** For complicated expressions, you must use the assume command to extract the desired variable. You may have encountered this situation before without realizing it, when you were using the assume facility to remove an assumption. The assume facility attaches various definitions to the variable you specify, with one result being that the name subsequently appears as a *local* name with an appended tilde. No relationship exists between the *local* variable $b$ with an assumption, which is displayed as b~, and the *global* variable name containing a tilde b~.

```
> assume(b>0);
> x := b + 1;
```

$$x := b\tilde{} + 1$$

```
> subs( `b~`=c, x);
```

$$b\tilde{} + 1$$

When you clear the definition of the named variable, the association between the name and the local name with the tilde is lost, but expressions created with the local name still contain it.

```
> b := evaln(b);
```

$$b := b$$

```
> x;
```

$$b\tilde{} + 1$$

To reuse the expression, you must either perform a substitution before removing the assumption or perform some manipulations of the expressions similar to those used for the equation eqn.

## Procedure as a Returned Object

An important use for returning local objects arises when the returned object is a procedure. When you write a procedure, which returns a procedure, you will often find it useful to have the procedure create a variable that holds information pertinent only to the returned procedure. This allows different procedures (or different invocations of the same procedure) to pass information among themselves. The following examples illustrate how different procedures pass information.

## Example 3

**Creating the Cartesian Product of a Sequence of Sets** When you pass a sequence of sets to the procedure, it constructs a new procedure. The new procedure returns the next term in the Cartesian product each time you invoke it. Local variables from the outer procedure are used to keep track of which term to return next.

The *Cartesian product* of a sequence of sets is the set of all lists in which the $i$th entry is an element of the $i$th set. Thus, the Cartesian product of $\{\alpha, \beta, \gamma\}$ and $\{x, y\}$ is

$$\{\alpha, \beta, \gamma\} \times \{x, y\} = \{[\alpha, x], [\beta, x], [\gamma, x], [\alpha, y], [\beta, y], [\gamma, y]\}.$$

The number of elements in the Cartesian product of a sequence of sets grows very rapidly as the number of sets or size of the sets increases. It therefore requires a large amount of memory to store all the elements of the Cartesian product.

**Solution** You must write a procedure that returns a new element of the Cartesian product each time you call it. By calling such a procedure repeatedly, you can process every element in the Cartesian product without storing all its elements at once.

The following procedure returns the next element of the Cartesian product of the list of sets `s`. It uses an array, `c`, of counters to determine the next element. For example, `c[1]=3` and `c[2]=1` correspond to the third element of the first set and the first element of the second set.

```
> s := [ {alpha, beta, gamma}, {x, y} ];
```

$$s := [\{\gamma, \alpha, \beta\}, \{x, y\}]$$

```
> c := array( 1..2, [3, 1] );
```

$$c := [3, 1]$$

```
> [ seq( s[j][c[j]], j=1..2 ) ];
```

$$[\beta, x]$$

Before you call the `element` procedure you must initialize all the counters to 1, except the first one, which must be 0.

```
> c := array( [0, 1] );
```

$$c := [0, 1]$$

In following procedure `element`, `nops(s)` is the number of sets and `nops(s[i])` is the number of elements in the *i*th set. When you have seen all the elements, the procedure re-initializes the array of counters and returns `FAIL`. Therefore, you can repeatedly trace the Cartesian product by calling `element`.

```
> element := proc(s::list(set), c::array(1, nonnegint))
>    local i, j;
>    for i to nops(s) do
>       c[i] := c[i] + 1;
>       if c[i] <= nops( s[i] ) then
>          return [ seq(s[j][c[j]], j=1..nops(s)) ] ;
>       end if;
>       c[i] := 1;
>    end do;
>    c[1] := 0;
>    FAIL;
> end proc:
```

```
> element(s, c); element(s, c); element(s, c);
```

$$[\gamma, x]$$

$$[\alpha, x]$$

$$[\beta, x]$$

```
> element(s, c); element(s, c); element(s, c);
```

$$[\gamma, y]$$

$$[\alpha, y]$$

$$[\beta, y]$$

```
> element(s, c);
```

$$FAIL$$

```
> element(s, c);
```

$$[\gamma, x]$$

**Example 4**

Instead of writing a new procedure for each Cartesian product you study, you can write a procedure, `CartesianProduct`, that returns such a procedure. `CartesianProduct` creates a list, `s`, of its arguments, which must be sets, and then initializes the array, `c`, of counters and defines the subprocedure `element`. Finally, the `element` subprocedure is invoked inside a `proc` structure.

```
> CartesianProduct := proc()
>    local s, c, element;
>    s := [args];
>    if not type(s, list(set)) then
>       error "expected a sequence of sets, but received",
>             args ;
>    end if;
>    c := array( [0, 1$(nops(s)-1)] );
>
>    element := proc(s::list(set), c::array(1, nonnegint))
>       local i, j;
>       for i to nops(s) do
>          c[i] := c[i] + 1;
>          if c[i] <= nops( s[i] ) then
>             return [ seq(s[j][c[j]], j=1..nops(s)) ] ;
>          end if;
>          c[i] := 1;
>       end do;
>       c[1] := 0;
>       FAIL;
>    end proc;
>
>    proc()
>       element(s, c);
>    end proc;
> end proc:
```

Again, you can find all six elements of $\{\alpha, \beta, \gamma\} \times \{x, y\}$.

```
> f := CartesianProduct( {alpha, beta, gamma}, {x,y} );
```

$$f := \mathbf{proc}()\ element(s,\ c)\ \mathbf{end\ proc}$$

```
> to 7 do f() end do;
```

$$[\gamma,\ x]$$

$$[\alpha,\ x]$$

$$[\beta,\ x]$$

$$[\gamma,\ y]$$

$$[\alpha,\ y]$$

$$[\beta,\ y]$$

$$FAIL$$

You can use `CartesianProduct` to study several products simultaneously.

```
> g := CartesianProduct( {x, y}, {N, Z, R},
>                        {56, 23, 68, 92} );
```

$$g := \mathbf{proc}()\ element(s,\ c)\ \mathbf{end\ proc}$$

The following are the first few elements of $\{x, y\} \times \{N, Z, R\} \times \{56, 23, 68, 92\}$.

```
> to 5 do g() end do;
```

$$[x,\ N,\ 23]$$

$$[y,\ N,\ 23]$$

$$[x,\ Z,\ 23]$$

$$[y,\ Z,\ 23]$$

$$[x,\ R,\ 23]$$

The variables `s` in `f` and `g` are local variables to `CartesianProduct`, so they are not shared by different *invocations* of `CartesianProduct`. Similarly, the variable `c` in `f` and `g` is not shared. You can see that the two arrays of counters are different by invoking `f` and `g` a few more times.

```
> to 5 do f(), g() end do;
```

$$[\gamma, x], [y, R, 23]$$

$$[\alpha, x], [x, N, 56]$$

$$[\beta, x], [y, N, 56]$$

$$[\gamma, y], [x, Z, 56]$$

$$[\alpha, y], [y, Z, 56]$$

The `element` procedure in `g` is also local to `CartesianProduct`. Therefore, you can change the value of the global variable `element` without breaking `g`.

```
> element := 45;
```

$$element := 45$$

```
> g();
```

$$[x, R, 56]$$

**Summary** The previous examples demonstrate that local variables can escape the bounds of the procedures which create them, and that escaped variables allow you to write procedures which create specialized procedures.

## Exercises

1. The procedure that `CartesianProduct` generates does not work if one of the sets is empty.

```
> f := CartesianProduct( {}, {x,y} );
```

$$f := \textbf{proc}()\ element(s, c)\ \textbf{end proc}$$

```
> f();
```

```
Error, (in element) invalid subscript selector
```

Improve the type-checking in `CartesianProduct` so that it generates an informative error message in each such case.

2. A *partition* of a positive integer, $n$, is a list of positive integers whose sum is $n$. The same integer can appear several times in the partition but the order of the integers in the partition is irrelevant. Thus, the following are all the partitions of 5:

$$[1,1,1,1,1],[1,1,1,2],[1,1,3],[1,2,2],[1,4],[2,3],[5].$$

Write a procedure that generates a procedure that returns a new partition of $n$ each time you call it.

## 1.4 Interactive Input

Normally you pass input to Maple procedures as parameters. Sometimes, however, you need a procedure to request input directly from the user. For example, you can write a procedure that tests students on some topic by generating random problems and verifying the students' answers. The input can be the value of a parameter, or the answer to a question such as whether a parameter is positive. The two commands in Maple for reading input from the terminal are the **`readline`** command and the **`readstat`** command.

### Reading Strings from the Terminal

The **`readline`** command reads one line of text from a file or the keyboard. Use the **`readline`** command as follows.

```
readline( filename )
```

If *filename* is the special name **`terminal`**, then **`readline`** reads a line of text from the keyboard. The **`readline`** command returns the text as a string.

```
> s := readline( terminal );
```

```
Maplesoft
```

$$s := \text{“Maplesoft”}$$

### Example 1

The following application prompts the user for an answer to a question.

```
> DetermineSign := proc(a::algebraic) local s;
>     printf("Is the sign of %a positive?  Answer yes or no: ",a);
>     s := readline(terminal);
>     evalb( s="yes" or s = "y" );
> end proc:
```

```
> DetermineSign(u-1);
```

```
Is the sign of u-1 positive?  Answer yes or no: y
```

$$true$$

**Information:** For more details on the `readline` command, see **Reading Text Lines from a File** on page 197.

### Reading Expressions from the Terminal

You can write procedures that interpret user input as a Maple expression rather than a string. The `readstat` command reads one expression from the keyboard.

```
readstat( prompt )
```

The *prompt* is an optional string.

```
> readstat("Enter degree: ");
```

```
Enter degree: n-1;
```

$$n - 1$$

The user input for a `readstat` command must have a terminating semi-colon or colon, or an error is raised.

**Advantages** Unlike the `readline` command, which only reads one line, the `readstat` allows you to break a large expression across multiple lines. Another advantage of using the `readstat` command is that if there is an error in the input, the `readstat` command automatically repeats the prompt for user input.

```
> readstat("Enter a number: ");
```

```
Enter a number: 5^^8;
syntax error, `^` unexpected:
5^^8;
 ^
```

```
Enter a number: 5^8;
```

$$390625$$

**Example 2**

The following is an application of the **readstat** command that implements an interface to the limit command. The procedure, given the function $f(x)$, assumes $x$ is the variable if only one variable is present. Otherwise, the user is asked for the variable and the limit point.

```
> GetLimitInput := proc(f::algebraic)
>    local x, a, K;
>    # choose all variables in f
>    K := select(type, indets(f), name);
>
>    if nops(K) = 1 then
>       x := K[1];
>    else
>          x := readstat("Input limit variable: ");
>          while not type(x, name) do
>             printf("A variable is required: received %a\n", x);
>             x := readstat("Please re-input limit variable: ");
>          end do;
>    end if;
>    a := readstat("Input limit point: ");
>    x = a;
> end proc:
```

The expression $\sin(x)/x$ depends only on one variable, so GetLimitInput does not prompt for a limit variable.

```
> GetLimitInput( sin(x)/x );
```

```
Input limit point: 0;
```

$$x = 0$$

In the following output, the user first tries to use the number 1 as the limit variable. Because 1 is not a name, GetLimitInput requests another limit variable.

```
> GetLimitInput( exp(u*x) );

Input limit variable: 1;
A variable is required: received 1

Please re-input limit variable: x;

Input limit point: infinity;
```

$$x = \infty$$

**Information:** You can specify a number of options to readstat. For more information, see **Reading Maple Statements** on page 204.

## Converting Strings to Expressions

For greater control of how and when Maple evaluates user input to a procedure, use the readline command instead of readstat. The readline command reads the input as a string, and the parse command converts the string to an expression. The string must represent a complete expression.

```
> s := "a*x^2 + 1";
```

$$s := \text{“a*x\^{}2 + 1”}$$

```
> y := parse( s );
```

$$y := a\,x^2 + 1$$

When you parse the string s you get an expression. In this case, you get a sum.

```
> type(s, string), type(y, `+`);
```

*true*, *true*

The parse command does not evaluate the expression it returns. You must use eval to evaluate the expression explicitly. In the following output, the variable a is not evaluted to its value, 2, until you explicitly use the eval command.

```
> a := 2;
```

$$a := 2$$

```
> z := parse( s );
```

$$z := a\,x^2 + 1$$

```
> eval(z);
```

$$2\,x^2 + 1$$

**Information:** For more details about the parse command, see **Parsing Maple Expressions and Statements** on page 218.

**Summary** The techniques in this section are very simple, but you can use them to create useful applications such as Maple tutorials, procedures that test students, or interactive lessons.

## 1.5 Extending Maple

Although it may be useful to write custom procedures to perform new tasks, sometimes extending the abilities of Maple commands is most beneficial. This section familiarizes you with:

- Defining custom types and operators
- Modifying how Maple displays expressions
- Extending commands such as simplify and expand.

### Defining New Types

If you are using a complicated structured type, it is recommended that you assign the structured type to a variable of the form `type/name`.

Writing the structure once reduces the risk of errors. When you have defined the variable `` `type/name` ``, you can use *name* as a type.

```
> `type/Variables` := {name, list(name), set(name)}:
> type( x, Variables );
```

*true*

```
> type( { x[1], x[2] }, Variables );
```

*true*

If the structured type mechanism is not powerful enough, you can define a new type by assigning a procedure to a variable of the form `` `type/name` ``. When you test whether an expression is of type *name*, Maple invokes the procedure `` `type/name` `` on the expression if such a procedure exists. The procedure should return `true` or `false`. The following `` `type/permutation` `` procedure determines if $p$ is a permutation of the first $n$ positive integers. That is, $p$ should contain exactly one copy of each integer from 1 through $n$.

```
> `type/permutation` := proc(p)
>    local i;
>    type(p,list) and { op(p) } = { seq(i, i=1..nops(p)) };
> end proc:
> type( [1,5,2,3], permutation );
```

*false*

```
> type( [1,4,2,3], permutation );
```

*true*

The type-testing procedure can accept more than one parameter. When you test if an expression, *expr*, has type `name(parameters)`, then Maple invokes

```
`type/name`( expr, parameters )
```

if such a procedure exists. The following `` `type/LINEAR` `` procedure determines if $f$ is a polynomial in $V$ of degree 1.

```
> `type/LINEAR` := proc(f, V::name)
>    type( f, polynom(anything, V) ) and degree(f, V) = 1;
> end proc:
```

```
> type( a*x+b, LINEAR(x) );
```

$$true$$

```
> type( x^2, LINEAR(x) );
```

$$false$$

```
> type( a, LINEAR(x) );
```

$$false$$

### Exercises

1. Modify the `` `type/LINEAR` `` procedure so that you can use it to test if an expression is linear in a set of variables. For example, $x + ay + 1$ is linear in both $x$ and $y$, but $xy + a + 1$ is not.

2. Define the type `POLYNOM(X)` which tests if an algebraic expression is a polynomial in $X$ where $X$ is a name, a list of names, or a set of names.

### Neutral Operators

The Maple software recognizes many operators, for example `+`, `*`, `^`, `and`, `not`, and `union`. These operators have special meaning to Maple. The operators can represent:

- Algebraic operations, such as addition or multiplication
- Logical operations
- Operations performed on sets

Maple also has a special class of operators, the *neutral operators*, on which it does not impose any meaning. Instead, Maple allows *you* to define the meaning of any neutral operator. The name of a neutral operator begins with the ampersand character (&).

```
> 7 &^ 8 &^ 9;
```

$$(7\,\&\hat{}\,8)\,\&\hat{}\,9$$

```
> evalb( 7 &^ 8 = 8 &^ 7 );
```

$$false$$

```
> evalb( (7&^8)&^9 = 7&^(8&^9) );
```

$$false$$

Internally, Maple represents neutral operators as procedure calls. Thus, `7&^8` is a convenient way of writing `&^(7,8)`.

```
> &^(7, 8);
```

$$7\,\&\hat{}\,8$$

Maple uses the infix notation, in which the operator is placed between the operands, only if the neutral operator has exactly two arguments.

```
> &^(4),  &^(5, 6), &^(7, 8, 9);
```

$$\&\hat{}(4),\ 5\,\&\hat{}\,6,\ \&\hat{}(7,\,8,\,9)$$

**Information:** For more information on naming conventions for neutral operators, refer to chapter 3 of the *Introductory Programming Guide*.

## Example 1

You can define the actions of a neutral operator by assigning a procedure to its name. The following example implements the Hamiltonians by assigning a neutral operator to a procedure that multiplies two Hamiltonians.

**Mathematical Premise** The *Hamiltonians* or *Quaternions* extend the complex numbers in the same way the complex numbers extend the real numbers. Each Hamiltonian has the form $a + bi + cj + dk$ where $a$, $b$, $c$, and $d$ are real numbers. The special symbols $i$, $j$, and $k$ satisfy the following multiplication rules: $i^2 = -1$, $j^2 = -1$, $k^2 = -1$, $ij = k$, $ji = -k$, $ik = -j$, $ki = j$, $jk = i$, and $kj = -i$.

The following `&^` procedure uses $I$, $J$, and $K$ as the three special symbols. However, $I$ is implemented as the *complex* imaginary unit in Maple. Therefore, you should assign another letter to represent the imaginary unit by using the `interface` function. For more information, refer to `?interface`.

```
> interface(imaginaryunit=j);
```

You can multiply many types of expressions by using `&^`, making it convenient to define a new type, `Hamiltonian`, by assigning a structured type to the name `type/Hamiltonian`.

```
> `type/Hamiltonian` := { `+`, `*`, name, realcons,
>     specfunc(anything, `&^`) };
```

$$type/Hamiltonian := \{*, +, realcons, name, \mathrm{specfunc}(anything, \&\hat{}\,)\}$$

The `&^` procedure multiplies the two Hamiltonians, $x$ and $y$. If either $x$ or $y$ is a real number or variable, then their product is the usual product denoted by $*$ in Maple. If $x$ or $y$ is a sum, `&^` maps the product onto the sum; that is, `&^` applies the distributive laws: $x(u+v) = xu + xv$ and $(u+v)x = ux + vx$. If $x$ or $y$ is a product, `&^` extracts any real factors. You must take special care to avoid infinite recursion when $x$ or $y$ is a product that does not contain real factors. If none of the multiplication rules apply, `&^` returns the product unevaluated.

```
> `&^` := proc( x::Hamiltonian, y::Hamiltonian )
>     local Real, unReal, isReal;
>     isReal := z -> evalb( is(z, real) = true );
>
>     if isReal(x) or isReal(y) then
>        x * y;
>
>     elif type(x, `+`) then
>        # x is a sum, u+v, so x&^y = u&^y + v&^y.
>        map(`&^`, x, y);
>
>     elif type(y, `+`) then
>        # y is a sum, u+v, so x&^y = x&^u + x&^v.
>        map2(`&^`, x, y);
>
>     elif type(x, `*`) then
>        # Pick out the real factors of x.
>        Real, unReal := selectremove(isReal, x);
>        # Now x&^y = Real * (unReal&^y)
>        if Real=1 then
>           if type(y, `*`) then
```

```
>             Real, unReal := selectremove(isReal, x);
>             Real * '`&^`'(x, unReal);
>          else
>             '`&^`'(x, y);
>          end if;
>       else
>          Real * `&^`(unReal, y);
>       end if;
>
>    elif type(y, `*`) then
>       # Similar to the x-case but easier since
>       # x cannot be a product here.
>       Real, unReal := selectremove(isReal, y);
>       if Real=1 then
>          '`&^`'(x, y);
>       else
>          Real * `&^`(x, unReal);
>       end if;
>
>    else
>       '`&^`'(x,y);
>    end if;
> end proc:
```

You can place all the special multiplication rules for the symbols $I$, $J$, and $K$ in the remember table of `&^`.

**Information:** For more information on remember tables, refer to chapter 6 of the *Introductory Programming Guide.*

```
> `&^`(I,I) := -1: `&^`(J,J) := -1: `&^`(K,K) := -1:
> `&^`(I,J) := K: `&^`(J,I) := -K:
> `&^`(I,K) := -J: `&^`(K,I) := J:
> `&^`(J,K) := I: `&^`(K,J) := -I:
```

Since `&^` is a neutral operator, you can write products of Hamiltonians using &^ as the multiplication symbol.

```
> (1 + 2*I + 3*J + 4*K) &^ (5 + 3*I - 7*J);
```

$$20 + 41\,I + 20\,J - 3\,K$$

```
> (5 + 3*I - 7*J) &^ (1 + 2*I + 3*J + 4*K);
```

$$20 - 15\,I - 4\,J + 43\,K$$

```
> 56 &^ I;
```

$$56\, I$$

In the following example, $a$ is an unknown Hamiltonian until you enter the assumption that $a$ is an unknown real number.

```
> a &^ J;
```

$$a \,\&\hat{}\; J$$

```
> assume(a, real);
> a &^ J;
```

$$a\tilde{}\; J$$

## Exercise

1. The inverse of a general Hamiltonian, $a + bi + cj + dk$, is $(a - bi - cj - dk)/(a^2 + b^2 + c^2 + d^2)$. You can demonstrate this fact by assuming that $a$, $b$, $c$, and $d$ are real and define a general Hamiltonian, $h$.

```
> assume(a, real); assume(b, real);
```

```
> assume(c, real); assume(d, real);
```

```
> h := a + b*I + c*J + d*K;
```

$$h := a\tilde{} + b\tilde{}\; I + c\tilde{}\; J + d\tilde{}\; K$$

By the formula above, the following should be the inverse of $h$.

```
> hinv := (a-b*I-c*J-d*K) / (a^2+b^2+c^2+d^2);
```

$$hinv := \frac{a\tilde{} - b\tilde{}\; I - c\tilde{}\; J - d\tilde{}\; K}{a\tilde{}^2 + b\tilde{}^2 + c\tilde{}^2 + d\tilde{}^2}$$

Check that `h &^ hinv` and `hinv &^ h` simplify to 1.

```
> h &^ hinv;
```

$$\frac{a\tilde{}\,(a\tilde{} - b\tilde{}\,I - c\tilde{}\,J - d\tilde{}\,K)}{\%1} + \frac{b\tilde{}\,(I\,a\tilde{} + b\tilde{} - c\tilde{}\,K + d\tilde{}\,J)}{\%1} + \frac{c\tilde{}\,(J\,a\tilde{} + b\tilde{}\,K + c\tilde{} - d\tilde{}\,I)}{\%1} + \frac{d\tilde{}\,(K\,a\tilde{} - b\tilde{}\,J + c\tilde{}\,I + d\tilde{})}{\%1}$$

$$\%1 := a\tilde{}^2 + b\tilde{}^2 + c\tilde{}^2 + d\tilde{}^2$$

```
> simplify(%);
```

$$1$$

```
> hinv &^ h;
```

$$\frac{a\tilde{}\,(a\tilde{} - b\tilde{}\,I - c\tilde{}\,J - d\tilde{}\,K)}{\%1} + \frac{a\tilde{}\,b\tilde{}\,I + b\tilde{}^2 + b\tilde{}\,c\tilde{}\,K - b\tilde{}\,d\tilde{}\,J}{\%1} + \frac{a\tilde{}\,c\tilde{}\,J - b\tilde{}\,c\tilde{}\,K + c\tilde{}^2 + c\tilde{}\,d\tilde{}\,I}{\%1} + \frac{a\tilde{}\,d\tilde{}\,K + b\tilde{}\,d\tilde{}\,J - c\tilde{}\,d\tilde{}\,I + d\tilde{}^2}{\%1}$$

$$\%1 := a\tilde{}^2 + b\tilde{}^2 + c\tilde{}^2 + d\tilde{}^2$$

```
> simplify(%);
```

$$1$$

Write a procedure, '&/', that computes the inverse of a Hamiltonian. It is recommended that you implement the following rules.

```
&/( &/x ) = x,   &/(x&^y) = (&/y) &^ (&/x),
       x &^ (&/x) = 1 = (&/x) &^ x.
```

## Extending Commands

If you introduce custom data structures, there are no manipulation rules for them. In most cases, you write special-purpose procedures that manipulate new data structures. However, sometimes extending the capabilities of one or more of the Maple built-in commands is easier than developing new data structures and special-purpose procedures. You can extend several Maple commands, among them `expand`, `simplify`, `diff`, `series`, and `evalf`.

**Extending the `Diff` Command** You can represent a polynomial $a_n u^n + a_{n-1} u^{n-1} + \cdots + a_1 u + a_0$ by using the data structure

```
POLYNOM( u, a_0, a_1, ..., a_n )
```

You can then extend the `diff` command so that you can differentiate polynomials represented in that way. If you write a procedure with a name of the form `` `diff/F` `` then `diff` invokes it on any unevaluated calls to $F$. Specifically, if you use `diff` to differentiate `F(arguments)` with respect to x, then `diff` invokes `` `diff/F` `` as follows.

```
`diff/F`( arguments, x )
```

The following procedure differentiates a polynomial in $u$ with constant coefficients with respect to $x$.

```
> `diff/POLYNOM` := proc(u)
>    local i, s, x;
>    x := args[-1];
>    s := seq( i*args[i+2], i=1..nargs-3 );
>    'POLYNOM'(u, s) * diff(u, x);
> end proc:
```

```
> diff( POLYNOM(x, 1, 1, 1, 1, 1, 1, 1, 1, 1, 1), x );
```

$$\mathrm{POLYNOM}(x, 1, 2, 3, 4, 5, 6, 7, 8, 9)$$

```
> diff( POLYNOM(x*y, 34, 12, 876, 11, 76), x );
```

$$\mathrm{POLYNOM}(x\,y, 12, 1752, 33, 304)\,y$$

**Extending the** `simplify` **Command** The implementation of the Hamiltonians in this section 1.5 does not include the associative rule for multiplication of Hamiltonians, that is $(xy)z = x(yz)$. Sometimes, using associativity simplifies a result. Recall that `I` here is *not* the complex imaginary unit, but rather, one of the special symbols $I$, $J$, and $K$ that are part of the definition of the Hamiltonians.

```
> x &^ I &^ J;
```

$$(x \,\&\hat{}\, I) \,\&\hat{}\, J$$

```
> x &^ ( I &^ J );
```

$$x \,\&\hat{}\, K$$

You can extend the `simplify` command so that it applies the associative law to unevaluated products of Hamiltonians. If you write a procedure with a name of the form `‘simplify/F‘`, then `simplify` invokes it on any unevaluated function calls to $F$. Thus, you must write a procedure `‘simplify/&^‘` that applies the associative law to Hamiltonians.

The following procedure uses the `typematch` command to determine if its argument is of the form `(a&^b)&^c` and, if so, it selects the `a`, `b`, and `c`.

```
> s := x &^ y &^ z;
```

$$s := (x \,\&\hat{}\, y) \,\&\hat{}\, z$$

```
> typematch( s, '‘&^‘'( '‘&^‘'( a::anything, b::anything ),
>                     c::anything ) );
```

$$true$$

```
> a, b, c;
```

$$x,\ y,\ z$$

**The `userinfo` Command** You can give the user details about procedure simplifications using the `userinfo` command. The `` `simplify/&^` `` procedure prints an informative message if you set `infolevel[simplify]` or `infolevel[all]` to greater than or equal to least 2.

```
> `simplify/&^` := proc( x )
>   local a, b, c;
>   if typematch( x,
>         '`&^`'( '`&^`'( a::anything, b::anything ),
>                c::anything ) ) then
>     userinfo(2, simplify, "applying the associative law");
>     a &^ ( b &^ c );
>   else
>     x;
>   end if;
> end proc:
```

Applying the associative law simplifies some products of Hamiltonians.

```
> x &^ I &^ J &^ K;
```

$$((x \,\&\hat{}\, I) \,\&\hat{}\, J) \,\&\hat{}\, K$$

```
> simplify(%);
```

$$-x$$

If you set `infolevel[simplify]` to a sufficiently large value, Maple prints information on the methods used by `simplify` while attempting to simplify the expression.

```
> infolevel[simplify] := 5;
```

$$infolevel_{simplify} := 5$$

```
> w &^ x &^ y &^ z;
```

$$((w \,\&\hat{}\, x) \,\&\hat{}\, y) \,\&\hat{}\, z$$

```
> simplify(%);

simplify/&^:    "applying the associative law"
simplify/&^:    "applying the associative law"
```

$$w \,\&\hat{}\, ((x \,\&\hat{}\, y) \,\&\hat{}\, z)$$

**Information:** For details on how to extend these commands, refer to `?expand`, `?series`, and `?evalf`. For information on extending the `evalf` command, see also **4.4 Extending the `evalf` Command**.

## 1.6 Conclusion

Procedures which return procedures and local variables are fundamental to advanced programming. Interactive input and extending Maple are also important topics in advanced programming.

# 2 Programming with Modules

Procedures allow you to associate a sequence of commands with a single command. Similarly, modules allow you to associate related procedures and data.

## Modules

This chapter describes Maple modules. Modules are a type of Maple expression (like numbers, equations, and procedures), that enable you to write generic algorithms, create packages, or use Pascal-style records in programs.

The use of modules satifies four important software engineering concepts.

- Encapsulation
- Packages
- Object Modeling
- Generic Programming

**Encapsulation** guarantees that an abstraction is used only according to its specified interface. You can write significant software systems that are transportable and reusable and that offer clean, well-defined user interfaces. This makes code easier to maintain and understand—important properties for large software systems.

**Packages** are a vehicle for bundling Maple procedures related to a problem domain. Much of the functionality of the standard Maple library resides in packages.

**Objects** are easily represented using modules. In software engineering or object-oriented programming, an object is defined as something that has both state and behavior. You compute with objects by sending them messages, to which they respond by performing services.

**Generic Programs** accept objects that possess specific properties or behaviors. The underlying representation of the object is transparent to generic programs.

## Examples

For better understanding, it is helpful to examine a small module.

**Example 1: Simple Module** When Maple evaluates the right side of the assignment to `TempGenerator`, it creates a *module* using the *module definition* that begins with `module()...` and ends with `end module`.

```
> TempGenerator := module()
>         description "generator for temporary symbols";
>         export  gentemp;
>         local   count;
>
>         count := 0;
>         gentemp := proc()
>                 count := 1 + count;
>                 `tools/gensym`( T || count )
>         end proc;
> end module;
```

*TempGenerator* := **module**()
**local** *count*;
**export** *gentemp*;
**description** "generator for temporary symbols";
**end module**

**Example Summary** The module definition resembles a procedure definition. The main differences are the use of the keyword **module** instead of **proc** (and the corresponding terminator) and the **export** declaration following the description string.

**Example 2: Procedure** In the following example, the previous module is written using only procedures.

```
> TempGeneratorProc := proc()
>         description "generator for temporary symbols";
>         local   count, gentemp;
>       count := 0;
```

```
>     gentemp := proc()
>             count := 1 + count;
>             `tools/gensym`( T || count )
>     end proc;
>     eval( gentemp, 1 )
> end proc:
```

You can assign the procedure returned by TempGeneratorProc, and then use it to generate temporary symbols.

```
> f := TempGeneratorProc();
```

$$f := \textbf{proc}()\ count := 1 + count\,;\ \text{`tools/gensym`}(T||count)\ \textbf{end proc}$$

```
> f();
```

$$T1$$

```
> f();
```

$$T2$$

## Module Versus Procedure

The module TempGenerator and the procedure TempGeneratorProc are similar.

In the procedure version, the local variable gentemp is assigned a procedure that references another local variable count; the value of gentemp is returned by the procedure to its caller. The module version of the generator behaves similarly. Its structure differs: its gentemp variable is declared as an *export*, not a *local*, and there is no explicit return.

In both versions of the generator, the variables count and gentemp *are* local variables. The significant difference here is that, in the module version, one of those local variables is *exported*. This means that it is available outside the scope of the structure in which it was created. Special syntax is used access exported local variables. For example, to call the exported variable gentemp of the module, enter

```
> TempGenerator:-gentemp();
```

$$T1$$

using the member selection operator `:-`. A module definition returns a data structure (a module) that contains all of its exported local variables.

## Accessing Module Exports

The `use` statement allows you to access module exports.

```
> use TempGenerator in
>     gentemp();
>     gentemp();
>     gentemp();
> end use;
```

$$T2$$

$$T3$$

$$T4$$

Within the body of a **use** statement, the exported local variables of the module that appears after the **use** keyword can be accessed directly, without using the member selection operator `:-`.

## In This Chapter

This chapter provides many example modules. Some examples are very simple, designed to illustrate a specific point. Others are more substantial. Many of the nontrivial examples are available as Maple source code in the `samples` directory of the Maple installation. You can load them into the private Maple library and experiment with them. You can modify, extend, and improve these code samples, and use them in custom programs.

The following topics are covered in this chapter.

- Syntax and Semantics
- Using Modules as Records or Structures
- Using Modules To Write Maple Packages
- The `use` Statement
- Modeling Objects
- Interfaces and Implementations

## 2.1 Syntax and Semantics

The syntax of module definitions is very similar to that of procedures, given in chapter 6 of the *Introductory Programming Guide*. Here is an example of a simple module definition.

```
> module()
>     export e1;
>     local a, b;
>
>     a := 2;
>     b := 3;
>     e1 := x -> a^x/b^x;
> end module:
```

Evaluating this expression results in a module with one export, e1, and two local variables, a and b.

A template for a module definition looks like:

```
module()
    local L;
    export E;
    global G;
    options O;
    description D;
    B
end module
```

The simplest valid module definition is

```
> module() end;
```

**module() end module**

This module definition does *not* have: exported variables, locals, references, global variables, or a body of statements. The module to which this evaluates is not very useful.

### The Module Definition

Every module definition begins with the keyword **module**, followed by an empty pair of parentheses. Following that is an optional declaration section and the module body. The keyword combination `end module` (or just **end**) terminates a module definition.

## The Module Body

The body of a module definition consists of the following.

- Zero or more Maple statements. The body is executed when the module definition is evaluated, producing a module.
- A number of assignment statements that give values to the exported names of the module.

The body of a module definition can also contain:

- Assignments to local variables, and performance of arbitrary computations.
- A `return` statement, but cannot contain a **break** or **next** statement outside a loop. Executing a `return` statement terminates the execution of the body of the module definition.

## Module Parameters

Module definitions begin with the Maple keyword **module**, followed by an (empty) pair of parentheses. This is similar to the parentheses that follow the **proc** keyword in a procedure definition. Unlike procedures, however, module definitions do not have explicit parameters because modules are not called (or invoked) with arguments.

**Implicit Parameters** Every module definition has an *implicit* parameter called **thismodule**. Within the body of a module definition, this special name evaluates to the module in which it occurs. This allows you to refer to a module within its own definition (before the result of evaluating it has been assigned to a name).

All procedure definitions can reference the implicit parameters **procname**, **args**, and **nargs**. Module definitions *cannot* reference these implicit parameters. Additionally, the difference between **thismodule** and **procname** is that **procname** evaluates to a *name*, while **thismodule** evaluates to the module expression itself. This is because the invocation phase of evaluating a module definition is part of its normal evaluation, and it occurs immediately. Procedures, on the other hand, are not invoked until called with arguments. Normally, at least one name for a procedure is known by the time it is called; this is not the case for modules.

## Named Modules

An optional symbol may appear after the **module** keyword in a module definition. Modules created with this variant on the syntax are called *named modules*. Semantically, named modules are nearly identical to normal modules, but the exported members of named modules are printed differently, allowing the module from which it was exported to be identified visually.

```
> NormalModule := module() export e; end;
```

$$NormalModule := \textbf{module}()\ \textbf{export}\ e;\ \ \textbf{end module}$$

```
> NormalModule:-e;
```

$$e$$

Here, the symbol (the name of the module) after the **module** keyword is `NamedModule`.

```
> module NamedModule() export e; end module;
```

$$\textbf{module}\ NamedModule\ ()\ \textbf{export}\ e;\ \ \textbf{end module}$$

```
> NamedModule:-e;
```

$$NamedModule : -e$$

When the definition of a named module is evaluated, the name (which appears immediately after the **module** keyword) is assigned the module as its value, *and the name is protected.* Therefore, a named module can, ordinarily, be created only once. For example, an attempt to execute the same named module definition yields an error.

```
> module NamedModule() export e; end module;
Error, (in NamedModule) attempting to assign to
`NamedModule` which is protected
```

Executing the normal module definition again creates a *new* instance of the module, but does not result in an error. (It simply reassigns the variable `NormalModule` to the new module instance.)

```
> NormalModule := module() export e; end;
```

$$NormalModule := \textbf{module}()\ \textbf{export}\ e;\ \ \textbf{end module}$$

**Important** Do not assign a named module to another variable.

```
> SomeName := eval( NamedModule );
```

$$SomeName :=$$
$$\textbf{module}\ NamedModule\,()\ \textbf{export}\ e;\ \textbf{end module}$$

```
> SomeName:-e;
```

$$NamedModule : -e$$

Exports of named modules are printed using the *distinguished* name that was given to the module when it was created, regardless of whether it has been assigned to another name.

Whether a module has a name also affects the reporting of errors that occur during its evaluation. When the second attempt to evaluate the named module definition above failed, the error message reported the location of the error by name. By contrast, when an error occurs during the evaluation of a normal module definition, the name **unknown** is used instead.

```
> NormalModule := module() export e; error "oops"; end;

Error, (in unknown) oops
```

This differs from procedure error reporting. Maple cannot report the name of a normal module (that is, the name of the variable to which the module is assigned), because the evaluation of the right side of an assignment occurs *before* the assignment to the name takes place. So the error occurs *before* any association between a variable and the module has occurred.

## Declarations

The declarations section of the module must appear immediately after the parentheses. All statements in the declarations section are optional, but at most one of each kind may appear. Most module declarations are the same as those for procedures.

**Description Strings** Provide a brief description outlining the purpose and function of any module you write. It is valuable to other users who read your code. Include an overview after the **description** keyword, just as you would in a procedure definition.

```
> Hello := module()
>     description "my first module";
>     export say;
>     say := proc()
>         print( "HELLO WORLD" )
>     end proc;
> end module:
```

When the module is printed, its description string is displayed.

```
> eval( Hello );
```

**module**()
**export** *say*;
**description** "my first module";
**end module**

The **export** declaration is explained later in this chapter.

**Global Variables** Global variables referenced within a module definition should be declared with the **global** declaration. Following the keyword **global** is a sequence of one or more symbols. These symbols are bound to their global instances. In certain cases you must declare a name as a global variable to prevent implicit scoping rules from making it local.

```
> Hello := module()
>     export say;
>     global message;
>     say := proc()
>         message := "HELLO WORLD!"
>     end proc;
> end module:
> message;
```

*message*

```
> Hello:-say();
```

"HELLO WORLD!"

```
> message;
```

"HELLO WORLD!"

**Local Variables** You can refer to variables that are local to the module definition by using the **local** declaration. Its format is the same as for procedures. Here is a variant on the previous `Hello` module which uses a local variable.

```
> Hello := module()
>     local loc;
>     export say;
>     loc := "HELLO WORLD!";
>     say := proc()
>         print( loc )
>     end proc;
> end module:
```

Local variables are not visible outside the definition of the module in which they occur. They are private to the module, and are exactly analogous to local variables of procedures.

A local variable in a module (or procedure) is a distinct object from a global variable with the same name. Local variables are normally short-lived variables; the normal lifetime of a local variable is the execution time of the body of code (a module or procedure body) to which it is local. (Local variables may persist once execution of the scope in which they occur has completed, but they are normally inaccessable and will eventually be recycled by the Maple automatic storage management system.)

## Exported Local Variables

Procedures and modules both support local variables. Only modules support *exported* local variables, often referred to simply as exports.

Module exports are declared using the **export** declaration. It begins with the keyword **export**, after which follows a (nonempty) sequence of symbols. A name is never exported implicitly; exports *must* be declared.

The result of evaluating a module definition is a module. You can view a module as a collection of its exports, which are also referred to as members of the module. These are simply names that can (but need not) be assigned values. You can establish initial values for the exports by assigning to them in the body of the module definition.

The word export is short for exported local variable. In most respects, a module export is a local variable (such as those declared via the **local** declaration.) The crucial difference is that you can access the exported local variables of a module after it has been created.

To access an export of a module, use the `:-` member selection operator. Its general syntax is:

```
modexpr :- membername
```

Here, modexpr must be an expression that evaluates to a module, and membername must be the name of an export of the module to which modexpr evaluates. Anything else signals an exception. You cannot access local variables of an instantiated module by using this syntax.

Local variables of a procedure are created when the procedure is called (or invoked). Normally, the locals persist only during the execution of the statements that form the body of the procedure. Sometimes, however, local variables persist beyond the procedure activation that instantiated them. For example:

```
> gen := proc()
>       local s, p;
>       s := 2;
>       p := x -> s * x;
>       p
> end proc:
> g := gen();
```

$$g := p$$

```
> g( 3 );
```

$$6$$

The local variable s of gen persists after gen has returned. It is captured in the closure of the procedure p, whose name is returned by gen. Thus, both local variables p and s of gen escape, but in different ways. The local name p is accessible because it is the assigned value of the global variable g. However, there is no way to refer to s once gen has returned. No Maple syntax exists for that purpose. The member selection operator :- provides a syntax for referencing certain local variables of modules–those declared as exports.

The most recent Hello example has one export, named say. In this case, say is assigned a procedure. To call it, enter

```
> Hello:-say();
```

"HELLO WORLD!"

The following expression raises an exception, because the name noSuchModule is not assigned a module expression.

```
> noSuchModule:-e;
```

```
Error, ‘noSuchModule‘ does not evaluate to a module
```

Here, a module expression is assigned to the name m, and the member selection expression m:-e evaluates to the value of the exported variable e of m.

```
> m := module() export e; e := 2 end module:
> m:-e;
```

$$2$$

Since m does not export a variable named noSuchExport, the following expression raises an exception.

```
> m:-noSuchExport;
```

```
Error, module does not export ‘noSuchExport‘
```

**Important** The following module exports an unassigned name. This illustrates the importance of distinguishing module exports from global variables.

```
> m := module() export e; end:
```

References to the exported name e in m evaluate to the name e.

```
> m:-e;
```

$$e$$

Note, however, that this is a *local* name e, not the global instance of the name.

```
> evalb( e = m:-e );
```

$$\mathit{false}$$

The first e in the previous expression refers to the global e, while the expression m:-e evaluates to the e that is local to the module m. This distinction between a global and export of the same name is useful. For example, you can create a module with an export sin. Assigning a value to the export sin does not affect the protected global name sin.

**The `exports` Procedure** You can determine the names of the exports of a module by using the `exports` procedure.

```
> exports( Hello );
```

*say*

```
> exports( NormalModule );
```

*e*

This returns the *global* instances of the export names.

```
> exports( m );
```

*e*

```
> evalb( % = e );
```

*true*

You can also obtain the local instances of those names by passing the option `instance`.

```
> exports( m, 'instance' );
```

*e*

```
> evalb( % = e );
```

*false*

```
> evalb( %% = m:-e );
```

*true*

For this reason, you cannot have the same name declared both as a local and an export.

```
> module() export e; local e; end;
Error, export and local `e` have the same name
```

(The declared exports and locals actually form a partition of the names that are local to a module.)

**The `member` Procedure** You have already seen the built-in procedure `member` that is used to test for membership in a set or list.

```
> member( 4, { 1, 2, 3 } );
```

*false*

This procedure can be used for membership tests in modules as well.

```
> member( say, Hello );
```

*true*

```
> member( cry, Hello );
```

*false*

The first argument is a (global) name whose membership is to be tested, and the second argument is a module. It returns the value `true` if the module has an export whose name is the same as the first argument.

The procedure `member` also has a three argument form that can be used with lists to determine the (first) position at which an item occurs.

```
> member( b, [ a, b, c ], 'pos' );
```

*true*

The name `pos` is now assigned the value 2 because `b` occurs at the second position of the list `[ a, b, c]`.

```
> pos;
```

2

When used with modules, the third argument is assigned the *local instance* of the name whose membership is being tested, provided that the return value is `true`.

```
> member( say, Hello, 'which' );
```

*true*

```
> which;
```

*say*

```
> eval( which );
```

**proc**() print(*loc*) **end proc**

If the return value from `member` is `false`, then the name remains unassigned (or maintains its previously assigned value).

```
> unassign( 'which' ):
> member( cry, Hello, 'which' );
```

*false*

```
> eval( which );
```

*which*

## Module Options

As with procedures, a module definition may contain options. The options available for modules are different from those for procedures. Only the options `trace`, and `‘Copyright...‘` are common to procedures and modules. The following four options have a predefined meaning for modules: `load`, `unload`, `package`, and `record`.

**The `load` and `unload` Options** The module initialization option is `load= pname` where `pname` is the name of a procedure in the declared exports or locals of the module. If this option is present, then the procedure is called when the module is read from the Maple repository in which it is found. The `unload = pname` option specifies the name of a local or exported procedure of the module that is called when the module is destroyed. A module is destroyed either when it is no longer accessible and is garbage collected, or when Maple exits.

There is a situation that can arise wherein a module is no longer accessible, and hence subject to garbage collection before the `unload=` procedure is executed, but becomes accessible again during the execution of that procedure. In that case, the module is *not* garbage collected. When it eventually is garbage collected or Maple exits, the `unload=` procedure is *not* executed again. The `load=` and `unload=` procedures are called with no arguments.

**The `package` Option** Modules with the option `package` represent Maple packages. The exports of a module created with the `package` option are automatically protected.

**The `record` Option** The `record` option is used to identify records. Records are produced by the `Record` constructor and are represented using modules.

## Implicit Scoping Rules

The bindings of names that appear within a module definition are determined when the module definition is simplified. Module definitions are subject to the same implicit scoping rules that procedure definitions are. Under no circumstances is a name ever implicitly determined to be exported by a module; implicitly scoped names can resolve only to locals or globals.

## Lexical Scoping Rules

Module definitions, along with procedure definitions, obey standard lexical scoping rules. Modules may be nested, in the sense that a module may have any of its exports assigned to a module whose definition occurs within the body of the outer module.

Here is a simple example of a submodule.

```
> m := module()
>     export s;
>     s := module()
>         export e;
>         e := proc()
>             print( "HELLO WORLD!" )
>         end proc;
>     end module
> end module:
```

The global name `m` is assigned a module that exports the name `s`. Within the body of `m`, the export `s` is assigned a module that exports the name `e`. As such, `s` is a *submodule* of `m`. The `Shapes` package, described later, illustrates a nontrivial use of submodules.

Modules and procedures can be mutually nested to an arbitrary depth. The rules for the visibility of local variables (including exported locals of modules) and procedure parameters are the same as the rules for nested procedures.

**Parameterized Modules** Modules do not take explicit parameters. You can write a generic module that could be specialized by providing one or more parameters.

For example, here is a module for arithmetic modulo 6.

```
> z6 := module()
>     export add, mul;
>     add := ( a, b ) -> a + b mod 6;
>     mul := ( a, b)  -> a * b mod 6;
> end module:
> z6:-add( 5, 4);
```

$$3$$

```
> z6:-mul( 2, 3);
```

$$0$$

You can write a *generic* module for arithmetic modulo any positive integer $n$, and then specialize it for any integer that you need. This is possible as a result of the standard lexical scoping rules. You must write a *constructor* procedure for the module that accepts the value of $n$ as an argument. Here is a generic version of the **z6** example.

```
> MakeZn := proc( n::posint )
>     module()
>         export add, mul;
>         add := ( a, b ) -> a + b mod n;
>         mul := ( a, b ) -> a * b mod n;
>     end module
> end proc:
```

To generate a module that does arithmetic modulo 7, call the constructor **MakeZn** with the number 7 as its argument.

```
> z7 := MakeZn( 7 );
```

$$z7 := \textbf{module}()\ \textbf{export}\ add,\ mul;\ \ \textbf{end module}$$

```
> z7:-add( 3, 4 );
```

$$0$$

## Modules and Types

Two Maple types are associated with modules. First, the name **module** is a type name. Naturally, an expression is of type **module** only if it is a module. When used as a type name, the name **module** must be enclosed in name quotes (`).

```
> type( module() end, ''module'' );
```

*true*

```
> type( LinearAlgebra, ''module'' );
```

*true*

Secondly, a type called `moduledefinition` identifies expressions that are module definitions. In the previous example, the module definition

```
> module() end:
```

was evaluated before being passed to `type`, so the expression that was tested was not the definition, but the module to which it evaluates. You must use unevaluation quotes (') to delay the evaluation of a module definition.

```
> type( 'module() end', 'moduledefinition' );
```

*true*

Other important type tests satisfied by modules are the types `atomic` and `last_name_eval`.

```
> type( module() end, 'atomic' );
```

*true*

The procedure `map` has no effect on modules; they pass through unchanged.

```
> map( print, module() export a, b, c; end );
```

**module()** **export** *a*, *b*, *c*; **end module**

Modules also follow last name evaluation rules. For more information on last name evaluation rules, refer to `?last_name_eval`.

```
> m := module() end:
> m;
```

$$m$$

```
> type( m, 'last_name_eval' );
```

*true*

Although type `module` is a surface type, it acts also as a structured type. Parameters passed as arguments to the unevaluated name **module** are taken to be the names of exports. For example, the module

```
> m := module() export a, b; end:
```

has the structured module type `` `module`( a, b ) ``:

```
> type( m, '`module`( a, b )' );
```

*true*

It also has type type `` `module`( a ) ``

```
> type( m, '`module`( a )' );
```

*true*

because any module that exports symbols `a` and `b` is a module that exports the symbol `a`.

## Example: A Symbolic Differentiator

This section illustrates the various module concepts through a symbolic differentiator example. Since Maple provides a built-in differentiator `diff`, the example symbolic differentiator is named `differentiate`. Its (final) implementation is in the module `DiffImpl` (later in this chapter), which holds all the local state for the program. Much of the code for the differentiator is designed to implement either a standard rule (such as the rule that the derivative of a sum is the sum of the derivatives of the summands), or special case rules for mathematical functions such as `sin` and `exp`. The example differentiator handles only real valued functions of a single real variable.

The following example shows several steps in the development of the module, from a very simple first try to the final, fully functional program. The final form of the differentiator is a good illustration of a very common Maple design pattern. This pattern arises when you have a single top-level routine that dispatches a number of subroutines to handle special cases using special purpose algorithms.

**The First Attempt** This initial example presents the differentiator as an ordinary procedure, not a module.

```
> differentiate := proc( expr, var )
>     local a, b;
>
>     if type( expr, 'constant' ) then
>         0
>     elif expr = var then
>         1
>     elif type( expr, '`+`' ) then
>         map( procname, args )
>     elif type( expr, '`^`' ) then
>         a, b := op( expr );
>         if a = var and not has( b, var ) then
>             b * a ^ ( b - 1 )
>         else
>             'procname( args )'
>         end if
>     elif type( expr, '`*`' ) then
>         a, b := op( 1, expr ), subsop( 1 = 1, expr );
>         procname( a, var ) * b + a * procname( b, var )
>     else
>         'procname( args )'
>     end if
> end proc:
```

Trivial cases are handled first: The derivative of a constant expression is equal to 0, and the derivative of the variable with respect to which we are differentiating is equal to 1. The additivity of the derivative operator is expressed by mapping the procedure over sums, using the command

```
> map( procname, args );
```

This is commonly used to map a procedure over its first argument, passing along all the remaining arguments. Only the simple case of powers of the differentiation variable is handled so far, provided also that the power is independent of the differentiation variable. The product rule for derivatives is expressed by splitting expressions of type product into two pieces:

- the first factor in the product, and
- the product of all the remaining factors.

This is achieved by the double assignment of

```
> a, b := op( 1, expr ), subsop( 1 = 1, expr );
```

so the input expression `expr` is expressed as `expr = a * b`. The standard technique of returning unevaluated is used so that computation can proceed symbolically on expressions that the procedure is unable to differentiate.

This first example is simple, but it is already able to handle polynomials with numeric coefficients.

```
> differentiate( 2 - x + x^2 + 3*x^9, x );
```

$$-1 + 2\,x + 27\,x^8$$

However, it fails on expressions containing calls to standard mathematical functions.

```
> differentiate( sin( x ), x );
```

$$\mathrm{differentiate}(\sin(x),\, x)$$

It is also unable to deal successfully with symbolic coefficients.

```
> differentiate( a*x^2 + b*x + c, x );
```

$$\mathrm{differentiate}(a,\, x)\, x^2 + 2\, a\, x + \mathrm{differentiate}(b,\, x)\, x + b \\ + \mathrm{differentiate}(c,\, x)$$

**Adding Missing Functionality** To add the missing functionality, add a case for expressions of type `function`.

```
> differentiate := proc( expr, var )
>     local a, b;
>
>     if not has( expr, var ) then
>         0
>     elif expr = var then
>         1
>     elif type( expr, '`+`' ) then
>         map( procname, args )
>     elif type( expr, '`^`' ) then
>         a, b := op( expr );
>         if not has( b, var ) then
>             b * a ^ ( b - 1 ) * procname( a, var )
>         else
>             'procname( args )'
```

```
>             end if
>         elif type( expr, ''*'' ) then
>             a, b := op( 1, expr ), subsop( 1 = 1, expr );
>             procname( a, var ) * b + a * procname( b, var )
>         elif type( expr, 'function' ) and nops( expr ) = 1 then
>             # functions of a single variable; chain rule
>             b := op( 0, expr ); # the name of the function
>             a := op( 1, expr ); # the argument
>             if b = 'sin' then
>                 cos( a ) * procname( a, var )
>             elif b = 'cos' then
>                 -sin( a ) * procname( a, var )
>             elif b = 'exp' then
>                 exp( a ) * procname( a, var )
>             elif b = 'ln' then
>                 ( 1 / a ) * procname( a, var )
>             else
>                 'procname( args )'
>             end if
>         else
>             'procname( args )'
>         end if
> end proc:
```

This uses the chain rule to compute the derivatives of calls to known functions.

```
> differentiate( sin( x ) + cos( exp( x ) ), x );
```

$$\cos(x) - \sin(e^x)\, e^x$$

```
> differentiate( sin( x^2 ) + cos( x^2 ), x );
```

$$2\cos(x^2)\, x - 2\sin(x^2)\, x$$

```
> differentiate( sin( x )^2 + cos( x )^3, x );
```

$$2\sin(x)\cos(x) - 3\cos(x)^2\sin(x)$$

At the same time, this has also improved the handling of expressions independent of the variable of differentiation.

```
> differentiate( a*x^2 + b*x + c, x );
```

$$2\, a\, x + b$$

This is effected by using the expression has( expr, var ) instead of the weaker test type( expr, 'constant' ). The power rule now handles more than just powers of var.

```
> differentiate( sin( x )^2, x );
```

$$2\sin(x)\cos(x)$$

However, adding new functions to the differentiator is tedious and error prone, and the job of handling the chain rule must be repeated for each function recognized by it.

**Introducing a Function Table** Many functions (that you need to add) and the rules used for their differentiation can be stored in a table as follows:

```
> differentiate := proc( expr, var )
>     local a, b, functab;
>
>     functab := table();
>     functab[ 'sin' ] := 'cos';
>     functab[ 'cos' ] := x -> -sin( x );
>     functab[ 'exp' ] := exp;
>     functab[ 'ln' ] := x -> 1 / x;
>
>     if not has( expr, var ) then
>         0
>     elif expr = var then
>         1
>     elif type( expr, '`+`' ) then
>         map( procname, args )
>     elif type( expr, '`^`' ) then
>         a, b := op( expr );
>         if a = var and not has( b, var ) then
>             b * a^ ( b - 1 ) * procname( a, var )
>         else
>             'procname( args )'
>         end if
>     elif type( expr, '`*`' ) then
>         a, b := op( 1, expr ), subsop( 1 = 1, expr );
>         procname( a, var ) * b + a * procname( b, var )
>     elif type( expr, 'function' ) and nops( expr ) = 1 then
>         # functions of a single variable; chain rule
>         b := op( 0, expr ); # the name of the function
>         a := op( 1, expr ); # the argument
>         if assigned( functab[ b ] ) then
>             # This is a ``known'' function
>             functab[ b ]( a ) * procname( a, var )
>         else
>             # This function is not known; return unevaluated
>             'procname( args )'
```

```
>            end if
>        else
>            'procname( args )'
>        end if
> end proc:
```

This not only simplifies the code used for the function case, but also makes it very easy to add new functions.

**Drawbacks** Unfortunately, this implementation has serious drawbacks.

- It is not extensible. The known functions are hardcoded as part of the procedure definition for differentiate. New functions cannot be added without editing this source code.
- A second problem relates to performance. A complete implementation would require a table of dozens or hundreds of functions. That large table would need to be created and initialized each time differentiate is invoked.

**Encapsulation and Extensibility** One way to fix both problems is to make the table of functions a global variable. However, using global variables can be dangerous, because they pollute the user namespace and are subject to unwanted inspection and tampering.

**Solution** A better solution is to put the differentiate procedure, along with its table of functions, into a module. The table is then initialized only once–when the module is created–and can be saved to a Maple repository with the rest of the module by using a savelib call. By making the table a local variable of the module, you prevent users from modifying the table or otherwise inspecting it in unwanted ways.

This does not prevent you from making the differentiator user-extensible, however. You can add an access procedure addFunc that allows users to add rules for differentiating new functions. For example, you can use the call

```
> addFunc( 'cos', x -> -sin(x) );
```

to add the derivative of the sin function. The export addFunc of the DiffImpl module is a procedure that requires two arguments. The first is the name of a function whose derivative is to be made known to the differentiator. The second is a Maple procedure of one argument that expresses the derivative of the function being added.

With this strategy in mind, you can create a module `DiffImpl`, with principal export `differentiate`. At the same time, you can also make the basic differentiation rules extensible.

Here is the complete source code for the differentiator with these improvements.

```
> DiffImpl := module()
>     description "a symbolic differentiator";
>     local       functab, ruletab, diffPower;
>     export      differentiate, addFunc, addRule, rule;
>
>     addFunc := proc( fname::symbol, impl )
>         functab[ fname ] := impl
>     end proc;
>
>     addRule := proc( T, impl )
>         if type( T, '{ set, list }' ) then
>             map( procname, args )
>         elif type( T, 'And( name, type )') then
>             ruletab[ T ] := impl
>         else
>             error "expecting a type name, but got %1", T
>         end if
>     end proc;
>
>     rule := proc( T )
>         if type( T, 'And( name, type )' ) then
>             if assigned( ruletab[ T ] ) then
>                 eval( ruletab[ T ], 1 )
>             else
>                 error "no rule for expressions of type %1", T
>             end if
>         else
>             error "expecting a type symbol, but got %1", T
>         end if
>     end proc;
>
>     differentiate := proc( expr, var )
>         local a, b, e;
>         if not has( expr, var ) then
>             0
>         elif expr = var then
>                   1
>         elif type( expr, 'function' ) and nops( expr ) = 1 then
>             e := op( 0, expr );
>             a := op( expr );
>             if assigned( functab[ e ] ) then
>                 functab[ e ]( a ) * procname( a, var )
>             else
>                 'procname( args )'
>             end if
>         else
>             b := whattype( expr );
```

```
>             if assigned( ruletab[ b ] ) then
>                 ruletab[ b ]( expr, var )
>             else
>                     'procname( args )'
>             end if
>         end if
>     end proc;
>
>     addRule( '{list,set,tabular}',
>             () -> map( differentiate, args ) );
>     addRule( '`+`',
>             () -> map( differentiate, args ) );
>     addRule( '`*`',
>       (expr,var) ->
>         op(1,expr)*differentiate(subsop(1=1,expr),var)
>            + differentiate(op(1,expr),var)*subsop(1=1,expr) );
>     diffPower := proc( expr, var )
>         local  b, e;
>         Assert( type( expr, '`^`' ) );
>         b, e := op( expr );
>         if has( e, var ) then
>             expr * ( differentiate( e, var ) * ln( b )
>                 + e * differentiate( b, var ) / b )
>         else # simpler formula
>             e * b^(e - 1) * differentiate( b, var )
>         end if;
>     end proc;
>     addRule( '`^`', eval( diffPower ) );
>
>     addFunc( 'sin', cos );
>     addFunc( 'cos', x -> -sin(x) );
>     addFunc( 'exp', exp );
>     addFunc( 'ln', x -> 1/x );
>     # ... etc.
>
> end module:
> differentiate := DiffImpl:-differentiate:
```

To give the set of rules for nonfunctional expressions similar extensibility, you can store those rules in a table. The table is indexed by the primary (or basic) type name for the expression type, as given by the Maple procedure `whattype`.

```
> whattype( a + 2 );
```

$$+$$

```
> whattype( a / b );
```

$$*$$

```
> whattype( a^sqrt(2) );
```

$$\wedge$$

```
> whattype( [ f( x ), g( x ) ] );
```

$$list$$

A rule is expressed by a procedure of two arguments, expr and var, in which expr is the expression to be differentiated, and var is the variable of differentiation. For instance, to make the differentiator handle items such as sets and lists by differentiating their individual components, add the rule

```
> addRule( '{ list, set, tabular }', () -> map( differentiate,
>    args ) );
```

The first version of the differentiator dealt with sums by mapping itself over the sum expression. In the new scheme, this is expressed by the statement

```
> addRule( '`+`', () -> map( differentiate, args ) );
```

in the module body. The advantage of using this scheme is that, not only can the author of the differentiator extend the system, but so can users of the system. Having instantiated the module DiffImpl, any user can add rules or new functions, simply by issuing appropriate calls to addRule and addFunc.

The differentiator cannot handle the procedure tan.

```
> differentiate( tan( x )/exp( x ), x );
```

$$-\frac{\tan(x)}{e^x} + \frac{\text{differentiate}(\tan(x), x)}{e^x}$$

You must add it to the database of known functions.

```
> DiffImpl:-addFunc( 'tan', x -> 1 + tan(x)^2 );
```

$$x \to 1 + \tan(x)^2$$

```
> differentiate( tan( x )/exp( x ), x );
```

$$-\frac{\tan(x)}{e^x} + \frac{1 + \tan(x)^2}{e^x}$$

Similarly, there is not yet any rule for handling equations and other relations.

```
> differentiate( y( x ) = sin( x^2 ) - cos( x^3 ), x );
```

$$\mathrm{differentiate}(\mathrm{y}(x) = \sin(x^2) - \cos(x^3), x)$$

```
> DiffImpl:-addRule( '{ `=`, `<`, `<=` }',
>                   () -> map( differentiate, args ) );
```

$$\{() \to \mathrm{map}(\mathit{differentiate}, \mathrm{args})\}$$

```
> differentiate( y( x ) = sin( x^2 ) - cos( x^3 ), x );
```

$$\mathrm{differentiate}(\mathrm{y}(x), x) = 2\cos(x^2)\,x + 3\sin(x^3)\,x^2$$

**The Extension Mechanism is Module Aware** Do not confuse the extension mechanism previously proposed for the differentiator with the extension mechanism used by the built-in Maple command `diff`. The `diff` command uses a traditional string concatenation mechanism for adding knowledge of the derivatives of functions, and all its rules are built-in, so they cannot be extended. For instance, to add a new function `F` to the Maple built-in `diff` command, you can define a procedure `` `diff/F` `` that computes the derivative of `F`.

By contrast, the extension mechanism used in the `differentiate` example is *module aware*. To add knowledge of the derivative of some top-level function `F`, you can issue a command, such as

```
> DiffImpl:-addFunc( 'F', x -> sin( x ) + cos( x ) );
```

$$x \to \sin(x) + \cos(x)$$

The derivative of `F( x )` is `sin( x ) + cos( x )`.) Define a module with some special functions, one of which is also called `F`.

```
> SpecFuncs := module()
>     export F; # etc.
>     # definition of F() and others
> end module:
```

You can now add this new F to the known functions.

```
> DiffImpl:-addFunc( SpecFuncs:-F, x -> exp( 2 * x ) );
```

$$x \to e^{(2\,x)}$$

```
> differentiate( F( x ), x );
```

$$\sin(x) + \cos(x)$$

```
> use SpecFuncs in
>     differentiate( F( x ), x );
> end use;
```

$$e^{(2\,x)}$$

With the traditional mechanism, this does not work.

```
> `diff/` || F := x -> sin( x ) + cos( x );
```

$$\mathit{diff}/F := x \to \sin(x) + \cos(x)$$

```
> diff( F( x ), x );
```

$$\sin(x) + \cos(x)$$

```
> use SpecFuncs in
>     `diff/` || F := x -> exp( 2 * x );
>     diff( F( x ), x );
> end use;
```

$$\mathit{diff}/F := x \to e^{(2\,x)}$$

$$e^{(2\,x)}$$

The definition for the global F has been lost.

```
> diff( F( 2 * x ), x );
```

$$e^{(4\,x)}$$

(You can use a different argument to `diff` to avoid recalling the answer from its remember table.) The traditional mechanism fails because it relies on the *external representation* of names, and not upon their bindings, so each attempt to define an extension to `diff` in fact adds a definition for the derivative of *all* functions whose names are spelled `"F"`.

**Note:** A commented version of the `differentiate` module is available in the `samples/AdvPG` directory of the Maple installation. The implementation shown in the text has been somewhat simplified.

## 2.2 Records

The simplest way to use modules is as Pascal-style records (or structures, as in C and C++). A record is a data structure that has some number of named *slots* or *fields*. In Maple, these slots can be assigned arbitrary values. Although the underlying data structure of a Maple record is currently a module, records and modules represent distinct abstractions. A record is simply an aggregate data structure in which the members have fixed names. Modules provide additional facilities such as computation at initialization and access control.

**Instantiating Records** To create a record, use the `Record` constructor. In the simplest form, it takes the slot names as arguments.

```
> rec := Record( 'a', 'b', 'c' );
```

*rec* :=
**module**() **export** *a*, *b*, *c*; **option** *record*; **end module**

The name `rec` is now assigned a record with slots named `a`, `b`, and `c`. These are the slot names for the record `rec`. You can access and assign these slots by using the expressions `rec:-a`, `rec:-b`, and `rec:-c`.

```
> rec:-a := 2;
```

$$a := 2$$

```
> rec:-a;
```

$$2$$

If not assigned, the record slot evaluates to the *local* instance of the slot name.

```
> rec:-b;
```

$$b$$

```
> evalb( % = b );
```

$$false$$

This is useful because the entire record can be passed as an *aggregate* data structure.

The record constructor accepts initializers for record slots. That is, you can specify an initial value for any slot in a new or in an unassigned record by passing an equation with the slot name on the left side and the initial value on the right.

```
> r := Record( 'a' = 2, 'b' = sqrt( 3 ) );
```

$$r := \mathbf{module}()\,\mathbf{export}\, a,\, b;\;\; \mathbf{option}\, record;\;\; \mathbf{end\ module}$$

```
> r:-b;
```

$$\sqrt{3}$$

In addition, you can attach type assertions to record slots. To introduce a type assertion, use a '::' structure with the slot name specified as the first operand. Type assertions can be used in combination with initializers. An incompatible initializer value triggers an assertion failure when the `assertlevel` kernel option is set to 2. For more information, refer to `?kernelopts`.

```
> kernelopts( 'assertlevel' = 2 ):
> Record( a::integer = 2.3, b = 2 );

Error, (in assign/internal) assertion failed in
assignment, expected integer, got 2.3
```

```
> r := Record( 'a'::integer = 2, 'b'::numeric );
```

$r :=$ **module**()
**export** $a::integer$, $b::numeric$;
**option** *record*;

**end module**

```
> r:-b := "a string";
```

```
Error, assertion failed in assignment, expected
numeric, got a string
```

If the initializer for a record slot is a procedure, you can use the reserved name `self` to refer to the record you are constructing. This allows records to be self-referential. For example, you can write a complex number constructor as follows.

```
> MyComplex := ( r, i ) ->
>     Record( 're' = r, 'im' = i, 'abs' = (() -> sqrt(
>               self:-re^2 + self:-im^2 ))):
> c := MyComplex( 2, 3 ):
> c:-re, c:-im, c:-abs();
```

$$2, 3, \sqrt{13}$$

Combined with prototype-based inheritance, described on page 76, this facility makes the `Record` constructor a powerful tool for object-oriented programming.

**Record Types** Expressions created with the `Record` constructor are of type `record`.

```
> type( rec, 'record' );
```

*true*

This is a structured type that works the same way as the `'module'` type, but recognizes records specifically.

```
> r := Record( a = 2, b = "foo" ):
> type( r, 'record( a::integer, b::string )' );
```

*true*

**Note:** In a record type, the slot types are used to test against the values assigned to the slots (if any), and are not related to type assertions on the slot names (if any).

```
> r := Record( a::integer = 2, b::{symbol,string} = "foo" ):
> type( r, 'record( a::numeric, b::string )' );
```

$$true$$

**Using Records to Represent Quaternions** Records are useful for implementing simple aggregate data structures for which named access to slots is wanted. For example, four real numbers can be combined to form a quaternion, and you can represent this using a record structure, as follows.

```
> MakeQuaternion := proc( a, b, c, d )
>      Record( 're' = a, 'i' = b, 'j' = c, 'k' = d )
> end proc:
> z := MakeQuaternion( 2, 3, 2, sqrt( 5 ) );
```

$z :=$ **module()**
**export** *re*, *i*, *j*, *k*;
**option** *record*;

**end module**

In this example, **z** represents the quaternion $2+3i+2j+\sqrt{5}k$ (where $i$, $j$, and $k$ are the nonreal quaternion basis units). The quaternion records can now be manipulated as single quantities. The following procedure accepts a quaternion record as its sole argument and computes the Euclidean length of the quaternion that the record represents.

```
> qnorm := proc( q )
>      use re = q:-re, i = q:-i, j = q:-j, k = q:-k in
>           sqrt( re * re + i * i + j * j + k * k )
>      end use
> end proc:
> qnorm( z );
```

$$\sqrt{22}$$

A Maple type for quaternions can be introduced as a structured record type.

```
> TypeTools:-AddType( 'quaternion', 'record( re, i, j, k )' );
> type( z, 'quaternion' );
```

*true*

**Object Inheritance** The Record constructor supports a simple form of prototype-based inheritance. An object system based on prototypes does not involve classes; instead, it uses a simpler, more direct form of object-based inheritance. New objects are created from existing objects (called *prototypes*) by *cloning*, that is, copying and augmenting the data and behavior of the prototype.

The Record constructor supports prototype-based inheritance by accepting an index argument, which is the prototype for the new object record.

```
> p := Record( a = 2, b = 3 ); # create a prototype
```

$p :=$ **module() export** $a, b;$ **option** *record*; **end module**

```
> p:-a, p:-b;
```

2, 3

```
> r := Record[p]( c = 4 );
```

$r :=$
**module() export** $a, b, c;$ **option** *record*; **end module**

```
> r:-a, r:-b, r:-c;
```

2, 3, 4

In this example, the record p is the prototype, and the second record r inherits the slots a and b, and their values, from the prototype p. It also augments the slots obtained from p with a new slot c. The prototype p is not changed.

```
> r:-a := 9;
```

$a := 9$

```
> p:-a;
```

$$2$$

Behavior, as well as data, can be copied from a prototype. To copy behavior, use a constructor procedure for both the prototype and its clones.

```
> BaseComplex := proc( r, i )
>   Record( 're' = r, 'im' = i )
> end proc:
> NewComplex := proc( r, i )
>   Record[BaseComplex(r,i)]( 'abs' =
>     (() -> sqrt( self:-re^2 + self:-im^2 )) )
> end proc:
> c := NewComplex( 2, 3 ):
> c:-re, c:-im, c:-abs();
```

$$2, 3, \sqrt{13}$$

An object created from a prototype can serve as a prototype for another object.

```
> NewerComplex := proc( r, i )
>   Record[NewComplex(r,i)]( 'arg' =
>     (() -> arctan(self:-im,self:-re)) )
> end proc:
> c2 := NewerComplex( 2, 3 ):
> c2:-re, c2:-im, c2:-abs(), c2:-arg();
```

$$2, 3, \sqrt{13}, \arctan(\frac{3}{2})$$

**Note:** Prototypes are supertypes of their clones.

```
> subtype( 'record( re, im, abs )', 'record( re, im )' );
```

*true*

For example, NewComplex creates objects of a type that is a subtype of the objects created by BaseComplex.

## 2.3 Packages

Modules are ideal for writing Maple packages. They provide facilities for large software projects that are better than table and procedure based methods.

### What Is a Package

A *package* is a collection of procedures and other data, that can be treated as a whole. Packages typically gather a number of procedures that enable you to perform computations in some well-defined problem domain. Packages may contain data other than procedures, and may even contain other packages (subpackages).

**Packages in the Standard Library** A number of packages are shipped with the standard Maple library. For example, the `group`, `numtheory`, `codegen`, and `LinearAlgebra` packages are all provided with Maple, along with several dozen others. The `group` package provides procedures that allow you to compute with groups that have a finite representation in terms of permutations, or of generators and defining relations. The `LinearAlgebra` package has a large number of procedures available for computational linear algebra.

**Table-Based Packages** Many packages are implemented as tables. The essential idea underlying this implementation scheme is that the name of a package routine is used as the index into a table of procedures. The table itself is the concrete representation of the package.

**Use Modules for New Packages** Modules are the new implementation vehicle for packages. A module represents a package by its exported names. The exported names can be assigned arbitrary Maple expressions, typically procedures, and these names form the package.

**Package Exports** Some of the data in a package is normally made accessible to the user as an export of the package. For packages implemented as modules, the package exports are the same as the exports of the underlying module. For packages implemented as tables, the package exports are the names used to index the underlying table.

Accessing the exports of a package is a fundamental operation that is supported by all packages. If `P` is a Maple package, and `e` is one among its exports, you can access `e` by using the fully qualified reference `P[ e ]`. If `P` is a module, then you can also use the syntax `P:-e`. These methods of accessing the exports of a module are normally used when programming with a package.

Note that `:-` is a left-associative operator. If `S` is a submodule of a module `P`, and the name `e` is exported by `S`, then the notation `P:-S:-e` is parsed as `(P:-S):-e`, and so it refers to the instance of `e` local to `S`. This fact is important to reference members of subpackages. For example,

```
> m := Matrix(2,2,[[1-x,2-x],[3-x,4-x]],
>              'datatype' = 'polynom(integer)' );
```

$$m := \begin{bmatrix} 1-x & 2-x \\ 3-x & 4-x \end{bmatrix}$$

```
> LinearAlgebra:-LA_Main:-Norm( m, 1, conjugate = false );
```

$$\max(|x-1|+|x-3|\,,\,|x-2|+|x-4|)$$

calls the procedure `Norm` in the subpackage `LA_Main` of the `LinearAlgebra` package. You can use indexed notation for this.

```
> LinearAlgebra[LA_Main][Norm](m, 1, conjugate = false );
```

$$\max(|x-1|+|x-3|\,,\,|x-2|+|x-4|)$$

**Using Packages Interactively** For interactive use, it is inconvenient to enter fully-qualified references to all the exports of a package. To ease this burden, the Maple procedure `with` is provided for the interactive management of package namespaces. Using `with`, you can globally impose the exported names of a package. This allows you to access the package exports, without typing the package prefix, by making the names of the exports visible at the top-level of the Maple session. For example, to use the `numtheory` package, you can issue the command

```
> with( numtheory );

Warning, the protected name order has been redefined
and unprotected
```

$$[GIgcd, bigomega, cfrac, cfracpol, cyclotomic, divisors, factorEQ, factorset, fermat, imagunit, index, integral\_basis, invcfrac, invphi, issqrfree, jacobi, kronecker, \lambda, legendre, mcombine, mersenne, migcdex, minkowski, mipolys, mlog, mobius, mroot, msqrt, nearestp, nthconver, nthdenom, nthnumer, nthpow, order, pdexpand, \phi, \pi, pprimroot, primroot, quadres, rootsunity, safeprime, \sigma, sq2factor, sum2sqr, \tau, thue]$$

The effect of this command is to make the names exported by the `numtheory` package (a list of which is returned by the call to `with`) available temporarily as top-level Maple commands.

```
> cfrac( ( 1 + x )^k, x, 5, 'subdiagonal', 'simregular' );
```

$$\cfrac{1}{1 - \cfrac{k\,x}{1 + \cfrac{1}{2}\,\cfrac{(k+1)\,x}{1 - \cfrac{1}{6}\,\cfrac{(k-1)\,x}{1 + \cfrac{1}{6}\,\cfrac{(k+2)\,x}{1 + \ldots}}}}}$$

## Writing Maple Packages by Using Modules

This section describes how to write Maple packages by using modules. The following subsections present several examples that illustrate how to do this.

### The LinkedList Package

The first example package is a small package called `LinkedList`. This example illustrates the basic structure of a package implemented by using modules.

**Background** Linked lists are a basic data structure used in programs for many different purposes. There are many kinds of linked lists, with variations on the basic idea intended to address performance and functionality issues. The example package shown in this subsection provides a few operations on the simplest possible form of linked lists.

The links in a linked list are formed from a very simple data structured called a *pair*. A pair is essentially a container with space for exactly two elements. Pairs can be modeled by fixed length records with two slots.

When used to implement linked lists, the first slot holds the data for the list entry, and the second slot stores a pointer to the next pair in the list.

The `LinkedList` package implements an abstract data definition for the pair data structure, and adds some higher level operations on pairs to effect the list abstraction. A linked list is effectively represented by its first pair.

The pair abstract data structure is very simple. It consists of a constructor pair, and two accessors called *head* and *tail* that satisfy the algebraic specification

$$p = \mathrm{pair}(\mathrm{head}(p), \mathrm{tail}(p))$$

for each pair $p$. In addition, there is a distinguished pair nil, satisfying this algebraic relation, that is unequal to any other pair, and satisfies

$$\mathrm{head}(\mathrm{nil}) = \mathrm{nil}, \mathrm{tail}(\mathrm{nil}) = \mathrm{nil}.$$

Note that linked lists are quite different from the Maple built-in list structures, which are really immutable arrays. Linked lists are best suited for applications in which you want to incrementally build up the list from its members.[1]

**Package Implementation** The `LinkedList` package is implemented as a module containing the primitive operations on pairs, and higher level operations that implement the list abstraction.

```
> macro( _PAIR = `` ): # for nice printing
> LinkedList := module()
>     description "routines for simple linked lists";
>     export
>         nil,
>         nullp,
>         pair,
>         head,
>         tail,
>         list,
>         length,
>         member,
>         reverse,
>         append,
>         map;
>     local
>         setup,
>         cleanup,
```

[1]Lisp programmers will recognize the pair, head, and tail operations as the more traditional operations known as "cons", "car" and "cdr".

```
>           map1,
>           reverse1,
>           _PAIR;
>       option
>           package,
>           load = setup,
>           unload = cleanup;
>
>       setup := proc()
>           global  `type/Pair`, `type/LinkedList`;
>           `type/Pair` := '{ _PAIR( anything, anything ),
>                             identical( nil ) }';
>           `type/LinkedList` := proc( expr )
>               if expr = nil then
>                   true
>               elif type( expr, Pair ) then
>                   type( tail( expr ), 'LinkedList' )
>               else
>                   false
>               end if
>           end proc;
>           userinfo( 1, 'LinkedList',
>               "new types `Pair` and `LinkedList` defined" );
>           NULL
>       end proc;
>
>       cleanup := proc()
>           global  `type/Pair`, `type/LinkedList`;
>           userinfo( 1, 'LinkedList',
>               "cleaning up global types" );
>           `type/Pair` := evaln( `type/Pair` );
>           `type/LinkedList` := evaln( `type/LinkedList` );
>           NULL
>       end proc;
>
>       pair := ( a, b )
>           -> setattribute( '_PAIR'( a, b ), 'inert' );
>       head := ( c::Pair )
>           -> `if`( c = nil, nil, op( 1, c ) );
>       tail := ( c::Pair )
>           -> `if`( c = nil, nil, op( 2, c ) );
>       nullp := ( pair )
>           -> evalb( pair = nil );
>
>       list := proc()
>           local   a, L;
>           L := nil;
>           for a in args do
>               L := pair( a, L )
>           end do
>       end proc;
>
>       length := proc( lst )
>           if nullp( lst ) then
```

```
>             0
>         else
>             1 + length( tail( lst ) )
>         end if
>     end proc;
>
>     member := proc( item, lst )
>         if nullp( lst ) then
>             false
>         elif item = head( lst ) then
>             true
>         else
>             procname( item, tail( lst ) )
>         end if
>     end proc;
>
>     map := proc( p, lst )
>         if nullp( lst ) then
>             nil
>         else
>             pair( p( head( lst ) ),
>                 procname( p, tail( lst ) ) )
>         end if
>     end proc;
>
>     append := proc( lst1, lst2 )
>         if nullp( lst1 ) then
>             lst2
>         else
>             pair( head( lst1 ),
>                 procname( tail( lst1 ), lst2 ) )
>         end if
>     end proc;
>
>     reverse1 := proc( sofar, todo )
>         if nullp( todo ) then
>             sofar
>         else
>             procname( pair( head( todo ), sofar ),
>                 tail( todo ) )
>         end if
>     end proc;
>
>     reverse := lst -> reverse1( nil, lst );
>
>     setup();
>
> end module:
```

Normally, a package definition like this would be entered into a Maple source file using a text editor, or in a worksheet using the Maple graphical user interface. In either case, the definition would then be followed by a call to the `savelib` procedure using the name of the module as its sole argument:

```
> savelib( 'LinkedList' );
```

Evaluating the `savelib` call saves the module to the first repository found in the global variable `libname`, or the repository named with the global variable `savelibname`, if it is defined. (At least one of these must be defined.)

**Important** Always ensure that the standard Maple library is write-protected to avoid saving expressions in it. If you accidentally save something to the standard Maple library, you may need to restore the original from the media on which you obtained the Maple software.

The package exports are listed as the exports of the module. A few local variables are used to implement the package. The local procedures `map1` and `reverse1` are part of the package implementation that is not available to users of the package. They are visible only within the module definition. This allows the package author to make improvements to the package without disturbing any code that uses it. If the local procedures `reverse1` and `map1` were exported (thus, available to users), it would be difficult for the author to replace these routines without breaking existing code that relies upon them.

The package includes two special (local) procedures, `setup` and `cleanup`. These are executed, respectively, when the module is first read from a repository, and when the package is either garbage collected or when Maple is about to exit.

**Using the Package** The package exports can always be accessed by using the long form of their names.

```
> LinkedList:-pair( a, b );
```

$$(a, b)$$

For consistency with the older table-based package implementations, an indexed notation can also be used.

```
> LinkedList[ 'pair' ]( a, b );
```

$$(a, b)$$

This form requires that the index (in this case, the symbol `pair`) be protected from evaluation, and the notation does not extend to packages with nested subpackages.

To access the package exports interactively, use the `with` command.

```
> with( LinkedList );
```

```
Warning, the protected names length, map and member
have been redefined and unprotected
```

$$[append, head, length, list, map, member, nil, nullp, pair, reverse, tail]$$

Note that, since some of the package exports shadow global procedures with the same name, the `with` command issues warnings. These warnings are normal. They remind you that these names now refer to expressions different from the expressions to which they referred previously. Once the exports of the package `LinkedList` have been bound, you can call them as you would global Maple routines with those names. Note that you can still access the global version of `member`, for example, by using the syntax `:-member`.

```
> use LinkedList in
>     member( a, %% );
>     :-member( a, [ a, b, c, d ] )
> end use;
```

$$true$$

$$true$$

This is one of the principal advantages of using modules and binding, rather than assignment, to implement packages.

Lists are either built incrementally using the `pair` export of the package, or by calling the `list` export.

```
> L := nil:
> for i from 1 to 10 do
>     L := pair( i, L )
> end do;
```

$$L := (1,\ nil)$$

$$L := (2,\ (1,\ nil))$$

$$L := (3,\ (2,\ (1,\ nil)))$$

$$L := (4,\ (3,\ (2,\ (1,\ nil))))$$

$$L := (5,\ (4,\ (3,\ (2,\ (1,\ nil)))))$$

$$L := (6,\ (5,\ (4,\ (3,\ (2,\ (1,\ nil))))))$$

$$L := (7,\ (6,\ (5,\ (4,\ (3,\ (2,\ (1,\ nil)))))))$$

$$L := (8,\ (7,\ (6,\ (5,\ (4,\ (3,\ (2,\ (1,\ nil))))))))$$

$$L := (9,\ (8,\ (7,\ (6,\ (5,\ (4,\ (3,\ (2,\ (1,\ nil)))))))))$$

$$L := (10,\ (9,\ (8,\ (7,\ (6,\ (5,\ (4,\ (3,\ (2,\ (1,\ nil))))))))))$$

```
> length( L );
```

$$10$$

```
> member( 3, L );
```

$$true$$

```
> member( 100, L );
```

$$false$$

```
> reverse( L );
```

$$(1,\ (2,\ (3,\ (4,\ (5,\ (6,\ (7,\ (8,\ (9,\ (10,\ nil))))))))))$$

```
> map( x -> x^2, L );
```

$$(100,\ (81,\ (64,\ (49,\ (36,\ (25,\ (16,\ (9,\ (4,\ (1,\ nil))))))))))$$

```
> member( 100, % );
```

$$true$$

```
> L2 := list( a, b, c, d );
```

$$L2 := (d,\ (c,\ (b,\ (a,\ nil))))$$

```
> map( sin, L2 );
```

$$(\sin(d),\ (\sin(c),\ (\sin(b),\ (\sin(a),\ nil))))$$

```
> eval( L2, { a = 1, b = 2, c = 3, d = 4 } );
```

$$(4,\ (3,\ (2,\ (1,\ nil))))$$

```
> map( evalf[ 10 ], % );
```

$$(4.,\ (3.,\ (2.,\ (1.,\ nil))))$$

## Code Coverage Profiling Package

The following example is a package called coverage. It instruments procedures and modules for coverage profiling, that is, turns on statement-level tracing. It serves as an example of a small package, and illustrates ways in which modules can be manipulated.[2]

**Design** You can write tests that exercise each part of the program to ensure that the program:

- Works correctly
- Continues to work when it, or other programs on which it depends, change over time.

It is important to be able to determine whether each statement in a procedure is executed by some test case. The traceproc option of the Maple command debugopts provides that capability. It takes the name p of a procedure, using the syntax

[2]The Maple CodeTools package provides tools for profiling code and testing code coverage. For more information, refer to ?CodeTools.

```
debugopts( 'traceproc' = p );
```

and instruments the procedure assigned to p for coverage profiling. Here is an example.

```
> p := proc( x )
>     if x < 0 then
>         2 * x
>     else
>         1 + 2 * x
>     end if
> end proc:
> debugopts( 'traceproc' = p ):
```

Once the procedure has been instrumented, each time it is executed, profiling information at the statement level is stored. To view the profiling information, use the procedure **showstat**.

```
> p( 2 );
```

$$5$$

```
> showstat( p );

p := proc(x)
     |Calls Seconds  Words|
PROC |    1   0.000     12|
   1 |    1   0.000     12| if x < 0 then
   2 |    0   0.000      0|   2*x
                            else
   3 |    1   0.000      0|   1+2*x
                            end if

end proc
```

The display shows that only one branch of the **if** statement that forms the body of p was taken so far. This is because only a non-negative argument has been supplied as an argument to p. To get complete coverage, a negative argument must also be supplied.

```
> p( -1 );
```

$$-2$$

```
> showstat( p );
```

```
p := proc(x)
     |Calls Seconds  Words|
PROC |     2   0.000     24|
   1 |     2   0.000     24| if x < 0 then
   2 |     1   0.000      0|   2*x
                             else
   3 |     1   0.000      0|   1+2*x
                             end if
end proc
```

The display shows that each statement in the body of p has been reached.

To display the profiling information, use the debugopts command with the traceproctable=procedure_name equation argument.

```
> debugopts( traceproctable=p );
```

$$\begin{bmatrix} 2 & 0 & 24 \\ 2 & 0 & 24 \\ 1 & 0 & 0 \\ 1 & 0 & 0 \end{bmatrix}$$

The package illustrated in this section helps extend this functionality to modules, and acts as an interface to the debugopts with the traceproc option.

The coverage package has two exports: profile and covered. Two private procedures, rprofile and traced, are used as subroutines. They are stored in local variables of the underlying module of the package.

**The Package Source** Here is the source code for the package.

```
> coverage := module()
>     description "a package of utilities for "
>                 "code coverage profiling";
>     option package;
>     export profile, covered;
>     local rprofile, traced, userprocs;
>
>     # Instrument a procedure or module
>     # for coverage profiling. Return the
>     # number of procedures instrumented.
>     profile := proc()
>         local arg;
>         add( rprofile( arg ), arg = [ args ] )
>     end proc;
```

```
>
>     rprofile := proc( s::name )
>         local e;
>         if type( s, 'procedure' ) then
>             debugopts( 'traceproc' = s );
>             1
>         elif type( s, '`module`' ) then
>             add( procname( e ),
>                 e = select( type,
>                         [ exports( s, 'instance' ) ],
>                         '{ `module`, procedure }' ) )
>         else
>             error "only procedures and modules can be profiled"
>         end if
>     end proc;
>
>     # Subroutine to recognize non-builtin procedures
>     userprocs := proc( s)
>         type( 's', procedure) and not( type( 's', builtin ) )
>     end proc;
>
>     # Subroutine to recognize profiled procedures
>     traced := proc( s )
>         debugopts( 'istraceproced' = 's' )
>     end proc;
>
>     # Determine which procedures have
>     # coverage information.
>     covered := proc()
>         local S;
>         S := [ anames( ) ];
>         S := select( userprocs, S );
>         S := select( traced, S );
>         if nargs > 0 and args[ 1 ] = 'nonzero' then
>             S := select( s -> evalb( s[1,1] <> 0 ), S )
>         elif nargs > 0 then
>             error "optional argument is the name nonzero"
>         end if;
>         map( parse, map( convert, S, 'string' ) )
>     end proc;
> end module:
```

**How the Package Works** The export `profile` is an interface to the package's principal facility: instrumenting procedures and modules for coverage profiling. It returns the number of procedures instrumented, and calls the private subroutine `rprofile` to do most of the work.

1. The procedure `rprofile` accepts a name `s` as an argument. If `s` is the name of a procedure, `rprofile` simply calls `debugopts` to instrument the procedure assigned to that name. Otherwise, if `s` is the name of a module, `rprofile` selects any exports of the module that are

procedures or modules and calls itself recursively to instrument them. If the parameter `s` is assigned a value of any other type, then an exception is raised.

2. The expression `[ exports( s, 'instance' ) ]` evaluates to a list of all the exported variables of the module that are assigned to `s`. It is important to pass the `instance` option to `exports`, because when those names are passed to `rprofile` in a recursive call, `rprofile` must test the type of their assigned values. This list contains *all* the module exports, so those that are of type `procedure`, or of type `module`, are selected by using a call to `select`. The recursion is effected in the call to `add`, which sums the return values of all the recursive calls to `rprofile`.

3. The exported procedure `covered` is used to determine which procedures have been instrumented and called, with profiling information stored. One possible design would store this information in a private table in the `coverage` package. With this design, `covered` could simply query that internal table for the names of the procedures that have been instrumented and that have profiling information stored. However, a user may have instrumented the procedure manually by calling `debugopts` directly, or historical profiling data may have been read from a Maple repository. Therefore, a design that queries the system directly, without regard to how a procedure was initially instrumented, is best used.

   The procedure `covered` queries Maple for all the names currently assigned values using the Maple command `anames` ("assigned names"). Names corresponding to profiled user procedures are selected using the subroutines `userprocs` and `traced`. If the `nonzero` option is passed to `covered`, then only those which have actually been called are chosen. The final statement

   ```
   > map( parse, map( convert, S, 'string' ) )
   ```

   first converts the names to strings, and then calls `parse` on each string to convert it to the procedure for which profiling data is stored.

**Using the Package** As with all packages, you can access the `coverage` package interactively by using the `with` command.

```
> with( coverage );
```

```
Warning, the protected name profile has been redefined
and unprotected
```

$$[covered, profile]$$

A list of the package exports is returned. Alternatively, the package exports can always be accessed by using the long forms `coverage:-profile` and `coverage:-covered`.

Suppose that you want to test the procedure `copy` (chosen because it is short). This procedure produces a new copy of a table, array, or rtable. Now that the `coverage` package has been globally imposed by using `with`, simply call

```
> profile( copy );
```

$$1$$

The return value of 1 indicates that, as expected, one procedure was instrumented. Next, call `copy` with a few arguments (output suppressed):

```
> copy( table() ):
> copy( array( 1 .. 3 ) ):
```

Using `covered`, `copy` has its profiling information stored.

```
> covered( 'nonzero' );
```

$$[p, copy]$$

From the output of `showstat`,

```
> showstat( copy );
```

```
copy := proc(A)
     |Calls Seconds  Words|
PROC |    2   0.000    664|
   1 |    2   0.000     50| if type(A,rtable) then
   2 |    0   0.000      0|   return rtable(rtable_indfns(A),
                                rtable_dims(A),A,rtable_options(A),
                                readonly = false)
                            elif type(A,{array, table}) then
   3 |    2   0.000     24|   if type(A,name) then
   4 |    0   0.000      0|     return map(proc () args end proc,
                                  eval(A))
                              else
   5 |    2   0.000    590|     return map(proc () args end proc,A)
                              end if
                            else
   6 |    0   0.000      0|   return A
                            end if
```

```
end proc
```

it appears that the rtable case (statement 2) has not been called. Add a test for the rtable case.

```
> copy( rtable() ):
> showstat( copy );
```

```
copy := proc(A)
     |Calls Seconds  Words|
PROC |    3   0.000    832|
   1 |    3   0.000     62| if type(A,rtable) then
   2 |    1   0.000    156|   return rtable(rtable_indfns(A),
                                 rtable_dims(A),A,rtable_options(A),
                                 readonly = false)
                            elif type(A,{array, table}) then
   3 |    2   0.000     24|   if type(A,name) then
   4 |    0   0.000      0|     return map(proc () args end proc,
                                   eval(A))
                              else
   5 |    2   0.000    590|     return map(proc () args end proc,A)
                              end if
                            else
   6 |    0   0.000      0|   return A
                            end if
end proc
```

Statement 4 has not been called. This statement can be reached by assigning an array or table to a name and by calling copy with that name as argument.

```
> t := table():
> copy( t ):
> showstat( copy );
```

```
copy := proc(A)
     |Calls Seconds  Words|
PROC |    4   0.000   1185|
   1 |    4   0.000     96| if type(A,rtable) then
   2 |    1   0.000    156|   return rtable(rtable_indfns(A),
                                 rtable_dims(A),A,rtable_options(A),
                                 readonly = false)
                            elif type(A,{array, table}) then
   3 |    3   0.000     28|   if type(A,name) then
   4 |    1   0.000    315|     return map(proc () args end proc,
                                   eval(A))
                              else
   5 |    2   0.000    590|     return map(proc () args end proc,A)
                              end if
                            else
```

```
     6 |      0    0.000        0|    return A
                                    end if
end proc
```

The only case that has not been called is the one in which the argument to copy is something other than an rtable, array, or table.

```
> copy( 2 ):
> showstat( copy );
```

```
copy := proc(A)
      |Calls Seconds  Words|
PROC  |     5   0.000   1221|
   1  |     5   0.000    122| if type(A,rtable) then
   2  |     1   0.000    156|   return rtable(rtable_indfns(A),
                                  rtable_dims(A),A,rtable_options(A),
                                  readonly = false)
                              elif type(A,{array, table}) then
   3  |     3   0.000     28|   if type(A,name) then
   4  |     1   0.000    315|     return map(proc () args end proc,
                                    eval(A))
                                else
   5  |     2   0.000    590|     return map(proc () args end proc,A)
                                end if
                              else
   6  |     1   0.000     10|   return A
                              end if
end proc
```

The final output shows that every statement has been reached by the test cases. This functionality is very useful for interactively developing unit tests for Maple programs.

**Note:** The source presented here for the `coverage` package has been simplified for presentation in printed form. The full source code is available in the `samples/AdvPG` directory of the Maple installation.

## The Shapes Package

Modules permit the construction of packages with hierarchical structure. This cannot be done with table-based implementations of packages. This section presents:

- How to organize the source code for a (potentially) large package that has a nontrivial substructure.
- A description of the `Shapes` package, including details of its design and implementation

- Hints related to source code organization.

The mathematical functionality of this package is trivial. It provides the means to compute areas and circumferences of various planar figures, which are called shapes.

**Note:** Only portions of the source code for this package are shown here. The fully commented source code can be found in the `samples/AdvPG/shapes` directory of the Maple installation.

**Source Code Organization** The `Shapes` package is organized into several source files:

```
shapes.mpl

    point.mpl
    segment.mpl
    circle.mpl
    square.mpl
    triangle.mpl
```

To avoid platform-specific differences, a flat directory structure is used. (All the source files reside in the same directory or folder.)

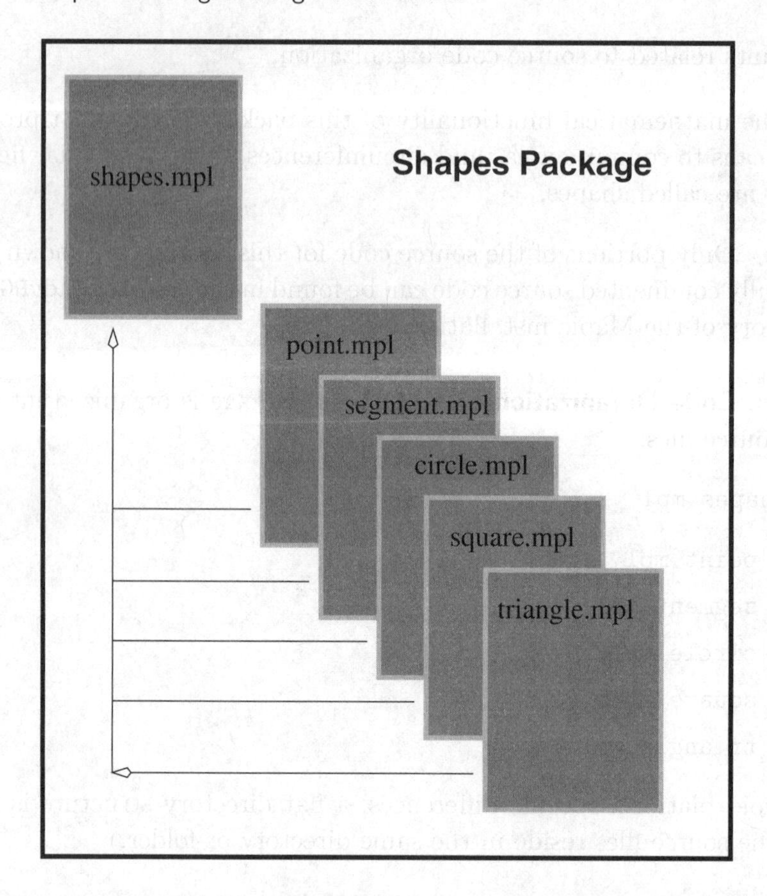


To define the module that implements this package, use the Maple preprocessor to include the remaining source files at the appropriate point in the master source file `shapes.mpl`. A number of `$include` directives are included in `shapes.mpl`, such as

```
$include          "point.mpl"
$include          "segment.mpl"
...
```

Splitting a large project into a number of source files makes it easier to manage, and allows several developers to work on a project simultaneously. The source file is divided into shape-specific functionality. Most of the functionality for points, for instance, is implemented by source code stored in the file `point.mpl`.

**Package Architecture** The `Shapes` package is structured as a module with a number of exported procedures. Individual submodules provide shape-specific functionality for each shape type supported by the package.

Each of these shape-specific submodules is stored in its own source file; these files are included into the main package source file, `shapes.mpl`.

The package module `Shapes` has a submodule, *also* called `Shapes`. The submodule `Shapes:-Shapes` contains one submodule for each shape supported. This submodule hierarchy is illustrated in the following diagram.

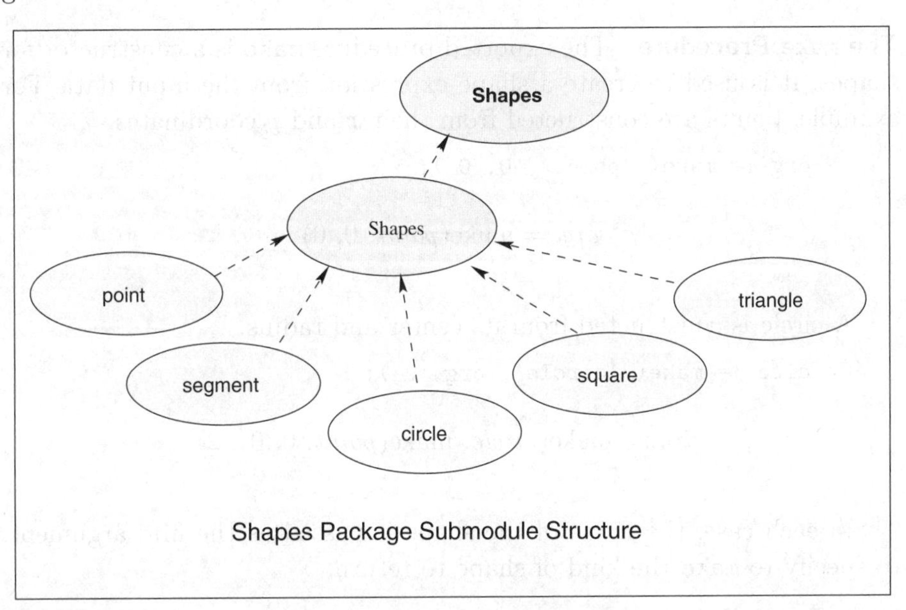


Shapes Package Submodule Structure

The result of preprocessing the main file `shapes.mpl` produces a module whose source has the following general outline.

```
Shapes := module()
    export make, area, circumference;
    local Shapes, circum_table;
    Shapes := module()
        export point, segment, circle, square, triangle;
        point := module() ... end;
        segment := module() ... end;
        .....
    end module;
    make := proc() ... end;
    area := proc() ... end;
    circum_table := table(); ...
    circumference := proc() ... end;
end module:
```

**The Package API** The `Shapes` package exports the following routines:

1. `make`
2. `area`
3. `circumference`

**The `make` Procedure** The exported procedure `make` is a constructor for shapes. It is used to create a shape expression from the input data. For example, points are constructed from their $x$ and $y$ coordinates.

```
> org := make( 'point', 0, 0 );
```

$$org := \mathrm{make}(point,\ 0,\ 0)$$

A circle is constructed from its center and radius.

```
> circ := make( 'circle', org, 2 );
```

$$circ := \mathrm{make}(circle,\ \mathrm{make}(point,\ 0,\ 0),\ 2)$$

In each case, the name of the shape is passed as the first argument, to specify to `make` the kind of shape to return.

**The `area` Procedure** To compute the area of a shape, call the exported procedure `area` with the shape as its argument.

```
> area( circ );
```

$$\mathrm{area}(\mathrm{make}(circle,\ \mathrm{make}(point,\ 0,\ 0),\ 2))$$

**The `circumference` Procedure** The exported procedure `circumference` computes the circumference of a given shape.

```
> circumference( circ );
```

$$\mathrm{circumference}(\mathrm{make}(circle,\ \mathrm{make}(point,\ 0,\ 0),\ 2))$$

**Shape Representation** Shapes are represented as unevaluated function calls. The arguments to the call are the instance-specific data for the shape. For example, a point with coordinates $(2, 3)$ is represented by the unevaluated function call `POINT( 2, 3 )`. Some instance data are shapes themselves. For example, a segment is represented, using its endpoints, as an unevaluated function call of the form `SEGMENT( start_point, end_point )`. The start and end points of the segment can be obtained by calls to the point constructor.

**Procedure Dispatch** The `Shapes` package illustrates three types of procedure dispatching:

1. Dispatching on submodule exports
2. Conditional dispatching
3. Table-based dispatching

**Dispatching on Submodule Exports** The procedure `make`, which is exported from the `Shapes` package, uses the submodule `Shapes:-Shapes` for procedure dispatching.

To test whether a method for a given shape is available, the procedure `make` tests whether there is a submodule by that name in the `Shapes:-Shapes` submodule. If no such submodule is found, an exception is raised. Otherwise, the export `make` *from the submodule* is passed the arguments that were given to the top-level `Shapes:-make` procedure. The `make` source code follows.

```
> make := proc( what::symbol )
>         description "constructor for shapes";
>         local   ctor,      # the shape constructor,
>                            # if found
>                 theShape; #the submodule for the
>                            # kind of shape requested
>
>         if not member( what, Shapes, 'theShape' ) then
>                 error "shape `%1' not available", what
>         end if;
>         if member( ':-make', theShape, 'ctor' ) then
>                 ctor( args[ 2 .. nargs ] )
>         else
>                 error "no constructor provided for "
>                       "shape %1", what
>         end if
> end proc:
```

**Summary** The first argument to make is a symbol that denotes the kind of shape to construct (point, circle, triangle). This symbol is used as an index in the Shapes:-Shapes submodule. The first statement uses member to test whether the symbol passed in the parameter what is exported by the submodule Shapes:-Shapes. If it is not found, an appropriate diagnostic is issued, and an exception raised. If member returns the value true, then its third argument, the local variable theShape, is assigned the export found in the submodule.

For example, if what is the symbol circle, then the local variable theShape is assigned the submodule Shapes:-Shapes:-circle that implements operations on circles. The same idea is used to select the shape-specific constructor; it is the value assigned to the local variable ctor upon a true return value from the second call to member. Any remaining arguments are used as data to construct the shape. These are passed to the make export in a shape-specific submodule, if found, and are not checked further at this level. This design localizes the shapes to the corresponding submodule.

**Conditional Dispatching** The procedure area uses a simple conditional dispatching mechanism. The tag of the input shape is extracted and is used in direct comparisons with hard-coded values to determine which shape-specific area subroutine to call to perform the area computation.

```
> area := proc( shape )
>         description "compute the area of a shape";
>         local   tag;
>
>         if not type( shape, 'function' ) then
>                 error "expecting a shape expression, "
>                   "but got %1", shape
>         end if;
>
>         # Extract the "tag" information from the shape
>         tag := op( 0, shape );
>
>         # Dispatch on the "tag" value
>         if tag = ':-POINT' then
>                 Shapes:-point:-area( shape )
>         elif tag = ':-SEGMENT' then
>                 Shapes:-segment:-area( shape )
>         elif tag = ':-CIRCLE' then
>                 Shapes:-circle:-area( shape )
>         elif tag = ':-SQUARE' then
>                 Shapes:-square:-area( shape )
>         elif tag = ':-TRIANGLE' then
>                 Shapes:-triangle:-area( shape )
>         else
>                 error "not a recognized shape: %1", tag
```

```
>           end if
> end proc:
```

**Table-based Dispatching** The third dispatch method illustrated in the `Shapes` package is table-based. This technique is used by the exported procedure `circumference`, which references the table `circum_table` to look up the appropriate routine to call. This table is built simply by assigning its entries in the body of the `Shapes` package.

```
> circum_table := table();
> circum_table[ 'POINT' ] := Shapes:-point:-circumference;
> circum_table[ 'SEGMENT' ] := Shapes:-segment:-circumference;
> circum_table[ 'CIRCLE' ] := Shapes:-circle:-circumference;
> circum_table[ 'SQUARE' ] := Shapes:-square:-circumference;
> circum_table[ 'TRIANGLE' ] := Shapes:-triangle:-circumference;
```

The source code for the procedure `circumference` follows.

```
> circumference := proc( shape )
>           description "compute the circumference of a "
>                   "shape expression";
>           if not type( shape, 'function' ) then
>                   error "expecting a shape, but got %1", shape
>           end if;
>           if assigned( circum_table[ op( 0, shape ) ] ) then
>                   circum_table[ op( 0, shape ) ]( shape )
>           else
>                   error "no circumference method available "
>                     "for shape %1. Supported shapes "
>                     "are: %2", tag,
>                           sprintf( "%q", op( ALL_SHAPES ) )
>           end if
> end proc:
```

Minimal checking is done to ensure that the input has the right structure. If an entry is found in the table `circum_table` for the shape tag (as with the `area` routine), then the corresponding procedure is called with the given shape as an argument. (The shape must be passed as an argument, so that the shape-specific subroutine can extract the instance data from it.) Otherwise, a diagnostic is issued, and an exception raised.

**Shape-specific Submodules** As already noted, each shape is implemented in a shape-specific submodule. The set of exports of each module varies, but each supports the required exports `make`, `area`, and `circumference` in the top-level `Shapes` module. Particular shapes support other operations. Only two submodules are described here. You can see the source for the other submodules in the sample source code.

**The point Submodule** The submodule that implements points is fairly simple. In fact, it makes no reference to any lexically scoped variables in its parent modules (Shapes and Shapes:-Shapes).

```
> point := module()
>     description "support routines for points";
>     export make, area, circumference, xcoord, ycoord;
>     option package;
>
>     make := ( x, y ) -> 'POINT'( x, y );
>     area := () -> 0;
>     circumference := () -> 0;
>     xcoord := p -> op( 1, p );
>     ycoord := p -> op( 2, p );
> end module:
```

Since the area and circumference of a point are both 0, these procedures are trivial to implement. In addition to the required exports, the point submodule also exports two utility routines, xcoord and ycoord, for retrieving the $x$ and $y$ coordinates of a point. Providing these makes it possible for clients of this submodule to use it without knowing anything about the concrete representation of points. This makes it easier to change the representation later, if required.

Within this submodule, the names make, area, and circumference shadow the names with the same external representation at the top-level Shapes module.

**The circle Submodule** This submodule provides the circle-specific subroutines for the Shapes package.

```
> circle := module()
>     export  make, center, radius, diameter,
>             area, circumference;
>     option package;
>
>     make := proc( cntrPt, radius )
>             'CIRCLE'( cntrPt, radius )
>     end proc;
>
>     center := circ -> op( 1, circ );
>     radius := circ -> op( 2, circ );
>     diameter := circ -> 2 * radius( circ );
>     circumference := circ ->  Pi * diameter( circ );
>     area := circ -> Pi * radius( circ )^2;
> end module:
```

Again, a few extra routines are provided in addition to those required at the top-level of the Shapes package. The exported procedure radius is used to define other routines. It can be made local to this submodule.

## 2.4 The use Statement

The use statement is formally unrelated to modules, but is expressly designed to complement them and to make programming with modules easier in some circumstances.

**Syntax and Semantics** The keyword **use** introduces the use statement, which has the following syntax template:

```
use env in
    body
end use;
```

Here, *env* is an expression sequence of *binding equations*, each of which is either a module or an equation whose left side is a symbol; and *body* is a sequence of Maple statements. The right side of a binding equation can be any Maple expression.

Executing a use statement executes the body of the statement. Each occurrence of a name that appears on the left side of any of the binding equations is replaced by the right side of the corresponding equation.

For example,

```
> use f = sin, g = cos in
>     f( x )^2 + g( x )^2
> end use;
```

$$\sin(x)^2 + \cos(x)^2$$

**Characteristics of the use Statement** The use statement can be nested.

```
> use f = sin in
>     use g = cos in
>         simplify( f(x)^2 + g(x)^2 )
>     end use
> end use;
```

$$1$$

When nested use statements are encountered, the name bindings established by the inner use statement take precedence over those of the outer one.

```
> use a = 2, b = 3 in
>     use a = 3 in a + b end
> end use;
```

$$6$$

In this example, the inner binding of the value 3 to the name a takes precedence, so the value of the expression `a + b` (and hence of the entire statement) is the number 6. The inner binding of 3 to a has an effect only within the body of the inner use statement. Once the execution has exited the inner use statement, the binding of 2 to a is restored.

```
> use a = 2, b = 3 in
>     # here a is bound to 2 and b to 3
>     use a = 3 in
>         # here, b is still bound to 3, but a is bound to 3
>         a + b
>     end use;
>     # binding of a to 2 is restored
>     a + b
> end use;
```

$$6$$

$$5$$

The use statement is unique in the Maple language because it is fully resolved during automatic simplification. It is not possible to *evaluate* a use statement. (Recall that Maple uses a modified read-eval-print loop, which actually involves the four stages: parsing (reading), *automatic simplification*, evaluation, and printing.)

To see how this works, consider an example in which the use statement appears inside a procedure.

```
> f := proc( a, b )
>     use x = a + b, y = a - b in
>         x * y
>     end use
> end proc;
```

$$f := \mathbf{proc}(a, b)\,(a+b)*(a-b)\ \ \mathbf{end\ proc}$$

Note that the body of the procedure f contains no use statement. During automatic simplification, the use statement that formed the body of `f` was expanded, yielding the expression that involves only the parameters `a` and `b`.

**Modules and use Statements** As a special case, a module `m` can appear in the binding sequence of a `use` statement. The module is regarded as an abbreviation for the sequence of equations `a = m:-a, b = m:-b, ...`, where `a,b,...` are the exports of the module `m`.

For example,

```
> m := module() export a, b; a := 2; b := 3; end:
> use m in a + b end;
```

$$5$$

This is useful for programming with packages.

```
> m := Matrix( 4, 4, [[ 26, 0,    0,    30 ],
>                     [ 0,   -41, -90, 0],
>                     [ 0,   -7,   -56, 0 ],
>                     [ 0,   0,    0,    0]] );
```

$$m := \begin{bmatrix} 26 & 0 & 0 & 30 \\ 0 & -41 & -90 & 0 \\ 0 & -7 & -56 & 0 \\ 0 & 0 & 0 & 0 \end{bmatrix}$$

```
> use LinearAlgebra in
>     Determinant( m );
>     Rank( m );
>     CharacteristicPolynomial( m, 'lambda' )
> end use;
```

$$0$$

$$3$$

$$\lambda^4 + 71\,\lambda^3 - 856\,\lambda^2 - 43316\,\lambda$$

Note that a name that appears in a binding list for a `use` statement, which is intended to be a module, must evaluate to a module *at the time the `use` statement is simplified.* This is necessary because the simplification of the `use` statement must be able to determine the exports of the module. In particular, the following attempt to pass a module as a parameter to a procedure does *not* work, and yields an error during the simplification of the procedure.

```
> proc( m, a, b )
>     use m in e( a, b ) end
> end proc;
```

```
Error, no bindings were specified or implied
```

The correct way to use a module as a parameter is to specify the names to be bound explicitly, such as in this example:

```
> proc( m, a, b )
>     use e = m:-e in a + b end
> end proc;
```

$$\mathbf{proc}(m,\, a,\, b)\, a + b\, \mathbf{end\ proc}$$

This is necessary because, until the procedure is called with a module expression as first argument, the reference to e is ambiguous. The variable e could refer to a module export or to something else (such as a global name). To expand the use statement, this must be known at the time the procedure is simplified.

## Operator Rebinding

An additional feature of the use statement is that it allows most infix and prefix operators in the Maple language to be rebound. This is not the operator overloading found in some programming languages (such as C++), because the rebinding occurs during automatic simplification in Maple.

If an operator name appears on the left side of a binding equation for a use statement (consequently, if it is an exported name of a module that is bound via use), then the corresponding operator expressions in the body of the use statement are transformed into function calls. For example:

```
> use `+` = F in a + b end;
```

$$\mathrm{F}(a,\, b)$$

```
> m := module()
>     export `*`, `+`;
>     `+` := ( a, b ) -> a + b - 1;
>     `*` := ( a, b ) -> a / b;
> end module:
> s * ( s + t );
```

$$s\,(s+t)$$

```
> use m in s * ( s + t ) end;
```

$$\frac{s}{s+t-1}$$

The operators that can be rebound are summarized in the following table.

| *Operator* | *Arity* | *Position* | *Description* |
|---|---|---|---|
| | *Arithmetic Operators* | | |
| `+` | binary | infix | addition |
| `*` | binary | infix | multiplication |
| `.` | binary | infix | multiplication |
| `^` | binary | infix | exponentiation |
| `-` | unary | prefix | negation |
| `/` | unary | prefix | inversion (reciprocal) |
| | *Logical Operators* | | |
| `and` | binary | infix | logical and |
| `or` | binary | infix | logical or |
| `not` | unary | prefix | logical negation |
| | *Relational Operators* | | |
| `<` | binary | infix | less than |
| `<=` | binary | infix | less than or equal |
| `>` | binary | infix | greater than |
| `>=` | binary | infix | greater than or equal |
| `=` | binary | infix | equality |
| `<>` | binary | infix | not equal |
| | *Other Operators* | | |
| `@` | binary | infix | composition |
| `@@` | binary | infix | power composition |
| `!` | unary | postfix | factorial |

Note that the operators `-` and `/` are treated as *unary* operators (that represent negation and inversion, respectively). Subtraction is represented internally in Maple by composing addition and negation: `a - b = a + (-b)`. Similarly for division. Therefore, it is not necessary to override the *binary* infix operators `-` and `/`.

Note also that an expression such as `a + b + c + d` is treated as though it were parenthesized as `((a + b) + c) + d`, so that each `+` operator is binary. For example,

```
> use `+` = F in
>     a + b + c + d;
>     a + ( ( b + c ) + d )
> end use;
```

$$F(F(F(a, b), c), d)$$

$$F(a, F(F(b, c), d))$$

## 2.5 Modeling Objects

A principle application of modules is modeling objects. An *object* is something that has both state and behavior. Many programming languages provide support for programming with objects. Some of these are called object-oriented; popular examples include Smalltalk, CLOS, Java™, and C++.

Maple is not an object-oriented programming language, but it does support programming with objects. In Maple, an object can be represented by a module. The state of the object (module) is stored in the local and exported data variables. The behavior of the object is represented by procedures assigned to the exported variables. In Maple, procedures stand on an equal footing with other expressions in the language; the distinction between state and behavior is somewhat artificial and exists only as a convention.

The essential idea behind programming with objects is that the objects carry their behavior with them. Clients of an object can elicit behavior by sending the object messages. Objects respond to these messages by performing some prescribed computation that is determined by both the recipient of the message (the object) and the message itself (which may be parameterized by other arguments). This is in contrast to non-object-oriented approaches to programming, in which the objects in a software system merely contain static data and serve as inputs and outputs of the algorithms, which are represented separately from the objects by procedures or other routines.

**Objects and Constructors** Objects are usually created by invoking a constructor. A *constructor* is a procedure that builds the object expression from some (possibly empty) set of inputs. Maple uses constructors for a number of its native expression types. For example, the procedure `table` is a constructor for Maple tables, and `series` is a constructor for Maple series expressions.

A constructor *must* be used to create objects that have no input syntax (such as series and tables, in Maple), but can also be used for expressions that do have an input syntax (the `Float` constructor is an example of the latter case). Therefore, most user-defined objects must be created by using a constructor. Most of the object examples in this section are defined by specifying a constructor for the object.

**Example: Complex Number Constructor** A simple example of an object is the following representation of a complex number.

```
> MakeComplex := proc( real, imag )
>     if nargs <> 2 then
>         error "real and imaginary parts are required"
>     end if;
>     module()
>         description "a complex number";
>         local real_part, imag_part;
>         export re, im, abs, arg;
>
>         real_part, imag_part := real, imag;
>         re := () -> real_part;
>         im := () -> imag_part;
>         abs := () -> sqrt( re()^2 + im()^2 );
>         arg := () -> arctan( im(), re() );
>     end module
> end proc:
```

To create the complex number $1 + i$, use the constructor.

```
> z := MakeComplex( 1, 1 );
```

$z :=$ **module**()
**local** *real_part*, *imag_part*;
**export** *re*, *im*, abs, *arg*;
**description** "a complex number";
**end module**

The procedure `MakeComplex` is a constructor for complex number objects. The value returned by the procedure is the instantiation of the module whose definition appears in the body of `MakeComplex`.

The local state of the complex number is represented by the local variables of the module, `real_part` and `imag_part`. The behavior is represented by the exported procedures `re`, `im`, `abs`, and `arg`.

The exports of a module that represents an object are sometimes viewed also as *messages*. Objects respond to these messages by exhibiting the behavior that the messages elicit.

```
> z:-re(), z:-im();
```

$$1, 1$$

```
> z:-abs();
```

$$\sqrt{2}$$

```
> z:-arg();
```

$$\frac{1}{4}\pi$$

For instance, the expression `z:-abs()` is viewed as sending the `abs` message to the complex number object `z`. The object responds by computing its absolute value.

Note that each time the procedure `MakeComplex` is invoked, a new module is created using the module definition that is visible within the procedure body. Thus, complex numbers created by different calls to the constructor are distinct, even if the arguments `real` and `imag` are the same. Whether a constructor should produce distinct objects for the same input (instance) data depends on the nature of the objects being modeled. For complex number objects, multiple calls with the same inputs should produce the same object. This can be achieved by using the `remember` option in the constructor. For more information, refer to chapter 6 of the *Introductory Programming Guide.*

**Effect of Immutable Local States** The previous `MakeComplex` constructor represents the local state of complex number objects by using two local variables `real_part` and `imag_part`. For many object constructors, some or all of the local state of the object is expected to be immutable. In these cases, local variables do not need to be allocated in the module to store the local state of the object. The state can instead be represented by the parameters to the constructor, which are visible within the module by the Maple lexical scoping rules. Using this idea, the previous constructor can be simplified as follows.

**Table 2.1** Priority Queue Methods

| | |
|---|---|
| empty | Test for an empty priority queue |
| top | Return the highest-priority item |
| insert | Insert a prioritized item |
| delete | Remove (and return) the highest priority item |

```
> MakeComplex := proc( real, imag )
>     if nargs <> 2 then
>          error "real and imaginary parts are required"
>     end if;
>     module()
>         description "a complex number";
>         export re, im, abs, arg;
>
>         re := () -> real;
>         im := () -> imag;
>         abs := () -> sqrt( real^2 + imag^2 );
>         arg := () -> arctan( imag, real );
>    end module
> end proc:
```

## Priority Queues

A useful data structure that can be implemented in an object-oriented way with modules is the priority queue. A *priority queue* is a container data structure that admits the following operations:

- Test for an empty priority queue
- Insert a prioritized item into a priority queue
- Return (non-destructively) the highest-priority item in the priority queue
- Delete the highest priority item from a priority queue

**Design** Table 2.1 lists the methods of an object representation of priority queues.

This representation leads directly to the following Maple type, which can be used to identify priority queues.

```
> `type/PriorityQueue` := ''module'( empty, top, insert,
>                                    delete )':
```

**Constructor Implementation** Priority queues can be implemented as Maple objects by writing a constructor for the objects.

```
> PriorityQueue := proc( priority::procedure )
>     description "priority queue constructor";
>     local largs, lnargs;
>
>     lnargs := nargs;
>     if lnargs > 1 then
>         largs := [ args[ 2 .. -1 ] ]
>     else
>         largs := []
>     end if;
>
>     module()
>         description "a priority queue";
>         export empty, top, insert,
>                size, delete, init;
>         local  heap, nitems,
>                bubbleup, bubbledown;
>
>         nitems := 0;
>         heap := table();
>
>         bubbleup := proc( child::posint )
>             local parent;
>             parent := iquo( child, 2 );
>             if child > 1
>               and priority( heap[ child ] ) > priority( heap[
>               parent ] ) then
>                 heap[ parent ], heap[ child ] := heap[ child ],
>                   heap[ parent ];
>                 procname( parent ) # recurse
>             end if
>         end proc;
>
>         bubbledown := proc( parent::posint )
>             local child;
>             child := 2 * parent;
>             if child < nitems
>               and priority( heap[ 1 + child ] ) > priority(
>               heap[ child ] ) then
>                 child := 1 + child
>             end if;
>             if child <= nitems
>               and priority( heap[ parent ] ) < priority( heap[
>               child ] ) then
>                 heap[ parent ], heap[ child ] := heap[ child ],
>                   heap[ parent ];
>                 procname( child ) # recurse (new parent)
>             end if
>         end proc;
>
>         # Initialize the priority queue.
```

```
>          init := proc()
>              heap := table();
>              nitems := 0
>          end proc;
>
>          # Test whether the priority queue is empty.
>          empty := () -> evalb( nitems < 1 );
>
>          # Return the number of items on the priority queue.
>          size := () -> nitems;
>
>          # Query the highest priority item.
>          top := proc()
>              if empty() then
>                  error "priority queue is empty"
>              else
>                  heap[ 1 ]
>              end if
>          end proc;
>
>          # Delete the highest priority item from the
>          # priority queue.
>          delete := proc()
>              local val;
>              val := heap[ 1 ]; # val := top()
>              # move bottom to the top
>              heap[ 1 ] := heap[ nitems ];
>              # allow expression to be collected
>              heap[ nitems ] := evaln( heap[ nitems ] );
>              # decrement the bottom of heap counter
>              nitems := nitems - 1;
>              # heapify the array
>              bubbledown( 1 );
>              # return the value
>              val
>          end proc;
>
>          # Insert an item into the priority queue.
>          insert := proc( v )
>              if nargs > 1 then
>                  op( map( procname, [ args ] ) )
>              else
>                  nitems := 1 + nitems;
>                  heap[ nitems ] := v;
>                  bubbleup( nitems )
>              end if
>          end proc;
>
>          # Insert any intially specified items.
>          if lnargs > 1 then
>              insert( op( largs ) )
>          end if
>      end module
> end proc:
```

The constructor takes a Maple procedure `priority` as its argument. For each expression placed on the queue, this procedure returns a numeric measure of its priority. Items on the queue are maintained in a prioritized order so that the highest priority items are removed first.

In this sample computation with a priority queue, use the Maple built-in procedure `length` as the priority of an expression. Here, the randomly generated expressions are all polynomials.

```
> pq := PriorityQueue( x -> length( x ) );
```

*pq* := **module**()
**local** *heap*, *nitems*, *bubbleup*, *bubbledown*;
**export** *empty*, *top*, *insert*, *size*, *delete*, *init*;
**description** "a priority queue";

**end module**

```
> for i from 1 to 10 do
>     pq:-insert( randpoly( x ) );
> end do:
> while not pq:-empty() do
>     pq:-delete()
> end do;
```

$$50 - 85\,x^5 - 55\,x^4 - 37\,x^3 - 35\,x^2 + 97\,x$$

$$72 - 99\,x^5 - 85\,x^4 - 86\,x^3 + 30\,x^2 + 80\,x$$

$$72 - 53\,x^5 + 85\,x^4 + 49\,x^3 + 78\,x^2 + 17\,x$$

$$-59 + 79\,x^5 + 56\,x^4 + 49\,x^3 + 63\,x^2 + 57\,x$$

$$88 - 86\,x^5 + 23\,x^4 - 84\,x^3 + 19\,x^2 - 50\,x$$

$$-62 - 50\,x^5 - 12\,x^4 - 18\,x^3 + 31\,x^2 - 26\,x$$

$$83 - 58\,x^5 - 90\,x^4 + 53\,x^3 - x^2 + 94\,x$$

$$-61 + 77\,x^5 + 66\,x^4 + 54\,x^3 - 5\,x^2 + 99\,x$$

$$-62 + 45\,x^5 - 8\,x^4 - 93\,x^3 + 92\,x^2 + 43\,x$$

$$41 + x^5 - 47\,x^4 - 91\,x^3 - 47\,x^2 - 61\,x$$

**Priority Queue Usage** Priority queues can be used to implement a heapsort algorithm.

```
> HeapSort := proc( L::list(numeric) )
>     local pq, t, count;
```

```
>       pq := PriorityQueue( x -> -x, op( L ) );
>       t := array( 1 .. nops( L ) );
>       count := 0;
>       while not pq:-empty() do
>           count := 1 + count;
>           t[ count ] := pq:-delete()
>       end do;
>       ASSERT( count = nops( L ) );
>       [ seq( t[ count ], count = 1 .. nops( L ) ) ]
> end proc:
> r := rand(100):
> L := [ seq( r(), i = 1 .. 20 ) ]:
> HeapSort( L );
```

[7, 7, 15, 25, 27, 27, 28, 29, 42, 51, 52, 55, 62, 74, 82,
88, 94, 97, 97, 98]

**Note:** The fully commented source code for the `PriorityQueue` constructor is available in the `samples/advPG/PriorityQueue` directory of the Maple installation.

## An Object-oriented Shapes Package

This section demonstrates an object-oriented approach to the `Shapes` package described in section 2.3. The earlier revision of the package used unevaluated function calls as the concrete representation of shapes. This section demonstrates how to build a package that offers the same functionality, but which represents shapes as objects. Each shape uses a module as its concrete representation. The package itself does not export the `area` and `circumference` features of the traditional style package, because these features are available as part of each shape object. Instead, the package is merely a collection of constructors for the various kinds of shapes. You could use the object representation at a lower level, and present exactly the same interface as the first `Shapes` package, but this section shows how to make the object-oriented nature of shape expressions more apparent to the user.

**The `point` Constructor** Points are simple shapes, so the corresponding constructor is similarly simple.

```
> point := proc( x, y )
>     module()
>         export area, circumference, xcoord, ycoord;
>         xcoord := () -> x;
>         ycoord := () -> y;
>         area := () -> 0;
>         circumference := () -> 0;
```

```
>       end module
> end proc:
```

The module returned by this constructor uses the lexically scoped parameters $x$ and $y$, representing the abscissa and ordinate of the point. These values are part of the local state, or instance data, of each point constructed. These points are captured in the closures of the exported methods, so that variables local to the module in which to store these values are not necessary.

**The segment Constructor** Segments are represented using the start and end points of the segment. These are the points returned by the point constructor.

```
> segment := proc( pt1, pt2 )
>       module()
>           export area,
>               circumference,
>               length,
>               start_point,
>               end_point;
>           local mymidpoint;
>
>           start_point := () -> pt1;
>           end_point := () -> pt2;
>           area := () -> 0;
>           circumference := () -> 0;
>           length := proc()
>               local   x, y;
>               x := pt1:-xcoord() - pt2:-xcoord();
>               y := pt1:-ycoord() - pt2:-ycoord();
>               sqrt( x^2 + y^2 )
>           end proc;
>           midpoint := proc()
>               local   x, y;
>               if assigned( mymidpoint ) then
>                   mymidpoint
>               else
>                   y := (pt1:-ycoord() + pt2:-ycoord())/2;
>                   x := (pt1:-xcoord() + pt2:-xcoord())/2;
>                   point( x, y )
>               end if
>           end proc;
>       end module
> end proc:
```

The segment objects implement methods in addition to the required area and circumference methods. Apart from the trivial syntax methods start_point and end_point, there are methods for computing the length of a segment and its midpoint.

**The circle Constructor** Circles are represented by using the center and radius of the circle as instance data.

```
> circle := proc( ctr, rad )
>     module()
>         export area, circumference, diameter,
>               center, centre, radius;
>         radius := () -> rad;
>         center := () -> ctr;
>         centre := eval( center ); # UK spelling
>         diameter := () -> 2 * radius();
>         circumference := () -> Pi * diameter();
>         area := () -> Pi * rad * rad;
>     end module
> end proc:
```

Again, the lexically scoped parameters `ctr` and `rad` encode the instance data of the circle object.

**Note:** The remainder of the object oriented version of the `Shapes` package can be read in `ShapeObj.mpl` file in the `samples/AdvPG` directory of your Maple installation.

## 2.6 Interfaces and Implementations

*Generic programming* is a programming style and a software engineering methodology for software reuse. In this sense, many Maple built-in operations are generic. The addition operator `+` computes sums of integers, rational numbers, complex numbers, polynomials, special functions, and so on. When using the addition operator `+`, it is not necessary to state how an expression is represented. (The automatic simplifier recognizes how Maple expressions are represented.) As with any dynamically typed language, Maple allows for a great deal of generic programming. Most built-in Maple operations (including many standard library routines) are naturally *polymorphic* in that they are able to perform successfully with a large variety of data formats.

**Generic Programming as Good Software Engineering Practice** On any large project, it is important to write *reusable* code; that is, code that can perform a well-defined function in a wide variety of situations. Generic programs do not rely on the details of how their inputs are represented. They are able to perform their function on *any* inputs that satisfy a specified set of constraints. Normally, these constraints are described in terms of the *behavior* of the inputs rather than on their physical representation or the storage layout of their concrete representation. This behavior is sometimes called a *contract.* Generic programs rely *only* on the object behavior specified by the contract. They do *not* rely on knowledge of how an object is implemented. So, generic software *separates* interfaces from implementations.

**Distinction Between Local and Exported Variables** The behavior specified by the contract for a module includes any module exports. Whatever is expressed through its local variables is private to the module, and is not to be relied upon, or even known, by clients of the module. (Client access is, in fact, the only technical difference between module locals and exports.)

Before the introduction of the module system, design by contract was enforced in Maple only by convention. Maple routines whose names had to be enclosed in name quotes (‘) were considered private, and not for client use. But this was only a convention. Moreover, it was necessary to use global variables to communicate information and state among the routines that comprised a subsystem (such as `solve` or `assume`). Now, using modules, it is possible to design software systems that enforce their contracts by a mechanism embedded in the Maple language.

### Interfaces

The contracts discussed previously in this section are represented formally in Maple by an *interface*. An interface is a special kind of structured type. It has the form

```
‘module‘( symseq );
```

in which `symseq` is a sequence of symbols or of typed symbols (expressions of the form `symbol::type`). For example, an interface for a ring can be written as

```
> ‘type/ring‘ := ’‘module‘( ‘+‘, ‘*‘, ‘-‘, zero, one )’:
```

while an (additive) abelian group can take the form

```
> ‘type/abgroup‘:= ’‘module‘( ‘+‘, ‘-‘, zero )’:
```

These symbols are the ones to which clients have access as module exports.

A module is said to *satisfy*, or to *implement*, an interface if it is of the type defined by the interface.

```
> z5 := module()
>     description "the integers modulo 5";
>     export `+`, `*`, `-`, zero, one;
>     `+` := (a,b) -> a+b mod 5;
>     `*` := (a,b) -> a*b mod 5;
>     `-` := s -> 5-s mod 5;
>     zero := 0;
>     one := 1;
> end module:
> type( z5, 'ring' );
```

$$true$$

A module can satisfy more than one interface.

```
> type( z5, 'abgroup' );
```

$$true$$

Interfaces are an abstraction that form part of the Maple type system. They provide a form of *constrained* polymorphism. Not every Maple type is an interface; only those that have the form described are. You can define a Maple type (that, as it happens, is not itself an interface) to describe interfaces.

```
> `type/interface` := 'specfunc( {symbol,symbol::type},
>                          `module` )':
```

This is a structured type. It describes expressions that are themselves structured types. They have the form of an unevaluated function call with the operator symbol `` `module` `` and all arguments of type `symbol`, or of type `symbol::type`. In the two previous examples in this section, the types `type/ring` and `type/abgroup` are the interface expressions, and the names `ring` and `abgroup` are the respective names of those interfaces.

**A Package for Manipulating Interfaces** Interfaces are sufficiently important that it is worthwhile to develop a package for manipulating them. The package is small enough that it can be reproduced here, in full, but it is also available in the `samples/AdvPG` directory of the Maple installation.

```
> Interface := module()
>     description "a package for manipulating interfaces";
>     global `type/interface`;
>     export define,      # define an interface
>            extend,      # extend an interface
>            extends,     # test for an extension
>            equivalent,# test equivalence
>            savelib,     # save an interface
```

```
>         satisfies;    # test whether a module satisfies
>                       # an interface
>     local  gassign,   # assign to a global variable
>            totype,    # convert from interface name to type
>            toset,     # convert from interface name to a set
>            setup;     # install `type/interface` globally
>     option package, load = setup;
>
>     # Define a global type for interfaces.
>     # This assignment takes care of installing the type
>     # in the Maple session in which this module definition
>     # is evaluated. Calling `setup()' ensures that this also
>     # happens when the instantiated module is read from a
>     # repository.
>     `type/interface`
>             := 'specfunc( {symbol, `::`}, `module` )';
>
>     # Ensure that `type/interface` is defined. This thunk is
>     # called when the instantiated `Interface' module is read
>     # from a Maple repository.
>     setup := proc()
>         global `type/interface`;
>         `type/interface`
>           := 'specfunc( {symbol, `::`}, `module` )';
>         NULL # quiet return
>     end proc;
>
>     # Assign to the global instance of a name
>     gassign := proc( nom::symbol, val )
>         option inline;
>         eval( subs( _X = nom,
>                     proc()
>                         global _X;
>                         _X := val
>                     end ) )()
>     end proc;
>
>     # Convert an interface name to the corresponding type.
>     totype := ( ifc::symbol ) -> ( `type/` || ifc );
>
>     # Convert an interface name to a set of symbols.
>     toset := ( ifc::symbol ) -> { op( ( `type/` || ifc ) ) };
>
>     # Install a new interface into the type system.
>     define := proc( ifc )
>         description "define an interface";
>         if map( type, {args}, 'symbol' ) <> { true } then
>             error "arguments must all be symbols"
>         end if;
>         gassign( `type/` || ifc,
>             '`module`'( args[ 2 .. nargs ] ) );
>         ifc # return the interface name
>     end proc;
>
```

```
>     # Implement subtyping.
>     extend := proc( new, old )
>         description "extend an existing inteface";
>         if map( type, {args}, 'symbol' ) <> { true } then
>             error "arguments must all be symbols"
>         end if;
>         if not type( totype( old ), 'interface' ) then
>             error "cannot find an interface named %1", old
>         end if;
>         define( new, op( totype( old ) ), args[3..nargs] )
>     end proc;
>
>     # Test whether ifc2 is an extension of ifc1.
>     extends := proc( ifc1, ifc2 )
>         description "test whether the second interface "
>                     "extends the first";
>         local t1, t2;
>         t1, t2 := op( map( totype, [ ifc1, ifc2 ] ) );
>         if not type( [t1,t2], '[interface,interface]' ) then
>             if not type( t1, 'interface') then
>                 error "arguments must be interface names, "
>                       "but got %1", ifc1
>             else
>                 error "arguments must be interface names, "
>                       "but got %1", ifc2
>             end if
>          end if;
>          toset( ifc1 ) subset toset( ifc2 )
>     end proc;
>
>     # Save an interface to the repository.
>     savelib := proc()
>         description "save a named interface to a "
>                     "repository";
>         local ifc;
>         for ifc in map( totype, [ args ] ) do
>             if not type( ifc, 'interface' ) then
>                 error "arguments must be interfaces, "
>                       "but got %1", ifc
>             end if;
>             :-savelib( totype( ifc ) )
>         end do
>     end proc;
>
>     # Test whether a module satisfies an interface.
>     # This is simply an alternative to a call
>     # to `type()'.
>     satisfies := proc( m, ifc )
>         description "test whether a module satisfies an interface";
>         if not type( totype( ifc ), 'interface' ) then
>             error "second argument must be an interface name, "
>                   "but got %1", ifc
>         end if;
>         type( m, ifc )
```

```
>       end proc;
>
>       # Test whether two interfaces are equivalent.
>       # Since unevaluated function calls compare
>       # differently if their arguments are in a
>       # different order, we convert them to sets first,
>       # and then test for equality.
>       equivalent := proc( ifc1, ifc2 )
>           description "test whether two interfaces "
>                  "are equivalent";
>           local t1, t2;
>           t1, t2 := totype( ifc1 ), totype( ifc2 );
>           if not type( t1, 'interface' ) then
>               error "expecting an interface name, "
>                     "but got %1", ifc1
>           elif not type( t2, 'interface' ) then
>               error "expecting an interface name, "
>                     "but got %1", ifc2
>           end if;
>           evalb( { op( t1 ) } = { op( t2 ) } )
>       end proc;
> end module:
```

This package implements the interface abstraction. It allows you to manipulate interfaces without having to worry about how they fit into the Maple type system.

```
> with( Interface );
```

```
Warning, the protected names define and savelib have
been redefined and unprotected
```

[*define*, *equivalent*, *extend*, *extends*, *satisfies*, *savelib*]

```
> define( 'abgroup', '`+`', '`-`', 'zero' );
```

*abgroup*

```
> type( `type/abgroup`, 'interface' );
```

*true*

```
> type( z5, 'abgroup' );
```

*true*

```
> satisfies( z5, 'abgroup' );
```

*true*

```
> extend( 'ring', 'abgroup', ''*'', 'one' );
```

*ring*

```
> type( `type/ring`, 'interface' );
```

*true*

```
> extends( abgroup, ring );
```

*true*

```
> satisfies( z5, 'ring' );
```

*true*

```
> type( z5, 'ring' );
```

*true*

**The `load=` Option** This package provides an abstraction of the interface concept in Maple and illustrates a module feature not previously demonstrated–the `load=procedure_name` option. In the `Interface` package, this option is used in a fairly typical way. The declaration

```
option load = setup;
```

that appears in the module definition instructs Maple that, when the instantiated module is read from a repository, it is to call the procedure `setup`. The procedure named must be a local or an exported local of the module. The local procedure `setup` in this module simply ensures that the global variable `type/interface` is assigned an appropriate value. This assignment is also made in the body of the module so that the assignment is also executed in the session in which the module is instantiated. This is done for illustrative purposes. A better scheme simply invokes `setup` in the body of the module definition.

## Generic Graph Algorithms

The following example uses simple graph algorithms to illustrate generic programming.

**Mathematical Description** A directed graph can be thought of as an object that consists of a set $V$ of vertices and a set $E \subseteq V \times V$ of ordered pairs of vertices, called *edges*. Graphs can be visualized by diagrams like the following.

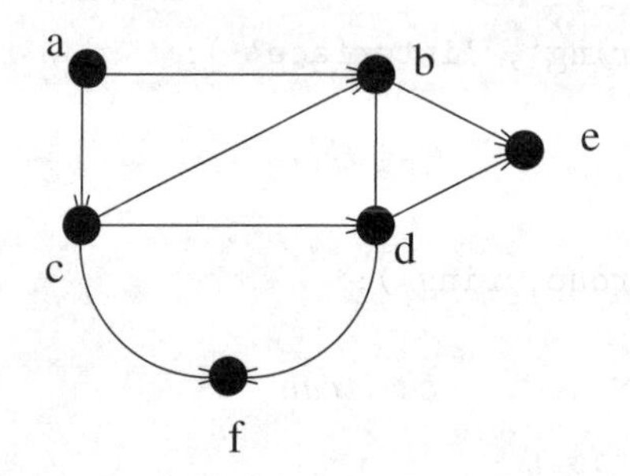


This diagram represents a graph with vertex set $V = \{a, b, c, d, e, f\}$, and edge set $E = \{(a, b), (a, c), (b, d), (c, f), (f, d), (b, e), (d, e), (c, b), (c, d)\}$.

**Software Models** Graphs can be represented in a variety of ways. The choice of storage mechanism depends on the expected applications of the graph. Three possibilities for representing graphs in software are:

1. Store the set $V$ of vertices and the set $E$ of edges explicitly.

2. Store the "adjacency matrix" of the graph.

3. Store, for each vertex of the graph, the set of all its neighbours.

(The *adjacency matrix* is a square matrix whose rows and columns are indexed by the vertices of the graph; the $(i, j)$-entry is equal to 1 if there is an edge from $i$ to $j$, and is equal to 0 otherwise.) You can write software that manipulates a graph independent of representation.

**Designing a Graph Interface** To demonstrate how this can be achieved, consider graphs as objects that implement the methods listed in Table 2.2.

Then, represent the *abstract interface* of a graph by a Maple type.

```
> `type/Graph` := ''module`( vertices, edges, addedge, order,
>                            size )':
```

An object *implements* the graph interface if it is of type `Graph`.

**Table 2.2** Graph Methods

| | |
|---|---|
| `vertices` | Returns the set of vertices of the graph |
| `edges` | Returns the set of edges of the graph |
| `addedge` | Allows one to add a new edge to a graph |
| `order` | Returns the number of vertices of the graph |
| `size` | Returns the number of edges of the graph |

**Computing Vertex Degrees Generically** If an object implements this interface, then you can write generic code based on that interface. For example, you can write the following procedure to compute the in-degree and out-degree of a vertex of a given graph.

```
> vdeg := proc( G::Graph, v )
>     local vs, vt;
>     description "compute the in- and out-degrees "
>                 "of a vertex in a graph";
>     if member( v, G:-vertices() ) then
>         vs := select( e -> evalb( v = e:-source() ),
>                       G:-edges() );
>         vt := select( e -> evalb( v = e:-target() ),
>                       G:-edges() );
>         nops( vs ), nops( vt )
>     else
>         0, 0
>     end if
> end proc:
```

You can write this procedure even though, at this point, you do not know the graph implementation. This capability is very important when you are designing a large software system.

**Edge Object Representation** Assume that edges are represented as objects that implement the interface `` `module`( source, target ) ``. The interface provides methods for extracting the source and target vertices from an edge. Writing a constructor **Edge** for edges is easy.

```
> Edge := proc( src, targ )
>     module()
>         local the_source, the_target;
>         export source, target, setsource, settarget;
>         the_source := src;
>         the_target := targ;
>         source := () -> the_source;
>         target := () -> the_target;
>         setsource := proc( v )
>             the_source := v
>         end proc;
>         settarget := proc( v )
>             the_target := v
```

```
>         end proc;
>     end module
> end proc:
```

**First Graph Constructor** At first, you might choose to adopt a graph representation that is simple to implement. Here is a graph constructor that produces graphs represented by storing the vertex and edge sets explicitly as part of the state of a module.

```
> Graph1 := proc()
>     local vertex_set, edge_set;
>     description "graph constructor";
>
>     edge_set := { args };
>     if not andmap( type, edge_set, '[ anything, anything ]' )
>         then
>         error "graph must be specified by a sequence of edges"
>     end if;
>     if not andmap( edge -> evalb( nops ( edge )= 2), edge_set )
>         then
>         error "each edge must be specified "
>                   "as a [ source, target ] pair"
>     end if;
>     vertex_set := map( op, edge_set );
>     edge_set := map( Edge@op, edge_set );
>     module()
>         export order, size,
>                vertices, edges,
>                addedge; # required exports
>         vertices := () -> vertex_set;
>         edges := () -> edge_set;
>         addedge := proc( src, targ )
>             edge_set := { Edge( src, targ ) }
>                         union edge_set;
>             vertex_set := { src, targ }
>                         union vertex_set;
>             NULL
>         end proc;
>         order := () -> nops( vertices() );
>         size := () -> nops( edges() );
>     end module
> end proc:
```

If you create a small graph using this constructor

```
> g1 := Graph1( [ a, b ], [ a, c ], [ b, c ] ):
> type( g1, 'Graph' );
```

$$true$$

you can use the routine **vdeg** with the graph **g1**, since graphs produced by **Graph1** implement the **Graph** interface.

```
> vdeg( g1, a );
```

$$2, 0$$

```
> vdeg( g1, b );
```

$$1, 1$$

```
> vdeg( g1, c );
```

$$0, 2$$

The important feature of the procedure **vdeg** is its generic quality. It can be used with *any* implementation of graphs that implements the **Graph** interface previously specified.

**Second Graph Constructor** Here is another, different implementation of the Graph interface. The graph is represented by using a table N in which the neighbors of each vertex are stored.

```
> Graph2 := proc()
>     local     vertex_set, edge_set;
>     description "graph constructor";
>
>     edge_set := { args };
>     vertex_set := map( op, edge_set );
>     if not andmap( type, edge_set, 'list' ) then
>         error "graph must be specified by a sequence of edges"
>     end if;
>     if not andmap( edge -> evalb( nops ( edge )= 2), edge_set )
>         then
>        error "each edge must be specified "
>               "as a [ source, target ] pair"
>     end if;
>     module()
>         export order, size,
>                vertices, edges,
>                addedge;
>         local N, e, v, n, edge_pairs;
>         N := table();
>         edge_pairs := () -> { seq(
>                 seq( [ v, n ], n = N[ v ] ),
>                 v = map( op, { indices( N ) } )
>             ) };
>         vertices := () -> map( op, edge_pairs() );
```

```
>             edges := () -> map( Edge@op, edge_pairs() );
>             addedge := proc( src, targ )
>                 if assigned( N[ src ] )
>                   and not member( targ, N[ src ] ) then
>                     N[ src ] := { op( N[ src ] ), targ }
>                 else
>                     N[ src ] := { targ };
>                 end if;
>                 NULL
>             end proc;
>             order := () -> nops( vertices() );
>             size := () -> nops( edges() );
>             for e in edge_set do
>                 addedge( op( 1, e ), op( 2, e ) )
>             end do
>         end module
> end proc:
```

A graph returned by the constructor `Graph2` also satisfies the `Graph` interface.

```
> g2 := Graph2( [ a, b ], [ a, c ], [ b, c ] ):
> type( g2, 'Graph' );
```

*true*

Therefore, the *generic* procedure `vdeg` works equally well with it.

```
> vdeg( g2, a );
```

2, 0

```
> vdeg( g2, b );
```

1, 1

```
> vdeg( g2, c );
```

0, 2

**Note:** The full source code for these procedures is available in the `samples/AdvPG/graph` directory of the Maple installation.

**Generic Computation of Adjacency Matrices** Another example of a generic procedure over the `Graph` interface is the following routine for computing the adjacency matrix of a graph.

```
> AdjacencyMatrix := proc( g::Graph )
>     local  a,   # the adjacency matrix; returned
>            n,   # the order of the graph g
>            V,   # the vertex set of the graph
>            E,   # the edge set of the graph
>            row, # row index for matrix
>            col, # column index for matrix
>            e;   # induction variable for loop
>
>     n := g:-order();
>     a := Matrix( n, n, 'storage' = 'sparse' );
>     V := sort( convert( g:-vertices(), 'list' ) );
>     E := g:-edges();
>     for e in E do
>         if not member( e:-source(), V, 'row' )
>           or not member( e:-target(), V, 'col' ) then
>             error "inconsistent graph structure detected"
>         end if;
>         a[ row, col ] := 1
>     end do;
>     a
> end proc:
> AdjacencyMatrix( g1 );
```

$$\begin{bmatrix} 0 & 1 & 1 \\ 0 & 0 & 1 \\ 0 & 0 & 0 \end{bmatrix}$$

```
> AdjacencyMatrix( g2 );
```

$$\begin{bmatrix} 0 & 1 & 1 \\ 0 & 0 & 1 \\ 0 & 0 & 0 \end{bmatrix}$$

## Quotient Fields

As an example of generic programming, a generic quotient field (or field of fractions) construction algorithm is discussed.

**Mathematical Description** Given an integral domain $D$, its quotient field is (up to isomorphism) the unique field $k$, paired with a nonzero ring homomorphism $\eta : D \longrightarrow k$, with the property that, for any nonzero ring homomorphism $\varphi : D \longrightarrow F$, in which $F$ is a field, there is a unique ring homomorphism $\sigma$ for which the diagram

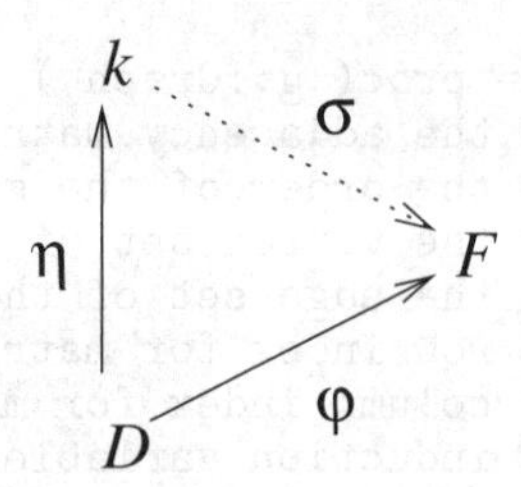


commutes. Because a nonzero ring homomorphism into a field must be injective, this says that every field $F$ that contains $D$ as a subring must also contain an isomorphic copy of $k$.

Concretely, the quotient field of an integral domain $D$ can be thought of as the set of "reduced fractions" $n/d$, with $n, d \in D$. A formal construction can be produced by defining an equivalence relation on the set $D \times (D \setminus \{0\})$, according to which two pairs $(n1, d1)$ and $(n2, d2)$ are equivalent only if,

$$n1 \cdot d2 = n2 \cdot d1.$$

A representative from each equivalence class is chosen to represent the field element defined by that class. This understanding guides the computer representation of the quotient field.

**Unit Normal Representatives** If $R$ is a commutative ring with multiplicative identity, then

$$U(R) \times R \longrightarrow R : (u, r) \to u \cdot r$$

is a natural action of the group $U(R)$ of units of $R$ on $R$. Each orbit of this action has a representative called the *unit normal* representative of the class. Consider an effective mapping $R \longrightarrow R$ that selects the unit normal representative of each class. For instance, for the ring $\mathbb{Z}$ of integers, the group $U(\mathbb{Z})$ of units is the set $\{1, -1\}$, the orbits are the sets $\{n, -n\}$ for $n \in \mathbb{Z} \setminus \{0\}$ together with $\{0\}$, and you take the unit normal representative to be the positive member of each orbit, and 0 for the orbit $\{0\}$. (Thus, the unit normal mapping simply computes the sign and absolute value of an integer.) The unit normal mapping on the ring $k[T]$ of polynomials in an indeterminate $T$ over a field $k$ is

$$p(T) \to \frac{1}{\mathrm{lc}(p(T))} \cdot p(T),$$

in which $\mathrm{lc}(p(T))$ denotes the leading coefficient of the polynomial $p(T)$. (The group of units in $k[T]$ is the set $k^* = k \setminus \{0\}$, of nonzero members of $k$, and each orbit of $k[T]$ under the action of $k^*$ contains an unique monic polynomial that is its representative.)

**Designing the Ring Interfaces** The first step in representing these ideas in software is to devise an interface that describes the rings. Suppose that the rings are equipped with the basic ring operations, as well as several methods that implement desired computations.

```
> `type/Ring` := ''module`(
>     `+`::procedure,
>     `*`::procedure,
>     `-`::procedure,
>     iszero::procedure,
>     isone::procedure,
>     zero, one
> )':
```

This interface corresponds naturally with a formal mathematical characterization of the ring as a tuple

$$\langle S, +, *, 0, 1 \rangle$$

that satisfies a number of properties, and to which some computational capabilities have been added. Given the way operator overrides work in Maple, unary negation (-) is added. (In a more tightly integrated system, you specify the number and types of arguments to each of the procedures.)

For these computations, you need a slightly richer structure.

```
> `type/GcdRing` := ''module`(
>     `+`::procedure,
>     `*`::procedure,
>     `-`::procedure,
>     quo::procedure,
>     rem::procedure,
>     gcd::procedure,
>     unormal::procedure,
>     iszero::procedure,
>     isone::procedure,
>     zero, one
> )':
```

This interface extends the `Ring` interface defined previously. Note that nothing in the signature enforces any ring-theoretic properties (such as being an integral domain, or having unique factorization). It merely specifies the admissible operations. To compute with infinite rings (and even large finite ones), you do not require an enumeration of the elements of the ring. You can focus entirely on the effectively computable operations that the ring must support.

**Representing the ring $\mathbb{Z}$ of Integers** One of the simplest examples of a ring that supports the computations is the ring of integers $\mathbb{Z}$ in its native Maple representation.

```
> MapleIntegers := module()
>     description "the ring of integers";
>     export `+`, `*`, `-`,
>            gcd, unormal, iszero,
>            isone, zero, one, rem, quo;
>     `+` := ( a, b ) -> a + b;
>     `*` := ( a, b ) -> a * b;
>     `-` := i -> -i;
>     quo := ( a, b ) -> :-iquo( a, b );
>     rem := ( a, b ) -> :-irem( a, b );
>     gcd := ( a, b ) -> :-igcd( a, b );
>     unormal := proc( i::integer )
>         if i < 0 then
>             -1, -i
>         else
>             1, i # includes 0
>         end if
>     end proc;
>     iszero := i -> evalb( i = 0 );
>     isone := i -> evalb( i = 1 );
>     zero := 0;
>     one := 1;
> end module:
```

This is a software representation of the ring of integers. The unit normal mapping is represented by the exported procedure `unormal`. It returns an expression sequence of length two, whose first member is a unit, and whose second member is the unit normal form of its argument. The product of the output values yields the input ring element. The other methods only invoke the corresponding built-in Maple operations.

```
> type( MapleIntegers, 'Ring' );
```

$$true$$

```
> type( MapleIntegers, 'GcdRing' );
```

$$true$$

**An Interface for Fields** The quotient field constructor produces a field. An interface that describes fields differs from the one for integral domains by the absence of a `gcd` method (since they are trivial) and the addition of the (unary) / operator that computes inverses. The methods `rem` and `quo` are also not included in the signature for fields, because they are trivial in a field. Two new methods are included:

- `make` for constructing field elements from their numerators and denominators

- embed, the natural embedding of the integral domain $D$ into its field $k$ of fractions.

Additionally, the two methods **numer** and **denom** allow the user to extract the components of a fraction.

```
> `type/Field` := ''module'(
>     `+`::procedure,
>     `*`::procedure,
>     `-`::procedure,
>     `/`::procedure,
>     normal::procedure,
>     iszero::procedure,
>     isone::procedure,
>     zero, one,
>     make::procedure,
>     embed::procedure,
>     numer::procedure,
>     denom::procedure
> )':
```

Naturally, the ring $\mathbb{Z}$ of integers is not a field.

```
> type( MapleIntegers, 'Field' );
```

$$false$$

Fields produced by the quotient field constructor satisfy this interface.

**The Quotient Field Functor** Here is the generic constructor for quotient fields.

```
> QuotientField := proc( R::GcdRing )
>    description "quotient field functor";
>    module()
>        description "a quotient field";
>        export `+`, `*`, `-`, `/`,
>               zero, one,
>               iszero, isone,
>               make,
>               numer, denom,
>               normal, embed;
>        make := proc( n, d )
>            local u, nd;
>            if R:-iszero( d ) then
>                error "division by zero"
>            end if;
>            u, nd := R:-unormal( d );
>            'FRACTION'( u*n, nd )
>        end proc;
>        embed := d -> make( d, R:-one );
>        numer := f -> op( 1, f );
>        denom := f -> op( 2, f );
```

```
>             zero := embed( R:-zero );
>             one := embed( R:-one );
>             iszero := f -> evalb( normal( f ) = zero );
>             isone := f -> evalb( normal( f ) = one );
>             normal := proc( f )
>                 local g, a, b;
>                 g := R:-gcd( numer( f ), denom( f ) );
>                 if R:-isone( g ) then
>                     f
>                 else
>                     a := R:-quo( numer( f ), g );
>                     b := R:-quo( denom( f ), g );
>                     make( a, b )
>                 end if
>             end proc;
>             `-` := f -> normal( R:-`-`( numer( f ) ), denom( f ) );
>             `/` := f -> normal( make( denom( f ), numer( f ) ) );
>             `+` := proc( a, b )
>                 use `+` = R:-`+`, `*` = R:-`*` in
>                     normal( make( numer( a ) * denom( b )
>                                       + denom( a ) * numer( b ),
>                                   denom( a ) * denom( b ) ) )
>                 end use
>             end proc;
>             `*` := proc( a, b )
>                 use `*` = R:-`*` in
>                     normal( make( numer( a ) * numer( b ),
>                                   denom( a ) * denom( b ) ) )
>                 end use
>             end proc;
>         end module
>     end proc:
```

**Note:** The source code for `QuotientField.mpl` is available in the `samples/AdvPG` directory of your Maple installation.

Most of the exported routines are straightforward. The fraction constructor `make` accepts two members of the ring $R$ as arguments and returns the constructed fraction, which is represented by an unevaluated function call of the form

```
FRACTION( numerator, denominator )
```

The exported procedure `embed` is the canonical embedding $\eta$ of the integral domain into its quotient field, described previously. This makes the constructor functorial. The arithmetic operators are simple implementations of the familiar rules for fraction arithmetic:

$$\frac{a}{b} + \frac{c}{d} = \frac{ad + bc}{bd}$$

$$\frac{a}{b} \times \frac{c}{d} = \frac{ac}{bd}$$
$$\left(\frac{a}{b}\right)^{-1} = \frac{b}{a}$$
$$-\left(\frac{a}{b}\right) = \frac{-a}{b}$$

After applying these simple formulae, the result is normalized by using a call to the *local* routine `normal` (not the top-level routine `:-normal`). The `normal` routine does most of the interesting work in the ring generated by this constructor. It uses the manifestation of the division algorithm in the ring $R$ via the exported procedures `quo` and `gcd` to reduce each fraction to the lowest terms. The fraction constructor `make` and the method `normal` represent field elements by the normal form representative of the appropriate equivalence class. The `make` routine prevents division by zero, and forces denominators to be unit normal representatives. The `normal` routine ensures that fractions are reduced to *lowest terms.*

The most important property of the `QuotientField` functor is that it is *generic*. It relies solely on the `GcdRing` interface. No knowledge of the concrete representation of the input integral domain `R` (other than that it is a module that satisfies the required interface) is used in the construction. Therefore, it works with *any* implementation of the `GcdRing` interface that:

- Implements the correct semantics for its public operations
- Satisfies the abstract constraint that it be a software representation of an integral domain. (This constraint is required to ensure that the arithmetic operations are well defined.)

**Constructing the Rationals as the Quotient Field of $\mathbb{Z}$** To construct the quotient ring of the ring `MapleIntegers` defined previously, proceed as follows.

```
> FF := QuotientField( MapleIntegers );
```

$FF :=$ **module**()
**export**‘ + ‘, ‘ ∗ ‘, ‘ − ‘, ‘/‘, *zero*, *one*, *iszero*, *isone*, *make*,
*numer*, *denom*, *normal*, *embed*;
**description** “a quotient field”;
**end module**

```
> type( FF, 'Field' );
```

$$true$$

```
> a := FF:-make( 2, 3 );
```

$$a := \mathrm{FRACTION}(2, 3)$$

```
> b := FF:-make( 2, 4 );
```

$$b := \mathrm{FRACTION}(2, 4)$$

```
> use FF in
>     a + b;
>     a * b;
>     a / b
> end use;
```

$$\mathrm{FRACTION}(7, 6)$$

$$\mathrm{FRACTION}(1, 3)$$

$$\mathrm{FRACTION}(4, 3)$$

**Note:** This is a complex representation of the field of rational numbers.

**The Quotient Field of the Polynomial Ring** $\mathbb{Q}[T]$ To illustrate the generic quality of this constructor, construct the field $\mathbb{Q}[T]$ of rational functions in a single indeterminate $T$ from a concrete representation of Maple rational polynomials.

```
> MaplePoly := module()
>       description "the ring of rational polynomials";
>       export `+`, `*`, `-`,
>               zero, one,
>               iszero, isone,
>               gcd, unormal,
>               quo, rem;
>       `+` := ( a, b ) -> expand( a + b );
>       `*` := ( a, b ) -> expand( a * b );
>       `-` := p -> -p;
>       gcd := ( a, b ) -> :-gcd( a, b );
>       unormal := proc( p )
>           local lc;
>           if iszero( p ) then
>               one, zero
>           else
>               use lc = lcoeff( p ) in
>                   lc, :-normal( p / lc )
```

```
>                 end use
>             end if
>         end proc;
>         iszero := p -> Testzero( p );
>         isone := p -> Testzero( p - 1 );
>         zero := 0;
>         one := 1;
>         rem := ( a, b ) -> :-rem( a, b );
>         quo := ( a, b ) -> :-quo( a, b );
> end module:
```

The `unormal` method produces the leading coefficient and monic associate of a given polynomial in $\mathbb{Q}[T]$. The remaining exports simply capture built-in Maple operations on univariate rational polynomials.

```
> RR := QuotientField( MaplePoly );
```

$RR :=$ **module**()
**export**' + ', ' * ', ' − ', '/', *zero*, *one*, *iszero*, *isone*, *make*, *numer*, *denom*, *normal*, *embed*;
**description** "a quotient field";

**end module**

```
> type( RR, 'Field' );
```

*true*

To make printed fractions more readable, introduce the following extension to the `print` command.

```
> `print/FRACTION` := ( n, d ) -> sort( n ) / sort( d ):
```

Finally, construct a few examples, and test the arithmetic.

```
> a := RR:-make( randpoly( 'T', 'degree' = 4, 'terms' = 3 ),
>                randpoly( 'T', 'degree' = 4, 'terms' = 3 ) );
```

$$a := \frac{-2072\,T^2 - 1960\,T + 5432}{T^3 + \frac{7}{8}\,T^2 + \frac{9}{8}}$$

```
> b := RR:-make( randpoly( 'T', 'degree' = 4, 'terms' = 3 ),
>                randpoly( 'T', 'degree' = 4, 'terms' = 3 ) );
```

$$b := \frac{-2790\,T^3 + 496\,T^2 + 5766}{T^2 - \frac{77}{62}\,T - \frac{33}{31}}$$

```
> use RR in
>     a + b;
>     a * b;
>     a / b
> end use;
```

$$(-2790\,T^6 - \frac{7781}{4}T^5 - 1638\,T^4 + \frac{401827}{124}T^3 + \frac{1943715}{124}T^2 - \frac{144452}{31}T + \frac{87333}{124}) \Big/ (T^5 - \frac{91}{248}T^4 - \frac{1067}{496}T^3 + \frac{6}{31}T^2 - \frac{693}{496}T - \frac{297}{248})$$

$$(5780880\,T^5 + 4440688\,T^4 - 16127440\,T^3 - 9252880\,T^2 - 11301360\,T + 31320912)/(T^5 - \frac{91}{248}T^4 - \frac{1067}{496}T^3 + \frac{6}{31}T^2 - \frac{693}{496}T - \frac{297}{248})$$

$$(5780880\,T^4 - 1711080\,T^3 - 28100520\,T^2 + 13000680\,T + 16133040)/(T^6 + \frac{251}{360}T^5 - \frac{7}{45}T^4 - \frac{113}{120}T^3 - \frac{241}{120}T^2 - \frac{93}{40})$$

## A Generic Group Implementation

This section illustrates how to develop a moderately complex software system by using features of the Maple module system. Generic programming is at the heart of the design. Only a fraction of the complete system from which the examples are taken is shown. A system for computing with finite groups comprises the examples that follow. Recall that a *group* is a set of objects together with an associative binary operation, for which there is an unique two-sided identity element, and with respect to which each member of the underlying set possesses an unique inverse. Examples of groups include:

- Systems of numbers, using addition
- Closed sets of invertible matrices (all of the same size, with a common ground field), using multiplication (linear groups)
- Closed sets of permutations (bijective mappings on a set), using composition (permutation groups)
- Groups of points on elliptic curves

Only finite groups are discussed.

**Table 2.3** Abstract Group Methods

| | |
|---|---|
| `id` | Returns the group identity |
| `` `.` `` | Performs the binary operation on the group |
| `mul` | $n$-ary version of `` `.` `` |
| `inv` | Performs the unary inversion operation |
| `pow` | Computes integral powers of group elements |
| `eq` | Tests whether two group elements are equal |
| `member` | Tests membership in the group and in sets |
| `gens` | Returns a generating set for the group |
| `order` | Returns the order of the group |
| `elements` | Returns an enumeration of the group's members |

**An Interface for Finite Groups** First, you must decide how to represent the generic group interface. This is determined by the proposed use of the group objects. Once again, the design takes a group to be a repository of data and computational services that you can query or invoke.

The `Group` signature used in the examples describes a computational model of abstract groups that supports the methods in Table 2.3.

```
> `type/Group` := '`module`(
>     id, `.`, mul, inv,
>     eq, member,
>     gens,
>     order, elements
> )':
```

A corresponding constructor for groups is easily written using the `Record` constructor introduced earlier. For the examples in this section, no default methods are introduced.

```
> Group := proc()
>     Record( op( `type/Group` ) );
> end proc:
```

This constructor does very little work on its own. It relies on more specialized constructors to establish useful values or defaults for the methods exported.

You can write generic algorithms using this interface immediately. A few simple examples are these routines for computing conjugates and commutators of group elements. The *conjugate* of a group member $a$ by a group member $b$ is $b^{-1}ab$. This routine computes the conjugate of an element `a` by an element `b` in a group `G`.

```
> Conjugate := proc( G, a, b )
>     description "compute the conjugate of a "
>                 "group element by another";
```

```
>       use `/` = G:-inv, `.` = G:-`.` in
>           b^(-1) . a . b
>       end use
> end proc:
```

Since the group operations `.` and inv in a generic group remain unassigned, the following computation is done symbolically.

```
> Conjugate( Group(), 'x', 'y' );
```

$$(\mathrm{inv}(y)) \;.\; x \;.\; y$$

Similarly, you can compute the commutator $[a, b] = a^{(-1)}b^{(-1)}ab$, generically, as follows.

```
> Commutator := proc( G, a, b )
>       description "compute the commutator of "
>                   "two group elements";
>       use `/` = G:-inv, mul = G:-mul in
>           mul( inv( a ), inv( b ), a, b )
>       end use
> end proc:
```

Again, this computation is done symbolically, so the group operations return unevaluated.

```
> Commutator( Group(), 'x', 'y' );
```

$$\mathrm{mul}(\mathrm{inv}(x),\, \mathrm{inv}(y),\, x,\, y)$$

The ability to write generic algorithms over a given interface is important for the management of large software projects involving many developers. One developer can be assigned the task of implementing particular group constructors along with the attendant arithmetic, while another developer can begin coding generic routines. The two developers can work independently, provided each ensures that the work conforms to some agreed-upon interface and semantics.

**Permutation Groups** Before attempting to develop any complicated algorithms, it is helpful to have a few constructors for specific kinds of groups. These can then be used to validate generic algorithms in specific instances. For this reason, develop a straightforward implementation of permutation groups.

Permutations are represented using Maple lists. For example, the list `[2,1,3]` represents the permutation that maps $1 \to 2$, maps $2 \to 1$, and leaves 3 fixed. (In cycle notation, this is written as the transposition

(12).) The constructor takes a positive integer as its first argument, indicating the degree of the permutation group. The remaining arguments are expected to be permutations (represented as lists) of the stated degree. These are used to form the generating set of the group returned by the constructor.

```
> PermutationGroup := proc( deg::posint )
>     description "permutation group constructor";
>     local G, gens;
>     gens := { args[ 2 .. -1 ] };
>     G := Group();
>     G:-id := [ $ 1 .. deg ];
>     G:-`.` := proc( a, b )
>         local i;
>         [ seq( b[ i ], i = a ) ]
>     end proc;
>     G:-mul := () -> foldl( G:-`.`, G:-id, args );
>     G:-inv := proc( g )
>         local i, a;
>         a := array( 1 .. deg );
>         for i from 1 to deg do
>             a[ g[ i ] ] := i
>         end do;
>         [ seq( a[ i ], i = 1 .. deg ) ]
>     end proc;
>     G:-member := proc( g, S, pos::name )
>         if nargs = 1 then
>             type( g, 'list( posint )' )
>               and { op( g ) } = { $ 1 .. deg }
>         else
>             :-member( args )
>         end if
>     end proc;
>     G:-eq := ( a, b ) -> evalb( a = b );
>     G:-gens := gens;
>     eval( G, 1 )
> end proc:
```

For example, to construct the group $\langle(12),(123)\rangle$ in the symmetric group $S_4$, use the PermutationGroup constructor as follows.

```
> G := PermutationGroup( 4, { [2,1,3,4], [2,3,1,4] } );
```

$G :=$ **module**()
**export**
*id*, '.', *mul*, *inv*, *eq*, *member*, *gens*, *order*, *elements*;
**option** *record*;
**end module**

To compute with its elements, use the methods exported by the instantiated group G.

```
> use G in
>     inv( [ 2,1,3,4 ] ) . [2,3,1,4];
> end use;
```

$$[3, 2, 1, 4]$$

It is useful to provide more specialized permutation group constructors for special kinds of groups. Using the general constructor PermutationGroup, and overriding some of the exported methods, you can define several of these specialized constructors as follows.

The full symmetric group $S_n$ on the $n$ points $\{1, 2, 3, \ldots, n\}$ is produced by specifying a particular set of generators for a given degree (which must be specified as an argument to the constructor).

```
> Symmetric := proc( n::posint )
>     description "symmetric group constructor";
>     if n < 2 then
>         error "argument must be an integer larger than 1"
>     elif n = 2 then
>         PermutationGroup( 2, [2,1] );
>     else
>         PermutationGroup( n, [2,1,$3..n], [$2..n,1] );
>     end if
> end proc:
```

This uses the fact that $S_n$ is the two-generator group

$$S_n = \langle (12), (123 \cdots n) \rangle,$$

for any integer $n \geq 3$.

A second special case is the class of dihedral groups. Think of these as the groups of symmetries of regular plane polygons. The symmetry group of the regular $n$-gon is the dihedral group of degree $n$ and order $2n$; it is denoted by $D_n$.

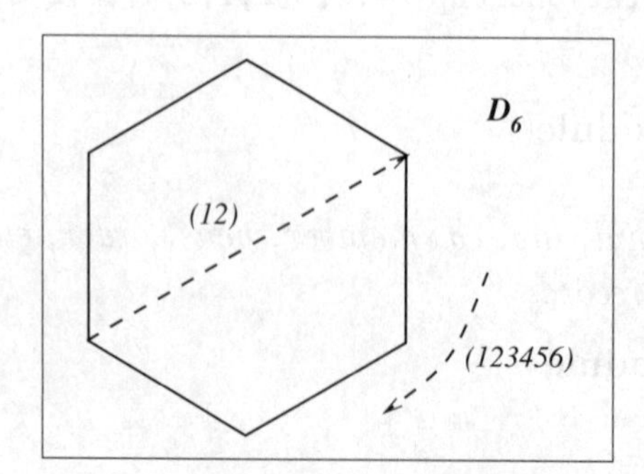

Use the following utility for reversing the order of a list.

```
> lreverse := proc( L::list )
>     description "reverse a list";
>     option inline;
>     [ seq( L[ -i ], i = 1 .. nops( L ) ) ]
> end proc:
> Dihedral := proc( n::posint )
>     description "dihedral group constructor";
>     local a, b, D;
>     if n = 2 or n = 3 then
>         return Symmetric( n )
>     end if;
>     a := [ $ 2 .. n, 1 ];
>     b := [ 1, op( lreverse( [ $ 2 .. n ] ) ) ];
>     D := PermutationGroup( n, { a, b } );
>     D:-order := () -> 2*n;
>     eval( D, 1 )
> end proc:
```

### Exercises

1. Use the fact that the alternating group $A_n$ of degree $n >= 3$ is generated by the set $\{(123), (234), (345), \ldots, (n-2, n-1, n)\}$ of 3-cycles to write a constructor `Alternating` for this class of groups.

**Dimino's Algorithm** Dimino's algorithm is used to compute a complete enumeration of the elements of a finite group, given a generating set for the group. Suppose that you are given a generating set $\{g_1, g_2, \ldots, g_n\}$ for a finite group $G$. The idea behind Dimino's algorithm is to enumerate, successively, the elements of each of the subgroups

$$G_k = \langle g_1, g_2, \ldots, g_k \rangle$$

of G, which form a chain

$$\langle g_1 \rangle = G_1 \leq G_2 \leq \cdots \leq G_k \leq \cdots \leq G_n = G.$$

These elements can be enumerated by forming products of the generators $g_1, g_2, \ldots, g_n$ in all possible ways, until all the elements of $G$ have been found. Dimino's algorithm does this in a careful way, avoiding unnecessary product computations.

Use the following utility routine to determine the entries assigned to a table. It can be used when you are certain no entry is a non-`NULL` expression sequence. Since it is sufficiently simple, it is defined with `option inline;`.

```
> Entries := proc( T )
>     description "return a set of simple table entries";
>     option inline;
>     map( op, { entries( T ) } )
> end proc:
```

Here is the code for Dimino's algorithm.

```
> Dimino := proc( G::Group )
>     description "enumerate the elements of a finite group";
>     local s, g, ord, elements, i, j, prev_ord, rep_pos,
>           elt, addElt, gens;
>
>     if nargs > 1 then
>         gens := args[ 2 ]
>     else
>         gens := G:-gens
>     end if;
>
>     if not type( gens, '{ set, list }' ) then
>         error "no generating set specified"
>     end if;
>
>     if nops( gens ) = 0 then
>         # trivial group
>         return { G:-id }
>     end if;
>
>     addElt := proc( h )
>         ord := 1 + ord;
>         elements[ ord ] := h
>     end proc;
>
>     elements := table();
>     ord := 0;
>     addElt( G:-id );
>
>     # Handle the first cyclic subgroup
>     s := gens[ 1 ];
>     g := s;
>     while not G:-eq( g, G:-id ) do
>         addElt( g );
>         g := G:-`.`( g, s )
>     end do;
>     userinfo( 1, 'Dimino', "finished first cycle; order is:", ord );
>
>     for i from 2 to nops( gens ) do
>         userinfo( 1, 'Dimino', "Adding generator number:", i );
>         s := gens[ i ];
>         if not G:-member( s, Entries( elements ) ) then
>             prev_ord := ord;
>             addElt( s );
>             for j from 2 to prev_ord do
>                 addElt( G:-`.`( elements[ j ], s ) )
```

```
>             end do;
>             rep_pos := 1 + prev_ord;
>             do
>                 for s in gens[ 1 .. i ] do
>                     elt := G:-mul( elements[ rep_pos ], s );
>                     if not G:-member( elt, Entries( elements ) ) then
>                         addElt( elt );
>                         for j from 2 to prev_ord do
>                             addElt( G:-`.`( elements[ j ], elt ) )
>                         end do
>                     end if
>                 end do;
>                 rep_pos := rep_pos + prev_ord;
>                 if rep_pos > ord then
>                     break
>                 end if
>             end do
>         end if
>     end do;
>     Entries( elements )
> end proc:
```

The coding of this algorithm is generic. The exported members of the group object `G` are used to effect computations within the procedure. Even comparisons of equality use the export `eq` instead of the built-in comparison operator `` `=` ``. (The need for this is illustrated below.)

Using the `Symmetric` constructor previously defined, you can compute the elements of the symmetric group $S_4$, using Dimino's algorithm, as follows.

```
> G := Symmetric( 4 );
```

$G :=$ **module**()
**export**
*id*, `.`, *mul*, *inv*, *eq*, *member*, *gens*, *order*, *elements*;
**option** *record*;
**end module**

```
> Dimino( G );
```

{[2, 1, 3, 4], [2, 3, 1, 4], [1, 2, 3, 4], [3, 2, 1, 4],
[2, 3, 4, 1], [3, 2, 4, 1], [1, 3, 4, 2], [3, 1, 4, 2],
[3, 4, 1, 2], [4, 3, 1, 2], [2, 4, 1, 3], [4, 2, 1, 3],
[3, 4, 2, 1], [4, 3, 2, 1], [4, 1, 2, 3], [1, 4, 2, 3],
[3, 1, 2, 4], [1, 3, 2, 4], [4, 1, 3, 2], [1, 4, 3, 2],
[4, 2, 3, 1], [2, 4, 3, 1], [1, 2, 4, 3], [2, 1, 4, 3]}

Anticipating later developments, the procedure Dimino has been coded to accept a second, optional argument that specifies an alternate set of generators to use. Thus, you could compute the same set using the set $\{(12), (23), \ldots, (n-1, n)\}$ of transpositions instead.

```
> Dimino( G, { [2,1,3,4], [1,3,2,4], [1,2,4,3] } );
```

$$\{[2, 1, 3, 4], [2, 3, 1, 4], [1, 2, 3, 4], [3, 2, 1, 4],
[2, 3, 4, 1], [3, 2, 4, 1], [1, 3, 4, 2], [3, 1, 4, 2],
[3, 4, 1, 2], [4, 3, 1, 2], [2, 4, 1, 3], [4, 2, 1, 3],
[3, 4, 2, 1], [4, 3, 2, 1], [4, 1, 2, 3], [1, 4, 2, 3],
[3, 1, 2, 4], [1, 3, 2, 4], [4, 1, 3, 2], [1, 4, 3, 2],
[4, 2, 3, 1], [2, 4, 3, 1], [1, 2, 4, 3], [2, 1, 4, 3]\}$$

You still need to pass the group object G for Dimino to access its operations.

Dimino's algorithm is a useful fallback algorithm, but many finite groups of interest can be enumerated more efficiently using specific knowledge of their structure. For *small* examples, the implementation presented here suffices, but a well-optimized implementation that takes advantage of fast arithmetic for group elements is required.

**Representing Subgroups** A subset of a group that forms a group for larger groups (using the operations inherited from the group, by restriction) is called a *subgroup*. For example, the 3-member set $\{(123), (132), (1)\}$ is a subgroup of the full symmetric group $S_3$ of degree 3 (which has 6 members). There are many approaches for representing of subgroups. One way is to represent a subgroup $H$ of a known group $G$ by specifying a generating set for $H$ and copying the computational services from the representation of $G$ to the representation of $H$. Thus, the Maple representations G and H of $G$ and $H$ would both be of type Group.

There is a different approach that is better suited to implicit representations of subgroups. This design can be extended to allow implicit representations of subgroups that you do not need to compute with directly. The idea is to represent a subgroup by a simpler structure that maintains a link to its parent group and an indication of how it is defined in terms of its parent group. Thus, a subgroup is represented by a module with an export parent that is assigned the group in which the subgroup is contained. A second export has a name depending upon the way in which the subgroup is defined. One way to define a subgroup in terms of its parent is to specify a generating set. Subgroups defined in this way are represented by a module having the export `gens` of type `set`. A second way to define a subgroup is by a property. For example, the center of a group is defined by the property that all its members commute with every element of the group (or, equivalently, that each member of the subgroup commutes with all the generators of the parent group). You can specify properties by using a procedure that tests for membership in the subgroup. Thus, subgroups can be described by either of the following interfaces.

| | |
|---|---|
| `parent` | Parent group |
| `test` | Membership test (a procedure) |
| `gens` | Set of generators |

Only one of the methods `test` and `gens` need be present. A Maple implementation of this interface is as follows.

```
> `type/SubGroup` := '{
>     `module`( parent::Group, gens::set ),
>     `module`( parent::Group, test::procedure )
> }':
```

The `SubGroup` constructor must dispatch on the type of its second argument to determine which kind of record to create to model the subgroup.

```
> SubGroup := proc( G::{Group,SubGroup}, how::{set,procedure} )
>     description "subgroup constructor";
>     local S;
>     if type( how, 'procedure' ) then
>         S:= Record( 'parent', 'test' = eval( how, 1 ) )
>     else
>         S := Record( 'parent', 'gens' = how )
>     end if;
>     S:-parent := G;
>     eval( S, 1 )
> end proc:
```

For example, the center of the symmetric group $S_3$ can be defined as follows.

```
> S3 := Symmetric( 3 ):
> Z := SubGroup( S3, proc( z )
>     local g;
>     use S3 in
>         for g in gens do
>             if not eq( mul( inv( g ), inv( z ), g ), z ) then
>                 return false
>             end if
>         end do;
>     end use;
>     true
> end proc );
```

$$Z := \textbf{module}()\ \textbf{export}\ parent, test;\ \textbf{option}\ record;\ \textbf{end module}$$

```
> Z:-test( [2,1,3] );
```

*false*

```
> Z:-test( [2,3,1] );
```

*false*

```
> Z:-test( [1,2,3] );
```

*true*

Similarly, you can write a constructor for the centralizer of an element in a group.

```
> Centralizer := proc( G, g )
>     SubGroup( G, proc( s )
>                      use `.` = G:-`.`, `=` = G:-eq in
>                          s . g = g . s
>                      end use end proc )
> end proc:
```

**Generic Interfaces** Dimino's algorithm is relatively slow. For many classes of groups, there are better alternatives for enumerating group elements. Use Dimino's algorithm only as a last resort. The advantage of Dimino's algorithm is that it works for *any* finite group. To provide a clean and uniform interface to the enumeration functionality, you can develop a frontend procedure, which hides the details, to choose the best available algorithm.

```
> GroupElements := proc( G )
>     description "enumerate the elements of a finite group";
>     if type( G, 'Group' ) then
>         if type( G:-elements, 'set' ) then
>             G:-elements
>         elif type( G:-elements, 'procedure' ) then
>             G:-procedure()
>         else
>             G:-elements := Dimino( G )
```

```
>             end if
>         else
>             'procname'( args )
>         end if
> end proc:
```

Several elements of the design allow you to take advantage of structural knowledge to improve efficiency. This routine first checks whether the export `elements` of its input group is of type `set`. If it is, then it is taken to be a stored enumeration of the group elements and is simply returned. Otherwise, if the export `elements` is a procedure, then it is taken to be a (perhaps specialized) routine for computing the requested enumeration. Finally, Dimino's algorithm is used as a last resort if no better alternative is provided. As a simple optimization, the result of Dimino's algorithm is stored as a new value for the `elements` export so that it need only be computed once.

Providing the `GroupElements` interface shields the user from needing to know what the available alternatives are and how to use them. An additional benefit of the design is that it allows you to *change* the algorithm selection criteria at any time (to correct software faults, or make functional or performance improvements). Code using this interface need not be modified, provided that the routine continues to honor its contract.

**Enumerating Elements in Subgroups** Once the elements of the parent group are known, the members of the subgroup can be computed using a call to the built-in Maple command `select`.

```
> select( C:-test, Dimino( G ) );
```

How best to enumerate the elements of a subgroup depends upon how it is defined and what is known about the parent group. The procedure `SubGroupElements` that follows takes a subgroup as argument and attempts to find the optimal way to compute the elements of the subgroup from among the available methods.

```
> SubGroupElements := proc( S )
>     description "enumerate the elements of "
>                 "a subgroup of a group";
>     local P;
>     P := S;
>     while type( P, 'SubGroup' ) do
>         P := P:-parent
>     end do;
>     if type( P, 'Group' ) then
>         if member( :-test, S ) then
>             select( S:-test, GroupElements( P ) )
>         else
>             ASSERT( member( :-gens, S ) );
```

```
>                Dimino( P, S:-gens )
>            end if
>        else
>            'procname'( args )
>        end if
>    end proc:
> G := Symmetric( 4 );
```

$G := \textbf{module}()$
**export**
*id*, '.', *mul*, *inv*, *eq*, *member*, *gens*, *order*, *elements*;
**option** *record*;
**end module**

```
> SubGroupElements( Centralizer( G, [ 1, 3, 2, 4 ] ) );
```

$$\{[1, 2, 3, 4], [4, 3, 2, 1], [1, 3, 2, 4], [4, 2, 3, 1]\}$$

With SubGroupElements implemented, it is a good idea to extend GroupElements to accept subgroups also, thus providing a common interface.

```
> GroupElements := proc( G )
>     description "enumerate the elements of a "
>                 "group or subgroup";
>     if type( G, 'SubGroup' ) then
>         SubGroupElements( G )
>     elif type( G, 'Group' ) then
>         if type( G:-elements, 'set' ) then
>             G:-elements
>         elif type( G:-elements, 'procedure' ) then
>             G:-elements()
>         else
>             G:-elements := Dimino( G )
>         end if
>     else
>         'procname'( args )
>     end if
> end proc:
```

**Computing the Order of a Group** As you can enumerate all of a group's elements, it is always possible to determine its order. (Note that this is rarely the best way to do this, however.) In many cases, it is possible to provide much better ways to compute the order of a group. For instance, the symmetric group of degree $n$ has order equal to $n!$, so its order export could be redefined to compute this number instead.

A generic interface to computing group orders, in the same spirit as GroupElements can be written as follows.

```
> GroupOrder := proc( G )
>     description "compute the order of a finite group";
>     if type( G, 'SubGroup' ) then
>         nops( GroupElements( G ) )
>     elif type( G, 'Group' ) then
>         if type( G:-order, 'posint' ) then
>             G:-order
>         elif type( G:-elements, 'set' ) then
>             G:-order := nops( G:-elements )
>         elif type( G:-order, 'procedure' ) then
>             G:-order()
>         else
>             nops( GroupElements( G ) )
>         end if
>     else
>         'procname'( args )
>     end if
> end proc:
```

As with GroupElements, this routine checks the possible shortcuts that might be available for a group. It begins with those that are likely to involve the least computation and progresses through more costly alternatives. Only as a last resort does the procedure call GroupElements to compute a full enumeration of the group elements only to return their number.

```
> G := Symmetric( 4 );
```

$G :=$ **module**()
**export**
*id*, '.', *mul*, *inv*, *eq*, *member*, *gens*, *order*, *elements*;
**option** *record*;

**end module**

```
> C := Centralizer( G, [ 1, 3, 2, 4 ] );
```

$C :=$ **module**()
**export** *parent*, *test*;
**option** *record*;

**end module**

```
> GroupOrder( G );
```

$$24$$

```
> GroupOrder( C );
```

$$4$$

Note that, when the argument `G` is neither a group nor a subgroup, the procedure `GroupElements` returns unevaluated. This allows you to extend other Maple operations, such as `expand`, `combine` or `simplify` to be effective on algebraic expressions involving unevaluated calls to `GroupOrder`.

**Matrix Groups** So far, all the groups have been permutation groups returned by one of the constructors previously presented. You must test the code on some other kinds of groups. A good source for examples of finite groups are the finite groups of exact matrices.

**Equality and Membership Tests for Matrices** Because distinct matrices with equal entries compare differently using the Maple equality comparison operator '`=`', it is necessary to implement a specialized test for membership in a set. For example, consider the matrices

```
> A := Matrix( [[1,0],[0,1]] );
```

$$A := \begin{bmatrix} 1 & 0 \\ 0 & 1 \end{bmatrix}$$

```
> B := Matrix( [[2,3],[3,4]] );
```

$$B := \begin{bmatrix} 2 & 3 \\ 3 & 4 \end{bmatrix}$$

```
> C := Matrix( [[1,0],[0,1]] );
```

$$C := \begin{bmatrix} 1 & 0 \\ 0 & 1 \end{bmatrix}$$

Both `A` and `C` have the same entries, and represent *mathematically* identical objects. However, because matrices are mutable data structures (necessary for efficiency in matrix computations), they are distinct as Maple objects. Thus, for instance:

```
> member( A, { B, C } );
```

*false*

To deal with this property of these data structures, you must implement a *generic* version of the Maple command `member`. The `gmember` routine accepts arguments like those required by the `member` routine in addition to the first argument, which specifies an equality test. This utility is used in the following implementation of the matrix group constructor.

```
> gmember := proc( test, g::anything, S::{set,list}, pos::name )
>     description "a generic membership predicate";
>     local i;
>     if type( test, 'procedure' ) then
>         for i from 1 to nops( S ) do
>             if test( g, S[ i ] ) then
>                 if nargs > 3 then
>                     pos := i
>                 end if;
>                 return true
>             end if
>         end do;
>         false
>     elif test = '`=`' then
>         # use the standard membership test
>         :-member( args[ 2 .. -1 ] )
>     else
>         'procname'( args )
>     end if
> end proc:
```

The built-in procedure `Equal` in the `LinearAlgebra` package provides an equality predicate that is suitable for use with matrices.

```
> gmember( LinearAlgebra:-Equal, A, { B, C } );
```

*true*

**The `MatrixGroup` Constructor** Except for the `member` export, most of the exported methods for matrix groups simply delegate to the appropriate routine in the `LinearAlgebra` package. The `MatrixGroup` constructor takes the degree $n$ of the matrix group as its first argument and, if given more than one argument, takes the remaining ones to be matrices that form a set of generators for the group.

```
> MatrixGroup := proc( n::posint )
>     description "matrix group constructor";
>     local matgens, G;
>     use LinearAlgebra in
```

```
>           matgens := { args[ 2 .. -1 ] };
>           G := Record(
>               'id' = Matrix( n, n, ( i, j ) -> `if`( i = j, 1, 0 ) ),
>               '`.`' = ( ( a, b ) -> MatrixMatrixMultiply( a, b ) ),
>               'mul' = ( () -> foldl( G:-`.`, G:-id, args ) ),
>               'inv' = ( m -> MatrixInverse( m ) ),
>               'gens' = matgens,
>               'eq' = ( ( a, b ) -> Equal( a, b ) ),
>               'member' = proc( g, S, pos::name )
>                   local i, s;
>                   if nargs = 1 then
>                       if type( g, 'Matrix( square )' ) then
>                           evalb( Determinant( g ) <> 0 )
>                       else
>                           false
>                       end if
>                   else
>                       gmember( G:-eq, args )
>                   end if
>               end proc,
>               'order', 'elements' );
>
>           if nargs = 1 then
>               G:-order := 1;
>               G:-elements := { G:-id }
>           end if
>       end use;
>       eval( G, 1 )
> end proc:
```

Here, the matrix group constructor is used to generate a dihedral matrix group of order 12.

```
> theta := Pi / 3;
```

$$\theta := \frac{1}{3}\pi$$

```
> a := Matrix( 2, 2, [[ 0, 1 ], [ 1, 0 ]] );
```

$$a := \begin{bmatrix} 0 & 1 \\ 1 & 0 \end{bmatrix}$$

```
> b := Matrix( 2, 2,
>       [[cos(theta),sin(theta)],
>        [-sin(theta),cos(theta)]] );
```

$$b := \begin{bmatrix} \frac{1}{2} & \frac{1}{2}\sqrt{3} \\ -\frac{1}{2}\sqrt{3} & \frac{1}{2} \end{bmatrix}$$

```
> B := MatrixGroup( 2, a, b );
```

$B :=$ **module**()
**export**
*id*, '.', *mul*, *inv*, *gens*, *eq*, *member*, *order*, *elements*;
**option** *record*;

**end module**

```
> GroupElements( B );
```

$$\left\{ \begin{bmatrix} 0 & 1 \\ 1 & 0 \end{bmatrix}, \begin{bmatrix} \frac{1}{2} & \frac{1}{2}\sqrt{3} \\ -\frac{1}{2}\sqrt{3} & \frac{1}{2} \end{bmatrix}, \begin{bmatrix} 1 & 0 \\ 0 & 1 \end{bmatrix}, \begin{bmatrix} -\frac{1}{2}\sqrt{3} & \frac{1}{2} \\ \frac{1}{2} & \frac{1}{2}\sqrt{3} \end{bmatrix}, \right.$$

$$\begin{bmatrix} \frac{1}{2}\sqrt{3} & \frac{1}{2} \\ \frac{1}{2} & -\frac{1}{2}\sqrt{3} \end{bmatrix}, \begin{bmatrix} \frac{1}{2} & -\frac{1}{2}\sqrt{3} \\ \frac{1}{2}\sqrt{3} & \frac{1}{2} \end{bmatrix}, \begin{bmatrix} \frac{-1}{2} & \frac{1}{2}\sqrt{3} \\ -\frac{1}{2}\sqrt{3} & \frac{-1}{2} \end{bmatrix},$$

$$\begin{bmatrix} -\frac{1}{2}\sqrt{3} & \frac{-1}{2} \\ \frac{-1}{2} & \frac{1}{2}\sqrt{3} \end{bmatrix}, \begin{bmatrix} \frac{1}{2}\sqrt{3} & \frac{-1}{2} \\ \frac{-1}{2} & -\frac{1}{2}\sqrt{3} \end{bmatrix}, \begin{bmatrix} \frac{-1}{2} & -\frac{1}{2}\sqrt{3} \\ \frac{1}{2}\sqrt{3} & \frac{-1}{2} \end{bmatrix}, \begin{bmatrix} -1 & 0 \\ 0 & -1 \end{bmatrix},$$

$$\left. \begin{bmatrix} 0 & -1 \\ -1 & 0 \end{bmatrix} \right\}$$

**Direct Products** To enrich the supply of example groups that you can use, develop a constructor for the direct product of (two) groups. (Extending the constructor to handle any finite number of groups is straightforward, but complicates the exposition unnecessarily.) Direct products are very important in the study of finite groups because all finitely generated abelian groups possess an unique factorization as a direct product of cyclic groups. (In the abelian theory, direct products are often referred to as direct *sums*.)

The direct product of two groups $A$ and $B$ is the group $G$ whose elements are all pairs $(a, b)$, with $a \in A$ and $b \in B$. The group product in $G$ is defined by $(a_1, b_1) \cdot (a_2, b_2) = (a_1 \cdot a_2, b_1 \cdot b_2)$. The inverse of an element $(a, b)$ is the pair $(a^{-1}, b^{-1})$. All the operations are defined component-wise. Represent the elements $(a, b)$ of the direct product by two-element lists. Here is the constructor `DirectProduct`.

```
> DirectProduct := proc( A::Group, B::Group )
>     description "direct product constructor";
>     local G, a, b;
>     if type( A, 'Group' ) and type( B, 'Group' ) then
>         G := Group();
>         G:-id := [ A:-id, B:-id ];
>         G:-`.` := ( u, v ) -> [ A:-`.`( u[1], v[1] ),
>                                  B:-`.`( u[2], v[2] ) ];
>         G:-mul := () -> foldl( G:-`.`, G:-id, args );
>         G:-inv := v -> [ A:-inv( v[ 1 ] ),
>                           B:-inv( v[ 2 ] ) ];
>         G:-gens := [ seq( seq( [ a, b ],
>                       a = A:-gens ), b = B:-gens ) ];
>         G:-eq := ( u, v ) -> A:-eq( u[ 1 ], v[ 1 ] )
>                           and B:-eq( u[ 2 ], v[ 2 ] );
>         G:-order := () -> GroupOrder( A ) * GroupOrder( B );
>         G:-member := proc( g, S, pos::name )
>             if nargs = 1 then
>                 A:-member( g[ 1 ] )
>                    and B:-member( g[ 2 ] )
>             else
>                 gmember( G:-eq, args )
>             end if
>         end proc;
>         G:-elements := () -> [ seq( seq( [ a, b ],
>             a = GroupElements( A ) ), b = GroupElements( B ) ) ];
>         eval( G, 1 )
>     else
>         'procname'( args )
>     end if
> end proc:
```

Most of the group methods are straightforward, but use the known group structure to reduce the complexity of some computations such as those for the `order` and `elements` exports.

```
> A := Symmetric( 3 ):
> G := DirectProduct( A, B ):
> GroupOrder( G );
```

$$72$$

```
> nops( GroupElements( G ) );
```

**Table 2.4** Homomorphism Interface

| | |
|---|---|
| domain | Domain of the homomorphism |
| codomain | Codomain of the homomorphism |
| genmap | Mapping of the generators of the domain into the codomain |

72

**Homomorphisms** In all algebraic theories, *homomorphisms* play a key role. A group homomorphism is a mapping from a group to another (possibly the same) group which commutes with the group operations. That is, a map $\varphi : A \longrightarrow B$ of groups $A$ and $B$ is a homomorphism if $\varphi(ab) = \varphi(a)\varphi(b)$, for all $a$ and $b$ in $A$. A homomorphism is determined uniquely by its effect on a generating set for its domain, so to define a homomorphism, it is enough to specify the images of each among a set of generators for the domain.

Use the interface in Table 2.4 for homomorphisms.

This leads directly to a simple constructor for homomorphism objects.

```
> `type/Homomorphism` := '`module`( domain, codomain, genmap )':
> Homomorphism := proc( A::Group, B::Group, p::procedure )
>    description "homomorphism constructor";
>     Record( 'domain' = A, 'codomain' = B, 'genmap' = p )
> end proc:
```

The *image* of a group homomorphism $\varphi : A \longrightarrow B$ is the subset $\varphi(A)$ of $B$ consisting of all elements of $B$ having the form $\varphi(a)$, for some element $a$ in $A$. It is a subgroup of $B$. These various design choices lead to a simple formulation for computing or representing images of homomorphisms.

```
> HomImage := proc( hom::Homomorphism )
>     description "compute the image of a homomorphism";
>     SubGroup( hom:-codomain,
>               map( hom:-genmap, hom:-domain:-gens ) )
> end proc:
```

As an example computation, compute the image of a homomorphism from the symmetric group $S_4$ onto a two-element matrix group generated by the reflection

```
> Matrix( [ [ 0, 1 ], [ 1, 0 ] ] );
```

$$\begin{bmatrix} 0 & 1 \\ 1 & 0 \end{bmatrix}$$

First, define the groups.

```
> A := Symmetric( 4 ):
> B := MatrixGroup( 2, Matrix( [[0,1],[1,0]] ) ):
```

Define a mapping from the generators of A to the group B by inserting the images of the generators into a procedure's remember table.

```
> h( [2,1,3,4] ) := Matrix( [[0,1],[1,0]] ):
> h( [2,3,4,1] ) := Matrix( [[1,0],[0,1]] ):
```

This defines a Maple procedure h that performs the indicated mapping and returns unevaluated for any other arguments.

```
> eval( h );
```

**proc**() **option** *remember*; 'procname(args)' **end proc**

Use A, B and h to construct the homomorphism object.

```
> hom := Homomorphism( A, B, h );
```

*hom* := **module**()
**export** *domain*, *codomain*, *genmap*;
**option** *record*;
**end module**

```
> type( hom, 'Homomorphism' );
```

*true*

Use the machinery developed earlier in this example to compute the order of the image of this homomorphism.

```
> GroupOrder( HomImage( hom ) );
```

2

Thus, the homomorphism is surjective (as expected). You can compute the elements explicitly.

```
> GroupElements( B );
```

$$\left\{\begin{bmatrix} 0 & 1 \\ 1 & 0 \end{bmatrix}, \begin{bmatrix} 1 & 0 \\ 0 & 1 \end{bmatrix}\right\}$$

```
> GroupElements( HomImage( hom ) );
```

$$\left\{\begin{bmatrix} 1 & 0 \\ 0 & 1 \end{bmatrix}, \begin{bmatrix} 0 & 1 \\ 1 & 0 \end{bmatrix}\right\}$$

**Exercises**

1. An automorphism $\alpha$ of a group $G$ is called *inner* if there is an element $a$ in $G$ for which $\alpha(g) = a^{-1}ga$, for all $g$ in $G$. Write a constructor for inner automorphisms of groups.

**Summary** With generic programming you need only implement computation in quotient fields or groups once — in the constructors and generic procedures. The functor `QuotientField` and the various generic group constructors and procedures are parameterized by the computational domains upon which their computed values depend. Rings, fields, groups, and subgroups are collections of computational capabilities, which you use to construct new instances with derived computational capabilities. Overriding default methods (which may not be efficient, but are always present) with methods that take advantage of specific structural information allows for efficient computation without sacrificing generality. This leads to a powerful paradigm for software reuse, and is the principal motivation underlying the Maple module system.

## 2.7 Extended Example: A Search Engine

Search engines are used in a variety of contexts to locate documents that match or satisfy a query. Queries consist of sequences of search terms – words that are meant to prescribe the subject matter of matching documents. Examples of search engines include Web search engines and database interfaces. However, search engines can be adapted to search a wide variety of structured or unstructured data.

This example illustrates how a simple search engine, based on the vector space model, can be constructed using Maple. Various Maple packages are used to pre- and post-process the data to be searched, as well as the queries, and the `LinearAlgebra` package is used to effect the computations necessary to locate relevant documents.

### Introduction to Searching

Prototypically, a document is a file of structured or unstructured text, but this section treats documents as abstract data items. A document can be a scientific article in LaTeX format, a web page, an integral formula, an image, or a simple string of text, as used here for illustrative purposes. The document is a raw piece of data that can be identified as a whole. Each document is equipped with a *document ID*, that is, an identifier that is used as a handle for the document data. The document ID is small, while the document (containing data) may be arbitrarily large.

For searching, documents are organized into *corpora*. A corpus is a collection of documents that can be searched collectively using search terms. A *query* is a list of search terms. A search term is typically a (natural language) word or phrase. The purpose of a search is to identify, among documents in a given corpus, those which match the search terms. Thus, search input consists of a corpus to search, and one or more search terms. The output is a ranked list of documents that the search criteria judge to be relevant to the search terms.

For this example, consider the following simple corpus of documents. Each document is a short string of text, which serves as both the document ID and the document data.

```
> doc1 := "The mathematician's patterns, like the painter's "
>   "or the poet's must be beautiful; the ideas, like "
>   "the colors or the words must fit together in a "
>   "harmonious way. Beauty is the first test: there "
>   "is no permanent place in this world "
>   "for ugly mathematics.": # Hardy
> doc2 := "God does arithmetic.":          # Karl Friedrich Gauss
> doc3 := "Anyone  who  cannot cope with mathematics is not"
>   " fully human.  At best he is a tolerable subhuman "
>   "who has learned to wear shoes, bathe, and not make "
>   "messes in the house.": # Robert A. Heinlein
> doc4 := "Things should be made as simple as possible, "
>   "but no simpler.":
> doc5 := "I don't believe in mathematics.":
> doc6 := "Imagination is more important than knowledge.":
> doc7 := "The most beautiful thing we can experience is "
>   "the mysterious.  It is the source of all true "
>   "art and science.":
> doc8 := "Common sense is the collection of prejudices "
>   "acquired by age eighteen.":
> doc9 := "God does not care about our mathematical "
>   "difficulties. He integrates empirically.": # A. Einstein
```

The corpus consists of these documents. To facilitate searches, the corpus is preprocessed to construct a search index. The index aids searches by making it easy to quickly locate documents in the corpus that are relevant to one or more of the search terms in a query.

## Inverted Term Occurrence Indexing

An inverted term occurrence index is a simple search index. An inverted term occurrence index constructs a list of all the potential search terms present in the corpus and maintains a list of the documents in which each search term occurs. Construction of an inverted term occurrence index begins by constructing a document-term mapping. For simple text strings, construct a list of document terms as follows.

```
> DocumentTerms := proc( text::string )
>   StringTools:-Words( text )
> end proc:
> DocumentTerms( doc1 );
```

["The", "mathematician's", "patterns", "like", "the", "painter's", "or", "the", "poet's", "must", "be", "beautiful", "the", "ideas", "like", "the", "colors", "or", "the", "words", "must", "fit", "together", "in", "a", "harmonious", "way", "Beauty", "is", "the", "first", "test", "there", "is", "no", "permanent", "place", "in", "this", "world", "for", "ugly", "mathematics"]

Using this, construct an inverted term occurrence index.

```
> BuildIndex := proc( corpus::list(string) )
>   local docterms, corpusterms, index, term, doc;
>   use StringTools in
>     # Construct all terms in the corpus
>     docterms := table( [seq]( doc = DocumentTerms( doc ),
>        doc = corpus ) );
>     corpusterms := `union`( seq( {op}( docterms[ doc ] ),
>        doc = corpus ) );
>     # Map each term to the documents containing it
>      index := table();
>      for doc in corpus do
>        for term in docterms[ doc ] do
>          if assigned( index[ term ] ) then
>            index[ term ] := index[ term ] union { doc }
>          else
>            index[ term ] := { doc }
>          end if
>        end do
>      end do
>   end use;
>   # Return the table
>   eval( index, 1 )
> end proc:
> Index := BuildIndex( [ doc || ($1..9) ] ):
> nops( {indices}( Index ) );
```

104

Searching is simple, using this index. Search for the terms "mathematical" and "beauty".

```
> Search := proc( query::list(string) )
>   global Index;
>   local results, term;
>   results := {};
>     for term in query do
>       if assigned( Index[ term ] ) then
>         results := results union Index[ term ]
>       end if
>     end do;
>   results
> end proc:
> Search( [ "mathematical", "beauty" ] );
```

{"God does not care about our mathematical diff \
iculties. He integrates empirically."}

```
> nops( % );
```

1

There are several problems with this index. One problem is that the index is quite large (relative to the size of the corpus). Many words that occur in the corpus convey little or no information about the content of the documents in which they occur. This can lead to irrelevant results, especially for poorly chosen search terms.

```
> nops( Search( [ "the" ] ) );
```

4

This problem can be solved by removing unimportant terms from the index. This set of unwanted terms is called a *stop list*.

```
> STOP_WORDS := { "a", "i", "an", "the", "in", "to",
>   "which", "that", "is", "and", "we", "it", "of",
>   "all", "can", "does", "don't", "most", "true",
>   "thing" }:
```

A second problem is *synonymy* in the corpus. That is, many distinct terms in the corpus have the same meaning in the context of searching. For example, searching for the term "mathematics" should return documents that contain the terms "mathematical", "math" and "mathematically", even if the exact term "mathematics" does not occur in the document. To solve this problem, map each term onto its *stem*, or root term.

To implement these changes in the DocumentTerms procedure, use the StringTools package.

```
> DocumentTerms := proc( text::string )
>   global STOP_WORDS;
>   local words;
>   use StringTools in
>     words := map( LowerCase, Words( text ) );
>     words := remove( type, words, STOP_WORDS );
>     map( Stem, words )
>   end use
> end proc:
```

By using the LowerCase function, case distinctions are removed, making the process more efficient. Apply the same preprocessing to search terms: convert to lowercase, remove stop list words, and map words onto their stems.

```
> Search := proc( query::list(string) )
>   global Index;
>   local  results, term, terms;
>   use StringTools in
>     terms := map( LowerCase, query );
>     terms := remove( type, terms, STOP_WORDS );
>     terms := map( Stem, terms )
>   end use;
>   results := {};
>   for term in terms do
>     if assigned( Index[ term ] ) then
>       results := results union Index[ term ]
>     end if
>   end do;
>   results
> end proc:
```

Because BuildIndex uses DocumentTerms, rebuild the index.

```
> Index := BuildIndex( [ doc || ($1..9) ] ):
> nops( {indices}( Index ) );
```

$$83$$

This has substantially reduced the size of the index.

```
> Search( [ "the" ] );
```

$$\{\}$$

Because the stop word "the" has been removed from the index, it returns no matches. This is also a user interface enhancement because queries can contain stop words without affecting the results.

```
> Search( [ "mathematical", "beauty" ] );
```

{"The mathematician's patterns, like the painter' \
s or the poet's must be beautiful; the ideas, like t \
he colors or the words must fit together in a har \
monious way. Beauty is the first test: there is no \
 permanent place in this world for ugly mathem\
atics.", "Anyone who cannot cope with mathem \
atics is not fully human. At best he is a tolerabl \
e subhuman who has learned to wear shoes, bat\
he, and not make messes in the house.",
"I don't believe in mathematics.", "The most bea \
utiful thing we can experience is the mysterious. \
 It is the source of all true art and science.", "Go\
d does not care about our mathematical difficult \
ies. He integrates empirically."}

```
> nops( % );
```

5

The new process returns many more documents relevant to the query.

## The Vector Space Model

It is possible to model the search by using a vector space model of the term-document indices for corpora. After collecting the relevant search terms for a corpus, represent each document by a vector in a Euclidean space $E^n$, where $n$ is the number of distinct terms in the corpus. Each coordinate in this vector space represents a term in the corpus. First determine an ordering of the corpus terms. Then map each document to a *term vector* in this Euclidean space. A simple mapping is to represent a document by a term vector whose $i$th coordinate is equal to 1 if the $i$th term occurs in the document, and is equal to 0 otherwise. For each query, construct a term vector. The dot product of the query term vector with a document term vector is the number of query terms that appear in the document. A document containing more query terms might reasonably be judged more relevant than one containing fewer query terms. To rank the documents, sort the dot products of the query term vector with the document term vectors.

For example, consider a smaller corpus comprising only the documents doc2, doc5, and doc7.

```
> SmallIndex := BuildIndex( [ doc2, doc5, doc7 ] ):
```

The ordered list of corpus terms is:

```
> SmallCorpusTerms := sort( [op]( map( op, {indices}(
>       SmallIndex ) ) ) );
```

$$SmallCorpusTerms := [\text{"arithmet"}, \text{"art"}, \text{"beauti"}, \text{"believ"}, \text{"experi"}, \text{"god"}, \text{"mathemat"}, \text{"mysteri"}, \text{"scienc"}, \text{"sourc"}]$$

**Note:** Terms in the documents are replaced by their stems and stop words are removed from the index. The document term vector can be computed using the following procedure.

```
> DocumentTermVector := proc( doc )
>   global  SmallCorpusTerms;
>   local  terms;
>   terms := DocumentTerms( doc );
>   Vector[row]( 1 .. nops( SmallCorpusTerms ),
>     i -> 'if'( member( SmallCorpusTerms[ i ], terms ), 1, 0 ) )
> end proc:
> doc5Vector := DocumentTermVector( doc5 );
```

$$doc5Vector := [0, 0, 0, 1, 0, 0, 1, 0, 0, 0]$$

Compute the query term vector for the search term "mathematical beauty".

```
> queryVector := DocumentTermVector( "mathematical beauty" );
```

$$queryVector := [0, 0, 1, 0, 0, 0, 1, 0, 0, 0]$$

The inner product is:

```
> LinearAlgebra:-DotProduct( queryVector, doc5Vector );
```

$$1$$

which indicates that one of the query terms (corresponding to "mathematical") appears in the document.

To rank the documents in the corpus for their relevance to the query, apply this process to each document in the corpus.

```
> use LinearAlgebra in
>   DotProduct( queryVector, DocumentTermVector( doc2 ) );
>   DotProduct( queryVector, DocumentTermVector( doc5 ) );
>   DotProduct( queryVector, DocumentTermVector( doc7 ) );
> end use;
```

$$0$$

$$1$$

$$1$$

It is more efficient to represent the entire corpus by a *term-document matrix*, in which the rows are the term vectors for the documents in the corpus. First determine a fixed ordering of the documents in the corpus. The dot products can then be computed by forming the product of the term-document matrix representing the corpus with the term vector for a query.

```
> TermDocumentMatrix := Matrix(
>   map( [s->s], map( DocumentTermVector,
>      [ doc2, doc5, doc7 ] ) ) );
```

$$\mathit{TermDocumentMatrix} := \begin{bmatrix} 1 & 0 & 0 & 0 & 0 & 1 & 0 & 0 & 0 & 0 \\ 0 & 0 & 0 & 1 & 0 & 0 & 1 & 0 & 0 & 0 \\ 0 & 1 & 1 & 0 & 1 & 0 & 0 & 1 & 1 & 1 \end{bmatrix}$$

```
> use LinearAlgebra in
>   Scores := TermDocumentMatrix . Transpose( queryVector )
> end use;
```

$$\mathit{Scores} := \begin{bmatrix} 0 \\ 1 \\ 1 \end{bmatrix}$$

There is a geometric interpretation of the search process. The dot product of two vectors, $u$ and $v$, is related to the angle between the vectors, for which the cosine is given by the formula:

$$\langle u, v\rangle/(\| u \| \cdot \| v \|).$$

Consider the projection of the document term vectors onto the hyperplane defined by the component vectors of the query vector, and then introduce appropriate scaling, using vector norms. In this context, searching can be viewed as a process of determining those vectors representing documents in a corpus for which the angle between their projections and the query vector is small.

## Term Weighting

A document that contains many instances of a given term is generally considered to be more relevant to queries containing that term than a document with fewer instances. To improve rankings, therefore, record not only the presence of a term in a document, but also its frequency. This is a simple change to DocumentTermMatrix. The term vector of a document is the vector of $E^n$ whose $i$th entry is equal to the number of times the $i$th corpus term occurs in the document.

```
> DocumentTermVector := proc( doc )
>   global  SmallCorpusTerms;
>   local  terms;
>   terms := DocumentTerms( doc );
>   Vector[row]( 1 .. nops( SmallCorpusTerms ),
>      i -> numboccur( terms, SmallCorpusTerms[ i ] ) )
> end proc:
```

This can lead to significantly improved results when searching a larger corpus.

To improve this method, scale the number of instances by the *size* (the total number of terms with multiplicities) of the document. For example, a book about cats is not more relevant than a short paper on cats merely because the term "cats" appears more often in the book than in the short article.

```
> DocumentTermVector := proc( doc )
>   global  SmallCorpusTerms;
>   local  terms;
>   terms := DocumentTerms( doc );
>   Vector[row]( 1 .. nops( SmallCorpusTerms ),
>      i -> evalf( numboccur( terms, SmallCorpusTerms[ i ] )
>                / nops( terms ) ) )
> end proc:
```

With this change, recompute the term-document matrix and the matrix of scores, which represents the search results. Also recompute the query term vector.

```
> TermDocumentMatrix := Matrix( map( [s->s],
>    map( DocumentTermVector, [ doc2, doc5, doc7 ] ) ) ):
> queryVector := DocumentTermVector( "mathematical beauty" ):
> use LinearAlgebra in
>   Scores := TermDocumentMatrix . Transpose( queryVector )
> end use;
```

$$Scores := \begin{bmatrix} 0. \\ 0.250000000000000000 \\ 0.0833333333499999968 \end{bmatrix}$$

According to these results, the second document in the corpus (doc5) is the most relevant to the query, followed by the third document (doc7). The first document (doc2) is judged to have no relevance to the query.

## Building a Search Engine Package

The next step is to design a search engine package that includes all the features described to this point. The search engine must also be as generic as possible, and accept a variety of document and term types.

The package manages two kinds of data objects: documents and corpora. Each is represented by an object that supports certain features.

A document is abstracted as a record object with three slots. The constructor is:

```
> Document := proc( id, fetch, filter )
>   Record(
>     ':-id' = id,
>     ':-fetch' = fetch,
>     ':-filter' = filter )
> end proc:
```

The id slot is the document ID. The document ID must uniquely represent the document within the corpus. For efficiency, document IDs are *small*, while their referents may be quite large. While enormous documents can be handled in the design, for simplicity, it is assumed that any document can reasonably be read into memory in its entirety. The fetch slot is a procedure that returns the body of a document, given its document ID. The filter slot contains a procedure that generates a list of terms appearing in the document, with multiplicities. Several accessor procedures for documents are also provided in the package.

A corpus is a collection of documents. It is represented by an object that supports methods for accessing, indexing, and searching the collection.

```
> SearchEngine := module()
>   description "a simple search engine";
```

```
>    option  package;
>    export
>      Filters,          # subpackage of filters
>      Document,         # document constructor
>      DocumentID,       # accessor procedure
>      FilterDocument, # accessor procedure
>      FetchDocument,  # accessor procedure
>      Corpus,           # corpus constructor
>      NumberOfDocuments, # returns number of documents in corpus
>      BuildIndex,       # index a corpus
>      GetDocumentIdByIndex, # retrieve a document ID
>      Search;           # perform a search
>    local
>      documentTermVector, # construct document term vector
>      queryTermVector;    # construct query term vector
>
>    # Exports
>
>    # Document constructor
>    Document := proc( id, fetch, filter )
>      Record(
>        ':-id' = id,
>        ':-fetch' = fetch,
>        ':-filter' = filter )
>    end proc;
>
>    # Accessor routines for documents.
>    DocumentID := doc -> doc:-id;
>    FetchDocument := doc -> doc:-fetch( doc:-id );
>    FilterDocument := doc -> doc:-filter( FetchDocument( doc ) );
>
>    # Corpus constructor. Called with either a sequence of
>    # documents or a list of document IDs, a fetcher, a document
>    # filter routine, and an optional query filter routine.
>
>    Corpus := proc( listOfIds::list, fetch, filter, _qfilter )
>      local  docs, qfilter;
>
>      # Process arguments.
>      if nargs = 0 then
>        error "expecting corpus description"
>      elif nargs > 3 then
>        # Allow the query filter to be different
>        # from the document filter
>        qfilter := eval( _qfilter, 2 )
>      else
>        # If query filter is not specified,
>        # use the document filter.
>        qfilter := eval( filter, 2 )
>      end if;
>
>      # Construct list of documents.
>      docs := map( Document, listOfIds, fetch, filter );
>
```

```
>       # Build the corpus.
>       module()
>         export  search, buildIndex,
>           numberOfDocuments,
>           getDocumentIdByIndex;
>         local  ids, corpusTerms,
>           documents,
>           term_document_matrix;
>
>         ids := listOfIds;
>         documents := docs;
>
>         numberOfDocuments := () -> nops( documents );
>         getDocumentIdByIndex := proc( idx::posint )
>           if idx <= numberOfDocuments() then
>             ids[ idx ]
>           else
>             error "there are fewer than %1 documents in the corpus",
>                   idx
>           end if
>         end proc;
>
>         buildIndex := proc()
>           local  docterms;
>           # Construct corpus terms.
>           docterms := map( FilterDocument, documents );
>           corpusTerms := sort( [op](
>                 `union`( op( map( {op}, docterms ) ) ) ) );
>           # Build the term-document matrix.
>           term_document_matrix := Matrix( map( [s -> s],
>             map( documentTermVector, docs, corpusTerms ) ),
>             'datatype' = 'float'[ 8 ], 'storage' = 'sparse' );
>           eval( thismodule, 1 )
>         end proc;
>
>         search := proc( query, numberOfResults::posint )
>           local  qt, qv, scores;
>           if not type( term_document_matrix, 'Matrix' ) then
>             error "corpus not yet indexed"
>           end if;
>           qt := qfilter( query );
>           qv := queryTermVector( qt, corpusTerms );
>           use LinearAlgebra in
>             scores := Transpose(
>                         MatrixVectorMultiply(
>                           term_document_matrix, qv ) )
>           end use
>         end proc;
>       end module
>     end proc;
>
>     NumberOfDocuments := corpus -> corpus:-numberOfDocuments();
>     GetDocumentIdByIndex := ( corpus, idx )
>            -> corpus:-getDocumentIdByIndex( idx );
```

```
>   BuildIndex := corpus -> corpus:-buildIndex();
>   Search := ( corpus, query ) -> corpus:-search( query );
>
>   # Locals
>   documentTermVector := proc( doc, corpusTerms::list )
>     local terms;
>     terms := FilterDocument( doc );
>     Vector[row]( 1 .. nops( corpusTerms ),
>       i -> evalf( numboccur( terms, corpusTerms[ i ] )
>                  / nops( terms ) ),
>       'datatype' = 'float'[ 8 ],
>       'storage' = 'sparse' )
>   end proc;
>
>   queryTermVector := proc( queryTerms::list, corpusTerms::list )
>     Vector[column]( 1 .. nops( corpusTerms ),
>       i -> evalf( numboccur( queryTerms, corpusTerms[ i ] )
>                  / nops( queryTerms ) ),
>       'datatype' = 'float'[ 8 ],
>       'storage' = 'sparse' )
>   end proc;
>
>   # Filters subpackage
>   Filters := module()
>     description "filter subpackage";
>     option package;
>     export  Text;
>     local  stopWords;
>
>     stopWords := { "a", "i", "an", "the", "in", "to",
>       "which", "that", "is", "and", "we", "it", "of",
>       "all", "can", "does", "don't", "most", "true",
>       "thing" }:
>
>     Text := proc( text::string )
>       local  words;
>       use StringTools in
>         words := map( LowerCase, Words( text ) );
>         words := remove( type, words, stopWords );
>         map( Stem, words )
>       end use
>     end proc;
>
>   end module;
>
> end module:
>
> with( SearchEngine ):
> corpus := Corpus( [ doc || ($1..9) ], s -> s, Filters:-Text ):
> NumberOfDocuments( corpus );
```

$$9$$

```
> GetDocumentIdByIndex( corpus, 1 );
```

"The mathematician's patterns, like the painter's \
or the poet's must be beautiful; the ideas, like th \
e colors or the words must fit together in a harm \
onious way. Beauty is the first test: there is no p \
ermanent place in this world for ugly mathemati\
cs."

```
> BuildIndex( corpus ):
> Search( corpus, "mathematical beauty" );
```

[0.04838709677499999992, 0., 0.02083333333349999990,
0., 0.2500000000000000000, 0.,
0.08333333333499999968, 0., 0.05000000000000000028
]

## Latent Semantic Analysis

The simple vector space model described previously has shortcomings. Suppose a user searches a corpus of documents about pets for the term "cat". The simple vector space model search engine locates all the documents that contain the term "cat". However, the search engine does not locate documents that contain the word "feline", but not the word "cat" (or any term for which the stem is "cat"). This issue is called synonymy – the problem that distinct search terms may represent the same concept. One way to circumvent this problem is to have a human domain expert prepare search term lists for each document in the corpus. All documents referring either to "cats" or "felines" would contain the search term "cat" included in their list of search terms. This solution is, however, very expensive.

An automatic indexing procedure known as *latent semantic analysis* (LSA) helps to discover relations between terms and documents that are latent in the corpus by analyzing the corpus as a whole. The process is related to factor analysis, and is essentially a statistical technique, relying heavily on linear algebra. When used to prepare a search index for a corpus, LSA is referred to as *latent semantic indexing* (LSI).

A thorough discussion of LSI is beyond the scope of this manual, so only the operational details necessary to construct the `SearchEngine` package are discussed.

LSI computes a lower rank approximation to the term-document matrix. The approximation is computed by using the singular value decomposition of the term-document matrix. The singular value decomposition of a matrix $A$ is a factorization:

$$A = U \cdot S \cdot V^T$$

where $U$ and $V$ are column orthogonal matrices, and $S$ is a diagonal matrix whose diagonal entries are arranged in descending order. The diagonal entries of $S$ are called the *singular values* of $A$, the columns of $U$ are called the *left singular vectors* of $A$, and the columns of $V$ are called the *right singular vectors* of $A$. If $A$ is a term-document matrix, then the columns of $U$ can be interpreted as an orthogonal basis for the semantic factors of term-term correlations between terms in the corpus represented by $A$, while the columns of $V$ can be interpreted as an orthogonal basis for the semantic factors of the correlations between documents. For large corpora, the rank of $S$ may be on the order of a few thousand. To obtain a rank $k$ approximation of $A$ that is closest, in the least squares sense, choose a rank $k$ smaller than the rank of $S$ (say, on the order of a few hundred), and form the matrix:

$$A_k = U_k \cdot S_k \cdot V_k^T$$

where $U_k$ consists of the first $k$ columns of $U$, $V_k$ consists of the first $k$ columns of $V$, and $S_k$ is the first $k \times k$ submatrix of $S$.

When the matrix $A$ is a term-document matrix, its approximation $A_k$ is used as a surrogate corpus index for searching. It can be argued that the matrix $A_k$ is better able to determine correlations between terms in such a way that searches using it are able to approximate results obtained by human expert indexing. For example, in a corpus on pets, some documents may contain the term "cat", others the term "feline", and still others may contain both terms. LSI places documents containing only one of these terms closer together in the lower dimensional projection by virtue of their co-occurrence in some of the documents in the corpus. In practice, the rank $k$ chosen for the approximation is an empirically determined value, based on the quality of search results. Because LSI is a statistical technique, in general, it produces useful results only for large corpora.

## The Search Engine Package

This section modifies the `SearchEngine` package to incorporate LSI without changing the interface that was designed for the simpler indexing scheme. The updated package contains more filters to allow for a greater variety of corpora.

```
> SearchEngine := module()
>   description "a generic search engine package";
>   option  package;
>   export
>     Filters,      # subpackage of filters
>     Document,     # document constructor
>     DocumentID,
>     FilterDocument,
>     FetchDocument,
>     Corpus,       # corpus constructor
>     NumberOfDocuments,
>     BuildIndex,
>     GetDocumentIdByIndex,
>     Search;
>   local
>     Tools,      # private submodule
>     documentTermVector,
>     queryTermVector;
>
>   # Exports
>
>   # Document constructor
>   Document := proc( id, fetch, filter )
>     description "document constructor";
>     Record(
>         ':-id' = id,
>         ':-fetch' = fetch,
>         ':-filter' = filter )
>   end proc;
>
>   # Document accessors.
>   DocumentID := doc -> doc:-id;
>   FetchDocument := doc -> doc:-fetch( doc:-id );
>   FilterDocument := doc -> doc:-filter( FetchDocument( doc ) );
>
>   # Corpus constructor. Called with either a sequence of documents,
>   # or a list of document IDs, a fetcher and a document filter
>   # routine, and a query filter routine.
>
>   Corpus := proc( listOfIds::list, fetch, filter, _qfilter )
>     description "corpus constructor";
>     local  docs, qfilter;
>
>     # Process arguments.
>     if nargs = 0 then
>       error "expecting corpus description"
>     elif nargs > 3 then
>       # Allow the query filter to be different
>       # than the document filter
>       qfilter := eval( _qfilter, 2 )
>     else
>       # If not query filter is specified,
>       # use the document filter
>       qfilter := eval( filter, 2 )
```

```
>       end if;
>
>       # Construct list of documents.
>       docs := map( Document, listOfIds, fetch, filter );
>
>       # Build the corpus.
>       module()
>         export  search, buildIndex,
>           numberOfDocuments,
>           getDocumentIdByIndex;
>         local  ids, corpusTerms,
>           documents,
>           term_document_matrix;
>
>         # Initialize private data.
>         ids := listOfIds;
>         documents := docs;
>
>         # Accessor methods.
>         numberOfDocuments := () -> nops( docs );
>         getDocumentIdByIndex := proc( idx::posint )
>           if idx <= numberOfDocuments() then
>             ids[ idx ]
>           else
>             error "there are fewer than %1 documents in the corpus",
>                   idx
>           end if
>         end proc;
>
>         # Construct an index based on a _k-dimensional approximation
>         # to the term-document matrix.
>         buildIndex := proc( _k::posint )
>           local  docterms, k, u, s, v;
>
>           # Construct corpus terms.
>           docterms := map( FilterDocument, documents );
>           corpusTerms := sort( [op]( `union`( op( map( {op},
>             docterms ) ) ) ) );
>
>           # Build the term-document matrix.
>           term_document_matrix := Matrix( map( [s -> s],
>             map( documentTermVector, docs, corpusTerms ) ),
>             'datatype' = 'float'[ 8 ], 'storage' = 'sparse' );
>
>           use LinearAlgebra in
>             u, s, v := SingularValues( term_document_matrix,
>               'output' = [ ':-U', ':-S', ':-Vt' ] );
>             v := Transpose( v );
>             if nargs > 0 then
>               k := _k
>             else
>               # Use a default if no dimension provided.
>               k := floor( Rank( DiagonalMatrix( s ) ) * 0.7 )
>             end if;
```

```
>           u := u[ 1 .. -1, 1 .. k ];
>           v := v[ 1 .. k, 1 .. -1 ];
>           s := DiagonalMatrix( s[ 1 .. k ] );
>           # Replace the term-document matrix with its rank
>           # k approximation
>           term_document_matrix := MatrixMatrixMultiply( u,
>             MatrixMatrixMultiply( s, v ) )
>         end use;
>         eval( thismodule, 1 )
>       end proc;
>
>       search := proc( query, numberOfResults::posint )
>         local  qt, qv, scores;
>         if not type( term_document_matrix, 'Matrix' ) then
>           error "corpus not yet indexed"
>         end if;
>         qt := qfilter( query );
>         qv := queryTermVector( qt, corpusTerms );
>         use LinearAlgebra in
>           scores := Transpose( MatrixVectorMultiply(
>             term_document_matrix, qv ) );
>           Tools:-permSort( scores )
>         end use
>       end proc;
>     end module
>   end proc;
>
>   NumberOfDocuments := corpus -> corpus:-numberOfDocuments();
>   GetDocumentIdByIndex := ( corpus, idx ) ->
>     corpus:-getDocumentIdByIndex( idx );
>   BuildIndex := ( corpus, k ) -> `if`( nargs = 1,
>     corpus:-buildIndex(), corpus:-buildIndex( k ) );
>   Search := ( corpus, query ) -> corpus:-search( query );
>
>   # Locals
>   documentTermVector := proc( doc, corpusTerms::list )
>     local  terms, norm;
>     terms := FilterDocument( doc );
>     Vector[row]( 1 .. nops( corpusTerms ),
>       i -> evalf( numboccur( terms, corpusTerms[ i ] ) /
>         nops( corpusTerms ) ),
>       'datatype' = 'float'[ 8 ],
>       'storage' = 'sparse' )
>   end proc;
>
>   queryTermVector := proc( queryTerms::list, corpusTerms::list )
>     Vector[column]( 1 .. nops( corpusTerms ),
>       i -> evalf( numboccur( queryTerms, corpusTerms[ i ] ) /
>         nops( corpusTerms ) ),
>       'datatype' = 'float'[ 8 ],
>       'storage' = 'sparse' )
>   end proc;
>
>   # The Tools submodule
```

```
> Tools := module()
>   export permSort;
>
>   permSort := proc( V::Vector )
>     local partition, quickSort, n, P, i;
>
>     partition := proc( a, lb, ub )
>       local i, j, k, v;
>       i, j, k := lb, 1 + ub, lb;
>       v := a[ k ];
>       while i < j do
>         i := 1 + i;
>         while i < j and a[ i ] < v do
>           i := 1 + i
>         end do;
>         j := j - 1;
>         while a[ j ] > v do
>           j := j - 1
>         end do;
>         if i < j then
>           P[ i ], P[ j ] := P[ j ], P[ i ];
>           a[ i ], a[ j ] := a[ j ], a[ i ]
>         end if
>       end do;
>       P[ k ], P[ j ] := P[ j ], P[ k ];
>       a[ k ], a[ j ] := a[ j ], a[ k ];
>       j
>     end proc;
>
>     quickSort := proc( a, lb, ub )
>       local k;
>       if lb < ub then
>         k := partition( a, lb, ub );
>         procname( a, lb, k - 1 );
>         procname( a, k + 1, ub )
>       end if;
>       a
>     end proc;
>
>     n := LinearAlgebra:-Dimensions( V );
>     P := Array( 1 .. n, [ $ 1 .. n ], 'datatype' =
>       'integer[ 4 ]' );
>     quickSort( V, 1, n );
>     [seq]( P[ i ], i = 1 .. n )
>   end proc;
>
> end module;
>
> # The Filters subpackage
> Filters := module()
>   option package;
>   export Text, XML, Maple, Worksheet;
>   local stopWords;
>
```

```
>       stopWords := {
>         # The 48 most common English words
>         "i", "a", "all", "an", "and", "are",
>         "as", "at", "be", "been", "but", "by",
>         "can", "do", "for", "from", "had", "has",
>         "have", "he", "his", "if", "in", "is",
>         "it", "not", "of", "on", "or", "she",
>         "that", "the", "their", "there", "they", "this",
>         "to", "was", "we", "were", "what", "which",
>         "who", "will", "with", "would", "you",
>         # a few others
>         "thing", "true", "most", "does", "don't",
>         NULL};
>
>       Text := proc( text::string )
>         description "compute the terms in a text string";
>         local  words;
>         use StringTools in
>           words := map( LowerCase, Words( text ) );
>           words := remove( type, words, stopWords );
>           map( Stem, words )
>         end use
>       end proc;
>
>       XML := proc( xml )
>         description "compute the terms in an XML document";
>           local   t, count, rec;
>
>           rec := proc( xml, t::table )
>           local  cm, texts, text, others;
>           use XMLTools in
>             if IsElement( xml ) then
>               cm := ContentModel( xml );
>               texts, others := selectremove( IsText, cm );
>               for text in texts do
>                 count := 1 + count;
>                 t[ count ] := text
>               end do;
>               map( procname, others, t )
>             end if
>           end use
>           end proc;
>           count := 0;
>           t := rec( xml, t )
>           [seq]( t[ i ], i = 1 .. count )
>       end proc;
>
>       Maple := proc( expr )
>         description "compute the terms in a Maple expression";
>         local       fns, terms, nocc;
>         fns := [op]( map2( op, 0, indets( expr, 'function' ) ) );
>         nocc := map2( numboccur, expr, fns );
>         terms := [seq]( [ seq( fns[ i ], j =  1 .. nocc[ i ] ) ],
>           i = 1 .. nops( fns ) );
```

```
>         sort( map( op, terms ), 'lexorder' )
>       end proc;
>
>       Worksheet := proc( mws )
>         description "compute the terms in a worksheet";
>         local  rec, wks, count, t, i;
>
>         rec := proc( x, t::table )
>           local  cm, texts, text, others;
>           use XMLTools in
>             if IsElement( x ) and ElementName( x ) = "Text-field" then
>               cm := ContentModel( x );
>               texts, others := selectremove( IsText, cm );
>               for text in texts do
>                 count := 1 + count;
>                 t[ count ] := text
>               end do;
>               map( procname, others, t )
>             elif not type( x, 'string' ) then
>               map( procname, args )
>             end if
>           end use
>         end proc;
>
>         use XMLTools in
>           if IsDocument( mws ) then
>             wks := select( IsElement, [op]( mws ) );
>             if nops( wks ) = 1 then
>               wks := wks[ 1 ]
>             else
>               error "ill-formed worksheet '%1'", fname
>             end if
>           end if
>         end use;
>
>         count := 0;
>         t := table();
>         rec( wks, t );
>         t := [seq]( t[ i ], i = 1 .. count );
>
>         use XMLTools in
>           t := map( TextText, t );
>           t := cat( op( t ) );
>           Filters:-Text( t )
>         end use;
>       end proc;
>
>     end module;
>
> end module:
```

The revised package contains several new document filters. To use document formats that are not directly supported, compose these filters with custom code. Rather than providing a vector of raw scores, the `Search` command in the package now returns a permutation of the document list indicating document rankings. This can be used directly with the `GetDocumentIdByIndex` routine.

## Using the Package

The package can be used with a variety of corpora. This subsection demonstrates two examples. The first is the corpus of short text strings used previously in this section.

```
> with( SearchEngine ):
> corpus := Corpus( [ doc || ($1..9) ], id -> id,
>     Filters:-Text ):
> NumberOfDocuments( corpus );
```

$$9$$

```
> GetDocumentIdByIndex( corpus, 1 );
```

"The mathematician's patterns, like the painter's \
or the poet's must be beautiful; the ideas, like th \
e colors or the words must fit together in a harm \
onious way. Beauty is the first test: there is no p \
ermanent place in this world for ugly mathemati\
cs."

```
> ranking := Search( BuildIndex( corpus ),
>     "mathematical beauty" );
```

$$ranking := [1, 3, 5, 6, 2, 7, 9, 8, 4]$$

```
> map2( GetDocumentIdByIndex, corpus, ranking[ 1 .. 3 ] );
```

["The mathematician's patterns, like the painter' \
s or the poet's must be beautiful; the ideas, like t \
he colors or the words must fit together in a har \
monious way. Beauty is the first test: there is no \
 permanent place in this world for ugly mathem\
atics.", "Anyone who cannot cope with mathem \
atics is not fully human. At best he is a tolerabl \
e subhuman who has learned to wear shoes, bat\
he, and not make messes in the house.",
"I don't believe in mathematics."]

The second example corpus is a database of formulae. The intent is to be able to locate formulae relevant to a search query consisting of function names. For the formula database, generate a list of identities among elementary functions using the `FunctionAdvisor` command.

```
> Formulae := map2( FunctionAdvisor, 'identities',
>     FunctionAdvisor( 'elementary', 'quiet' ), 'quiet' ):
> Formulae := map( op, sort( Formulae, 'length' ) ):
> nops( Formulae );
```

132

Use each formula as both the document and its ID. The `Maple` filter in the `Filters` subpackage extracts the terms from each document.

```
> corpus2 := Corpus( Formulae, id -> id, Filters:-Maple,
>     query -> [op]( {op}( query ) ) ):
> BuildIndex( corpus2 ):
```

It is possible to locate formulae relevant to, for example, the `sin` and `cos` functions.

```
> ranking := Search( corpus2, [ 'sin', 'cos' ] );
```

$$ranking := [120, 19, 103, 127, 29, 104, 126, 119, 59, 81, 131, 97, 125, 102, 101, 124, 49, 76, 107, 4, 9, 96, 132, 128, 83, 6, 82, 108, 22, 16, 114, 91, 116, 113, 92, 94, 118, 24, 86, 112, 90, 105, 42, 65, 33, 95, 25, 117, 20, 32, 23, 14, 17, 2, 12, 10, 7, 3, 5, 18, 80, 110, 111, 109, 21, 30, 89, 87, 88, 115, 44, 39, 64, 38, 85, 68, 61, 69, 93, 40, 36, 35, 62, 67, 1, 43, 37, 66, 34, 41, 63, 31, 13, 11, 60, 130, 122, 129, 121, 123, 48, 47, 26, 27, 53, 50, 57, 84, 106, 99, 100, 98, 77, 75, 56, 74, 55, 54, 45, 28, 72, 78, 52, 51, 58, 15, 79, 71, 70, 46, 8, 73]$$

```
> map2( GetDocumentIdByIndex, corpus2, ranking[ 1 .. 3 ] );
```

$$\left[\tan(z) = 2\,\frac{\tan(\frac{1}{2}\,z)}{1 - \tan(\frac{1}{2}\,z)^2},\ \frac{1}{\csc(\mathrm{arccsch}(x)\,I + \mathrm{arccsch}(y)\,I)^4} + (-\frac{1}{x^2} + \frac{1}{y^2})^2 - 2\,\frac{-y^2 - x^2 - 2}{\csc(\mathrm{arccsch}(x)\,I + \mathrm{arccsch}(y)\,I)^2\,x^2\,y^2} = 0,\ \cot(z) = \frac{1}{2}\,\frac{1 - \tan(\frac{1}{2}\,z)^2}{\tan(\frac{1}{2}\,z)}\right]$$

Construct a similar corpus using a different choice for the document IDs and the fetcher routine passed to the constructor. Instead of using formulae for both the document and its ID, use the position of the formula in the global list `Formulae` as the document ID, and pass a suitable fetcher routine.

```
> corpus3 := Corpus( [$1..nops(Formulae)], id -> Formulae[
>     id ], Filters:-Maple, query -> [op]( {op}( query ) ) ):
> ranking := Search( corpus2, [ 'sin', 'cos' ] );
```

$ranking := [120, 19, 103, 127, 29, 104, 126, 119, 59, 81, 131, 97, 125, 102, 101, 124, 49, 76, 107, 4, 9, 96, 132, 128, 83, 6, 82, 108, 22, 16, 114, 91, 116, 113, 92, 94, 118, 24, 86, 112, 90, 105, 42, 65, 33, 95, 25, 117, 20, 32, 23, 14, 17, 2, 12, 10, 7, 3, 5, 18, 80, 110, 111, 109, 21, 30, 89, 87, 88, 115, 44, 39, 64, 38, 85, 68, 61, 69, 93, 40, 36, 35, 62, 67, 1, 43, 37, 66, 34, 41, 63, 31, 13, 11, 60, 130, 122, 129, 121, 123, 48, 47, 26, 27, 53, 50, 57, 84, 106, 99, 100, 98, 77, 75, 56, 74, 55, 54, 45, 28, 72, 78, 52, 51, 58, 15, 79, 71, 70, 46, 8, 73]$

The common and practical case, in which a corpus represents a collection of files to be indexed, can be handled by using a constructor call such as the following.

```
> corpus := Corpus(
>   remove( type, listdir( "MyDocuments" ), { ".", ".." } ),
>   fname -> readbytes( fname, 'TEXT', infinity ),
>   Filters:-Text ):
```

If the documents contain structured text encoded as XML, then a similar invocation can be used.

```
> corpus := Corpus(
>   remove( type, listdir( "MyDocuments" ), { ".", ".." } ),
>   fname -> XMLTools:-ParseFile( fname ), Filters:-XML ):
```

Finally, a directory of Maple worksheets can be represented by a corpus constructed as follows.

```
> corpus := Corpus(
>   remove( type, listdir( "MyDocuments" ), { ".", ".." } ),
>   fname -> Worksheet:-ReadFile( fname ), Filters:-Worksheet
>   ):
```

A client of the `SearchEngine` package can provide a specialized filter routine to be used in constructing a corpus object to represent a collection of documents of a specific type. Generic interfaces and careful hiding of representational details provide considerable client flexibility and the ability to evolve the implementation.

## 2.8 Conclusion

This chapter introduced the concept of Maple modules. It described the structure and flexibility of modules.

Encapsulation and generic programming with modules allow you to write code that can be reused, transported, and easily maintained. By collecting procedures into a module called a package, you can organize procedures into distinct sets of related functions. You can also use modules to implement objects in Maple.

# 3 Input and Output

Although Maple is primarily a system and language for performing mathematical manipulations, many situations arise where such manipulations require:

- Data originating outside Maple
- Output of data in a form accepted by other applications
- Input directly from the user
- Output presented directly to the user

The Maple software includes a comprehensive collection of input and output (I/O) commands. *Maple I/O library* refers to these commands as a group.

## In This Chapter

- Tutorial Example
- File Types and Modes
- File Descriptors Versus File Names
- File Manipulation Commands
- Input Commands
- Output Commands
- Conversion Commands
- Notes to C Programmers

## 3.1 A Tutorial Example

This section illustrates how you can use the Maple I/O library. Specifically, the examples show how to write a table of numerical data to a file, and how to read such a table from a file. The examples refer to the following data set, given in the form of a list of lists and assumed to represent a list of $(x, y)$ pairs, where each $x$ is an integer and each $y$ is a real number.

```
> A := [[0, 0],
>       [1, .8427007929],
>       [2, .9953222650],
>       [3, .9999779095],
>       [4, .9999999846],
>       [5, 1.000000000]]:
```

In a real application, this list is generated by a Maple command or procedure. In this example, the list was simply entered as above.

If you want to use another program (like a presentation graphics program, or perhaps a custom C program) to process data that Maple has generated, then you often need to save the data to a file in a format that the other program recognizes. Using the I/O library, you can write such data to a file.

```
> for xy in A do fprintf("myfile", "%d %e\n", xy[1], xy[2])
>    end do:
> fclose("myfile");
```

The file `myfile` is saved in the current directory. To determine the current directory, use the `currentdir()` command. If you print the file `myfile`, or view it with a text editor, it looks like this:

```
0 0.000000e-01
1 8.427008e-01
2 9.953223e-01
3 9.999779e-01
4 1.000000e+00
5 1.000000e+00
```

The `fprintf` command writes each pair of numbers to the file. This command takes two or more arguments. The first argument specifies the file that Maple is to write, and the second argument specifies the format for the data items. The remaining arguments are the actual data items that Maple is to write.

**Opening a File** In the preceding example, the filename is `myfile`. The first time a given filename appears as an argument to `fprintf` (or any of the other output commands described later), the command creates the file if it does not already exist, and prepares (opens) it for writing. If the file exists, the new version overwrites the old one. You can override this behavior (for example, if you want to append to an already existing file) by using the `fopen` command. For more information on the `fopen` command, see **3.4 Opening and Closing Files**.

**Format String** The format string, `"%d %e\n"`, specifies that Maple write the data items as follows:

- First data item as a decimal integer (`%d`)
- Second data item in Fortran-like scientific notation (`%e`)
- A single space separates the first and second data items
- A line break (`\n`) follows the second data item (to write each pair of numbers on a new line)

By default, as in the example, Maple rounds floating-point numbers to six significant digits for output. You can specify more or fewer digits by using options to the `%e` format. The section on `fprintf` describes these options in more detail.

**Closing a File** When you are finished writing to a file, you must close it. Until you close a file, the data may not be in the file, because output is buffered under most operating systems. The `fclose` command closes a file. If you forget to close a file, Maple automatically closes it when you exit.

**One Command for Opening, Writing, and Closing a File** For a simple case like the one presented here, writing the data to a file by using the `writedata` command is easier.

```
> writedata("myfile2", A, [integer,float]):
```

The `writedata` command performs all the operations of opening the file, writing the data in the specified format (an integer and a floating-point number) and then closing the file. However, `writedata` does not provide the precise formatting control that you may need in some cases. For this, use `fprintf`.

**Reading Data From a File** In some applications, you need to read data from a file. For example, some data acquisition software supplies data that you need to analyze. Reading data from a file is almost as easy as writing to it.

```
> A := [];
```

$$A := []$$

```
> do
>    xy := fscanf("myfile2", "%d %e");
>    if xy = 0 then break end if;
>    A := [op(A),xy];
> end do;
```

$$xy := [0, 0.]$$

$$A := [[0, 0.]]$$

$$xy := [1, 0.8427007929]$$

$$A := [[0, 0.], [1, 0.8427007929]]$$

$$xy := [2, 0.995322265]$$

$$A := [[0, 0.], [1, 0.8427007929], [2, 0.995322265]]$$

$$xy := [3, 0.9999779095]$$

$$A := [[0, 0.], [1, 0.8427007929], [2, 0.995322265], [3, 0.9999779095]]$$

$$xy := [4, 0.9999999846]$$

$$A := [[0, 0.], [1, 0.8427007929], [2, 0.995322265], [3, 0.9999779095], [4, 0.9999999846]]$$

$$xy := [5, 1.000000000]$$

$$A := [[0, 0.], [1, 0.8427007929], [2, 0.995322265], [3, 0.9999779095], [4, 0.9999999846], [5, 1.000000000]]$$

$$xy := []$$

$$A := [[0, 0.], [1, 0.8427007929], [2, 0.995322265], [3, 0.9999779095], [4, 0.9999999846], [5, 1.000000000], []]$$

$$xy := 0$$

```
> fclose("myfile2");
```

This example starts by initializing `A` to be the empty list. Upon entering the loop, Maple reads pairs of numbers from the file.

The `fscanf` command reads characters from a specified file, and parses them according to the specified format (in this case, `"%d %e"`, indicating a decimal integer and a real number). It either returns a list of the resulting values or the integer 0 to indicate that it has reached the end of the file. The first time you call `fscanf` with a given file name, Maple prepares (opens) the file for reading. If it does not exist, Maple generates an error.

The second line of the loop checks if `fscanf` returned 0 to indicate the end of the file, and breaks the loop if it has. Otherwise, Maple appends the pair of numbers to the list of pairs in `A`. (The syntax `A := [op(A),xy]` tells Maple to assign to `A` a list consisting of the existing elements of `A`, and the new element `xy`.)

**One Command for Opening, Reading, and Closing a File** As when you write to a file, you can read from a file more easily by using the `readdata` command.

```
> A := readdata("myfile2", [integer,float]);
```

$$A := [[0, 0.], [1, 0.8427007929], [2, 0.995322265], [3, 0.9999779095], [4, 0.9999999846], [5, 1.000000000]]$$

The `readdata` command performs all the operations of opening the file, reading the data, parsing the specified format (an integer and a floating-point number), and then closing the file. However, `readdata` does not provide the precise parsing control that you may need in some cases. For this, use `fscanf` directly.

The next section expands on the basic concepts of the Maple I/O library.

## 3.2 File Types and Modes

Most of the Maple I/O library commands operate on files. In this chapter, the term *file* is not limited to a disk file. It can include the default output stream to a terminal or worksheet output region. Almost any operation that you can perform on a real file you can perform on a data output stream to the terminal or worksheet.

### Buffered Files versus Unbuffered Files

The Maple I/O library can use two file types: buffered (`STREAM`) and unbuffered (`RAW`). Maple uses these files similarly.

**Buffered Files:**

- When buffering a lot of I/O, buffered file operations are usually faster.
- Maple collects characters in a buffer and writes them to a file when the buffer is full or the file is closed. (Changes made in Maple may not appear on disk until later.)
- In general, you should use buffered files. They are used by default with most I/O library commands.

**Raw Files:**

- Raw files are useful when examining the properties of the underlying operating system, such as the block size on the disk.

**Identifiers** Commands that provide information about I/O status use the identifiers `STREAM` and `RAW` to indicate buffered and unbuffered files, respectively.

### Text Files versus Binary Files

Many operating systems, including DOS/Windows® and the Macintosh operating system (Mac OS®), distinguish between files containing sequences of characters (*text files*) and files containing sequences of bytes (*binary files*). The distinction lies primarily in the treatment of the newline character. Other distinctions may exist on some platforms, but they are not visible when using the Maple I/O library.

Within Maple, the newline character, which represents ending one line and beginning a new one, is a single character (although you can type it as the two characters "`\n`" within Maple strings). The internal representation of this character is the byte whose value is 10, the ASCII linefeed character. Many operating systems, however, represent the concept of newline within a file using a different character, or a sequence of two characters. For example, DOS/Windows represents a newline with two consecutive bytes whose values are 13 and 10 (carriage return and line feed). The Macintosh represents a newline with the single byte with value 13 (carriage return).

The Maple I/O library can use text files or binary files. When Maple writes to a text file, any newline characters that it writes to the file are translated into the appropriate character or character sequence that the underlying operating system uses. When Maple reads this character or character sequence from a file, it translates it to the single newline character. When Maple writes to a binary file, no translation takes place; it reads newline characters and writes them as the single byte with value 10.

When running Maple under the UNIX® operating system or one of its many variants, Maple makes no distinction between text and binary files. It treats both in the same way, and no translation takes place.

**Identifiers** Commands that can specify or query whether a file is a text file or a binary file use the identifiers `TEXT` and `BINARY`, respectively.

### Read Mode versus Write Mode

At any given time, a file may be open either for reading or for writing.

- You cannot write to a file that is open *only* for reading. If you attempt, using the Maple I/O library, to write to a file which is open for reading, Maple closes and reopens the file for writing. If the user does not have the necessary permissions to write to the file (if the file is read-only, or resides on a read-only file system), errors occur.

- You can write to and read from a file that is open for writing.

**Identifiers** Commands where you can specify or query whether a file is open for reading or writing use the identifiers `READ` and `WRITE`, respectively.

### The `default` and `terminal` Files

The Maple I/O library treats the Maple user interface as a file. The identifiers `default` and `terminal` refer to this file. The `default` identifier refers to the current input stream, the one from which Maple reads and processes commands. The `terminal` identifier refers to the top-level input stream, the one which was the current input stream when you started Maple.

When Maple is run interactively, `default` and `terminal` are equivalent. Only when reading commands from a source file using the `read` statement does a distinction arise. In that case, `default` refers to the file being read; whereas, `terminal` refers to the session. Under UNIX, if input is redirected from a file or pipe, `terminal` refers to that file or pipe.

Note that only the *symbols* `default` and `terminal` are special; the *strings* `"default"` and `"terminal"` refer to files with those names.

## 3.3 File Descriptors versus File Names

The commands of the Maple I/O library refer to files in one of two ways: by name or by descriptor.

**Name** Referring to a file by name is the simpler of the two methods. The first time Maple performs an operation on the file, it opens the file, either in `READ` mode or in `WRITE` mode and as a `TEXT` file or a `BINARY` file, as appropriate to the operation that it is performing. The primary advantage of referring to files by name is simplicity. However, you will experience a slight performance penalty for using this method, especially if performing many small operations on a file (such as writing individual characters).

**Descriptor** Referring to a file by descriptor is only slightly more complex and is a familiar concept to those who have programmed in more traditional environments. A descriptor simply identifies a file after you have opened it. Use the name of the file once to open it and create a descriptor. When you subsequently manipulate the file, use the descriptor instead of the file name. An example in **Opening and Closing Files** on page 194 illustrates the use of a file descriptor.

The advantages of the descriptor method include more flexibility when opening the file (you can specify whether the file is `TEXT` or `BINARY`, and whether Maple opens it in `READ` mode or in `WRITE` mode), improved efficiency when performing many operations on a file, and the ability to work with unbuffered files. The disadvantage is a slight increase in the amount of programming that you must do.

**Best Approach** Which approach is best depends on the task at hand. You can perform simple file I/O tasks most easily by using names, whereas, more complex tasks can benefit from the use of descriptors.

**Note:** In subsequent sections, the term *fileIdentifier* refers to a filename or a file descriptor.

## 3.4 File Manipulation Commands

### Opening and Closing Files

Before you can read from or write to a file, you must open it. When referring to files by name, this happens automatically with the first attempt at any file operation. When you use descriptors, however, you must explicitly open the file first to create the descriptor.

The two commands for opening files are `fopen` and `open`. The `fopen` command opens buffered (`STREAM`) files, whereas, the `open` command opens unbuffered (`RAW`) files.

Use the `fopen` command as follows.

```
fopen( fileName, accessMode, fileType )
```

The *fileName* specifies the name of the file to open. This name is specified as a string, and follows the conventions that the underlying operating system uses. The *accessMode* must be one of `READ`, `WRITE`, or `APPEND`, indicating whether you should initially open the file for reading, writing, or appending. The optional *fileType* is either `TEXT` or `BINARY`.

If you try to open the file for reading and it does not exist, `fopen` generates an error.

If you try to open the file for writing and it does not exist, Maple creates it. If it does exist and you specify `WRITE`, Maple truncates the file to zero length; if you specify `APPEND`, subsequent calls to commands that write to the file append to it.

Call the `open` command as follows.

```
open( fileName, accessMode )
```

The arguments to `open` are the same as those to `fopen`, except that you cannot specify a *fileType* (`TEXT` or `BINARY`). Maple opens an unbuffered file with type `BINARY`.

Both fopen and open return a file descriptor. Use this descriptor to refer to the file for subsequent operations. You can still use the filename.

When you have finished with a file, instruct Maple to close it. This ensures that Maple writes all information to the disk. It also frees resources of the underlying operating system, which often imposes a limit on the number of files that you can open simultaneously.

Close files by using the fclose or close commands. These two commands are equivalent. You can call them as follows.

```
fclose( fileIdentifier )
close( fileIdentifier )
```

The *fileIdentifier* is the name or descriptor of the file to close. Once you close a file, any descriptors referring to the file are no longer valid.

```
> f := fopen("testFile.txt",WRITE):

> writeline(f,"This is a test"):
> fclose(f);

> writeline(f,"This is another test"):

Error, (in fprintf) file descriptor not in use
```

When you exit Maple or issue a restart command, Maple automatically closes any open files, whether you opened them explicitly by using fopen or open, or implicitly through a file I/O command.

## Position Determination and Adjustment

Associated with each open file is the concept of its current position. This is the location within the file to which a subsequent write occurs, or from which a subsequent read occurs. Any reading or writing operation advances the position by the number of bytes read or written.

You can determine the current position within a file by using the filepos command. Use this command in the following manner.

```
filepos( fileIdentifier, position )
```

The *fileIdentifier* is the name or descriptor of the file whose position to determine or adjust. If you give a filename, and that file is not yet open, Maple opens it in READ mode with type BINARY.

The *position* is optional. If you do not specify the *position*, Maple returns the current position. If you supply the *position*, Maple sets the current position to *position* and returns the resulting position. In that case, the returned position is the same as the specified *position* unless the file is shorter than the specified *position*, in which case the returned position is that of the end of the file (that is, its length). You can specify the *position* either as an integer or as the name `infinity`, which specifies the end of the file.

The following command returns the length of the file `myfile.txt`.

```
> filepos("myfile.txt", infinity);
```

$$36$$

## Detecting the End of a File

The `feof` command determines whether you have reached the end of a file. Only use the `feof` command on files that you have opened as `STREAM`s implicitly or explicitly via `fopen`. Call `feof` in the following manner.

```
feof( fileIdentifier )
```

The *fileIdentifier* is the name or descriptor of the file to query. If you give a filename, and that file is not yet open, Maple opens it in `READ` mode with type `BINARY`.

The `feof` command returns `true` if and only if you have reached the end of the file during the most recent `readline`, `readbytes`, or `fscanf` operation. Otherwise, `feof` returns `false`. This means that if 20 bytes remain in a file and you use `readbytes` to read these 20 bytes, then `feof` still returns `false`. You encounter the end-of-file only after you attempt another `read`.

## Determining File Status

The `iostatus` command returns detailed information about all the files currently in use. Call the `iostatus` command with the following syntax.

```
iostatus()
```

The `iostatus` command returns a list. The list contains the following elements:

`iostatus()[1]` The number of files that the Maple I/O library is currently using.

`iostatus()[2]` The number of active nested `read` commands (when `read` reads a file, which itself contains a `read` statement).

`iostatus()[3]` The upper bound on `iostatus()[1] + iostatus()[2]` that the underlying operating system imposes.

`iostatus()[n]` for `n > 3`. A list giving information about a file currently in use by the Maple I/O library.

When $n > 3$, the lists that `iostatus()[n]` return each contain the following elements:

`iostatus()[n][1]` The file descriptor which `fopen` or `open` returned.

`iostatus()[n][2]` The filename.

`iostatus()[n][3]` The file kind (`STREAM`, `RAW`, or `DIRECT`).

`iostatus()[n][4]` The file pointer or file descriptor that the underlying operating system uses. The pointer is in the form `FP=`*`integer`* or `FD=`*`integer`*.

`iostatus()[n][5]` The file mode (`READ` or `WRITE`).

`iostatus()[n][6]` The file type (`TEXT` or `BINARY`).

## Removing Files

Many files are solely for temporary use. Because you do not need these files in future Maple sessions, remove them. Use the `fremove` command to do this.

```
fremove( fileIdentifier )
```

The *fileIdentifier* is the name or descriptor of the file to remove. If the file is open, Maple closes it before removing it. If the file does not exist, Maple generates an error.

To remove a file regardless of whether it exists, use a `try/catch` statement to trap the error that `fremove` might create.

```
> try fremove("myfile.txt") catch: end try:
```

# 3.5 Input Commands

## Reading Text Lines from a File

The `readline` command reads a single line of text from a file. Characters are read up to and including a new line. The `readline` command then discards the new line character, and returns the line of characters as a Maple string. If `readline` cannot read a whole line from the file, then it returns 0 instead of a string.

Call the `readline` command by using the following syntax.

```
readline( fileIdentifier )
```

The *fileIdentifier* is the name or descriptor of the file to read. For compatibility with earlier versions of Maple, you can omit the *fileIdentifier*, in which case Maple uses `default`. Thus `readline()` and `readline(default)` are equivalent.

If you use `-1` as the *fileIdentifier*, Maple also takes input from the `default` stream, except that the Maple command-line preprocessor runs on all input lines. This means that lines beginning with "`!`" pass to the operating system instead of returning through `readline`, and that lines beginning with "`?`" translate to calls to the `help` command.

If you call `readline` with a filename, and that file is not open, Maple opens it in `READ` mode as a `TEXT` file. If `readline` returns 0 (indicating the end of the file) when called with a filename, it automatically closes the file.

**Example** The following example defines a Maple procedure which reads a text file and displays it on the `default` output stream.

```
> ShowFile := proc( fileName::string )
>    local line;
>    do
>       line := readline(fileName);
>       if line = 0 then break end if;
>       printf("%s\n",line);
>    end do;
> end proc:
```

## Reading Arbitrary Bytes from a File

The `readbytes` command reads one or more individual characters or bytes from a file, returning a string or a list of integers. If there are no characters remaining in the file when you call `readbytes`, the command returns 0, indicating that you have reached the end of the file.

Use the following syntax to call the **readbytes** command.

```
readbytes( fileIdentifier, length, TEXT )
```

The *fileIdentifier* is the name or descriptor of the file to read. The *length*, which you may omit, specifies how many bytes Maple needs to read. If you omit *length*, Maple reads one byte. The optional parameter TEXT indicates that the result is to be returned as a string rather than a list of integers.

You can specify the *length* as infinity, in which case Maple reads the remainder of the file.

If you specify TEXT when a byte with value 0 resides among the bytes being read, the resulting string contains only those characters preceding the 0 byte.

If you call readbytes with a filename, and that file is not open, Maple opens it in READ mode. If you specify TEXT, Maple opens it as a TEXT file; otherwise, Maple opens it as a BINARY file. If readbytes returns 0 (indicating the end of the file) when you call it with a filename, it automatically closes the file.

**Example** The following example defines a Maple procedure which reads an entire file, by using readbytes, and copies it to a new file.

```
> CopyFile := proc( sourceFile::string, destFile::string )
>     writebytes(destFile, readbytes(sourceFile, infinity))
> end proc:
```

**Note:** For information on the writebytes function, refer to ?writebytes or see **Writing Bytes to a File** on page 210.

### Formatted Input

The fscanf and scanf commands read from a file, parsing numbers and substrings according to a specified format. The commands return a list of these parsed objects. If no more characters remain in the file when you call fscanf or scanf, they return 0 instead of a list, indicating that it has reached the end of the file.

Call the fscanf and scanf commands as follows.

```
fscanf( fileIdentifier, format )
scanf( format )
```

The *fileIdentifier* is the name or descriptor of the file to read. A call to scanf is equivalent to a call to fscanf with default as the *fileIdentifier*.

If you call `fscanf` with a filename, and that file is not open, Maple opens it in `READ` mode as a `TEXT` file. If `fscanf` returns 0 (indicating the end of the file) when you call it with a filename, Maple automatically closes the file.

**Format String** The *format* specifies how Maple is to parse the input. The *format* is a Maple string consists of a sequence of conversion specifications, that may be separated by other characters. Each conversion specification has the following format, where the brackets indicate optional components.

```
%[*][width][modifiers]code
```

- The "%" symbol begins the conversion specification.
- The optional "*" indicates that Maple is to scan the object, but not return it as part of the result. It is discarded.
- The optional *width* indicates the maximum number of characters to scan for this object. You can use this to scan one larger object as two smaller objects.

The optional *modifiers* are used to indicate the type of the value to be returned:

`l` **or** `L` The letters `l` and `L` are supported for compatibility with the C `scanf` function, and indicate that a "long int" or "long long" is to be returned. In Maple, these flags have no effect.

*z*`c` **or** `Z` One of these flags can precede any of the numeric formats, namely `d`, `o`, `x`, `e`, `f`, or `g`, indicating that a complex value is to be scanned. The real and imaginary parts of the complex value are scanned by using the specified format with the `z` or `Z` elided. The `z` format scans the real part, followed by the character specified by `c`, followed by the imaginary part. The `Z` format scans the real part, followed by a "+" or "-" sign, followed by the imaginary part, followed by a string of characters corresponding to the current setting of `interface(imaginaryunit)`.

The `z` and `Z` options can result in one of the few conditions in which `scanf` raises an exception. If `scanf` is scanning a complex value (for example, the real part has already been successfully scanned), and is unable to finish scanning the remainder (for example, there is no imaginary part after the real part), `scanf` raises an exception of the form "

`‘%1‘ expected in input for complex format `", where `%1` is replaced by the expected character (for example, a comma).

The *code* indicates the type of object to scan. It determines the type of object that Maple returns in the resulting list. The *code* can be one of the following.

`d` The next non-whitespace characters in the input must comprise a signed or unsigned decimal integer. A Maple integer is returned.

`o` The next non-whitespace characters in the input must make up an unsigned octal (base 8) integer. The integer is converted to a decimal, and then returned as a Maple integer.

`x` The next non-whitespace characters in the input must consist of an unsigned hexadecimal (base 16) integer. The letters `A` through `F` (upper or lower case) represent the digits corresponding to the decimal numbers 10 through 15. The integer is converted to a decimal, and then returned as a Maple integer.

`y` The next non-whitespace characters in the input must consist of an IEEE hex-dump format floating-point value. This value must consist of sixteen hexadecimal characters. The value is converted to and returned as a Maple float.

`e`, `f`, or `g` The next non-whitespace characters in the input must consist of a signed or unsigned decimal number, possibly including a decimal point, and possibly followed by `E` or `e`, an optional sign, and a decimal integer indicating a power of ten. The number is returned as a Maple floating-point value.

In addition to numeric values, the `e`, `f`, and `g` formats also recognize the special values "`inf`" and "`NaN`". If an `i` or `N` is encountered when `scanf` is looking for the first digit of a number, it assumes that one of these special values has been found, and proceeds to look for the subsequent `nf` or `aN`. If the rest of the special value is not found, an exception is raised.

`he`, `hf`, or `hg` These are special formats for reading one or two-dimensional numeric arrays. In general, such arrays should be read by using the more sophisticated functionality provided by the {} format, but the `he`, `hf`, and `hg` formats are provided for backward compatibility with `hfarrays`, and provide some intelligence in automatically dealing with a variety of textual layouts of such arrays.

The following input must consist of a one or two-dimensional array of floating-point (or integer) values. Characters encountered during scanning are categorized into three classes: numeric, separator, and terminator. All the characters that can appear within a number (the digits, decimal point, signs, `E`, `e`, `D`, and `d`) are numeric. Any white space, commas, or square brackets are separators. A square bracket not immediately followed by a comma, and any other character, is a terminator. If a backslash is encountered, it and the following character are ignored.

The dimensions of the array are determined by the number of lines read, and the number of values in the first line. If either of these is 1, or if the number of rows multiplied by the number of columns does not equal the total number of values read, a one-dimensional array is produced.

The definition of "the first line" is "everything read up to the first line break that does not immediately follow a comma or a backslash, or up to the first closing square bracket that *is* immediately followed by a comma".

This method can read anything that can be written by the corresponding `printf`, typical tables of numbers, and lprinted or saved (in text form) Maple lists and lists of lists.

The result is returned as an `hfarray` of one or two dimensions.

`hx` The following input must consist of a one or two dimensional array of floating-point numbers in IEEE hex-dump format (16 characters per number). The dimensions of the array are determined as described for the previous `"%he"`, `"%hf"`, and `"%hg"` formats.

`s` The next non-whitespace characters, up to but not including the following blank characters (or the end of the string), are returned as a Maple string.

`a` Maple collects and parses the next non-whitespace characters, up to but not including the following blank characters (or the end of the string). An unevaluated Maple expression is returned.

`m` The next characters must be a Maple expression encoded in the Maple `.m` file format. Maple reads enough characters to parse a single complete expression; it ignores the *width* specification. The Maple expression is returned.

c This code returns the next character (whitespace or otherwise) as a Maple string. If a width is specified, that many characters (blank or otherwise) are returned as a single Maple string.

[...] The characters between "[" and "]" become a list of characters that are acceptable as a character string. Maple scans characters from the input until it encounters one that is *not* in the list. The scanned characters are then returned as a Maple string.

If the list begins with a "^" character, the list represents all those characters *not* in the list.

If a "]" is to appear in the list, it must immediately follow the opening "[" or the "^" if one exists.

You can use a "-" in the list to represent a range of characters. For example, "A-Z" represents any capital letter. If a "-" is to appear as a character instead of representing a range, it must appear at the beginning or the end of the list.

{...}wft The characters between the left brace, "{", and the right brace, "}", are options for scanning Arrays, Matrices, or Vectors (that is, the various classes of rtable). The optional w is an integer specifying the width to scan for each element (any width specified before the opening "{" applies to the entire rtable being scanned, but is ignored). The character f specifies the format code, and can be any format code supported by scanf except [...] or {...}. The character t, which must be one of a, m, c, or r, specifies the type of object to be created (Array, Matrix, Vector[column], or Vector[row] respectively).

For more information on rtable formatting options, refer to ?rtable_scanf.

M The next sequence of characters must correspond to a well formed XML element. The result is a Maple function call whose name is constructed from the XML element, whose arguments are either function calls for the child elements or the CDATA as strings, and whose attributes are equations defining the XML attributes of the object.

n The total number of characters scanned up to the "%n" is returned as a Maple integer.

Maple skips non-whitespace characters in the *format* but not within a conversion specification (where they must match the corresponding characters in the input). It ignores white space in the *format*, except that a space immediately preceding a "%c" specification causes the "%c" specification to skip any blanks in the input. If it does not successfully scan any objects, Maple returns an empty list.

The fscanf and scanf commands use the underlying implementation that the hardware vendor provides for the "%o" and "%x" formats. As a result, input of octal and hexadecimal integers are subject to the restrictions of the operating system.

**Example** The following example defines a Maple procedure that reads a file containing a table of numbers, in which each row can have a different width. The first number in each row is an integer specifying how many real numbers follow it in that row, and commas separate all the numbers in each row.

```
> ReadRows := proc( fileName::string )
>    local A, count, row, num;
>    A := [];
>    do
>       # Determine how many numbers are in this row.
>       count := fscanf(fileName,"%d");
>       if count = 0 then break end if;
>       if count = [] then
>          error "integer expected in file"
>       end if;
>       count := count[1];
>
>       # Read the numbers in the row.
>       row := [];
>       while count > 0 do
>          num := fscanf(fileName,",%e");
>          if num = 0 then
>             error "unexpected end of file"
>          end if;
>          if num = [] then
>             error "number expected in file"
>          end if;
>          row := [op(row),num[1]];
>          count := count - 1
>       end do;
>
>       # Append the row to the accumulated result.
>       A := [op(A),row]
>    end do;
>    A
> end proc:
```

## Reading Maple Statements

The `readstat` command reads a single Maple statement from the `terminal` input stream. Maple parses and evaluates the statement, and returns the result. Call the `readstat` command as follows.

```
readstat( prompt, ditto3, ditto2, ditto1 )
```

The *prompt* argument specifies the prompt that `readstat` is to use. If you omit the *prompt* argument, Maple uses a blank prompt. You can either supply or omit all of the three arguments *ditto3*, *ditto2*, and *ditto1*. If you supply them, they specify the values which Maple uses for `%%%`, `%%`, and `%` in the statement that `readstat` reads. Specify each of these arguments as a Maple list containing the actual value for substitution. This allows for values that are expression sequences. For example, if `%` is to have the value `2*n+3` and `%%` is to have the value `a,b`, then use `[2*n+3]` for *ditto1* and `[a,b]` for *ditto2*.

The response to `readstat` must be a single Maple expression. The expression can span more than one input line, but `readstat` does not permit multiple expressions on one line. If the input contains a syntax error, `readstat` returns an error describing the nature of the error, and its position in the input.

**Example** The following example shows a trivial use of `readstat` within a procedure.

```
> InteractiveDiff := proc( )
>    local a, b;
>    a := readstat("Please enter an expression: ");
>    b := readstat("Differentiate with respect to: ");
>    printf("The derivative of %a with respect to %a is %a\n",
>            a,b,diff(a,b))
> end proc:
```

## Reading Tabular Data

The `readdata` command reads TEXT files containing tables of data. For simple tables, this is more convenient than writing a procedure by using a loop and the `fscanf` command.

Use the following syntax to call the `readdata` command.

```
readdata( fileIdentifier, dataType, numColumns )
```

The *fileIdentifier* is the name or descriptor of the file from which `readdata` reads the data. The *dataType* must be one of `integer` or `float`, or you can omit it, in which case `readdata` assumes `float`. If `readdata` needs to read more than one column, you can specify the type of each column by using a list of data types.

The *numColumns* argument indicates how many columns of data are to be read from the file. If you omit *numColumns*, `readdata` reads the number of columns specified by the number of data types that you specified (one column if you did not specify any *dataType*).

If Maple reads only one column, `readdata` returns a list of the values read. If Maple reads more than one column, `readdata` returns a list of lists, each sublist of which contains the data read from one line of the file.

If you call `readdata` with a filename, and that file is not open, Maple opens it in `READ` mode as a `TEXT` file. Furthermore, if you call `readdata` with a filename, it automatically closes the file when `readdata` returns.

**Example** The following two examples are equivalent uses of `readdata` to read a table of $(x, y, z)$-triples of real numbers from a file.

```
> A1 := readdata("my_xyz_file.text",3);
```

$$A1 := [[1.5, 2.2, 3.4], [2.7, 3.4, 5.6], [1.8, 3.1, 6.7]]$$

```
> A2 := readdata("my_xyz_file.text",[float,float,float]);
```

$$A2 := [[1.5, 2.2, 3.4], [2.7, 3.4, 5.6], [1.8, 3.1, 6.7]]$$

**Note:** Data elements in the file are white space delimited. Newlines separate rows, and white space separates columns. The `numColumns` argument defines how many columns to read and those columns are read from all rows. For the file:

1 2 3 4
5 6 7 8

`readdata(...,2)` returns [[1,2],5,6]] and `readdata(...,3)` returns [[1,2,3],[5,6,7]].

## 3.6 Output Commands

### Configuring Output Parameters Using the `interface` Command

The `interface` command is not an output command. It is a mechanism to provide communication between Maple and the user interface. You can use it to configure parameters affecting the output produced by various commands within Maple.

To set a parameter, call the `interface` command as follows.

```
interface( variable = expression )
```

The *variable* argument specifies which parameter to change, and the *expression* argument specifies the value that the parameter is to have. For a list of parameters you can use, see the following sections or refer to `?interface`. You can set multiple parameters by giving several arguments of the form *`variable = expression`*, with commas separating them.

To query the setting of a parameter, use the following syntax.

```
interface( variable )
```

The *variable* argument specifies the parameter to query. The `interface` command returns the current setting of the parameter. You can query only one parameter at a time.

## One-Dimensional Expression Output

The `lprint` command prints Maple expressions in a one-dimensional notation similar to the format Maple uses for input. In most cases, you can use this output as input, and the same expression would result. The single exception is if the expression contains Maple names containing non-alphanumeric characters.

The `lprint` command is called as follows.

```
lprint( expressionSequence )
```

The *expressionSequence* consists of one or more Maple expressions. Each of the expressions is printed in turn, with three spaces separating each of them. Maple prints a new line character after the last expression.

Maple always sends the output that `lprint` produces to the `default` output stream. You can use the `writeto` and `appendto` commands, described later, to temporarily redirect the `default` output stream to a file.

The `interface` parameter `screenwidth` affects the output of `lprint`. If possible, Maple wraps the output between tokens. If a single token is too long to display (for example, a very long name or number), Maple breaks it across lines, and prints a backslash, "\", before each line break.

**Example** The following command-line example illustrates `lprint` output, and how `screenwidth` affects it.

```
> lprint(expand((x+y)^5));

x^5+5*x^4*y+10*x^3*y^2+10*x^2*y^3+5*x*y^4+y^5


> interface(screenwidth=30);

> lprint(expand((x+y)^5));
x^5+5*x^4*y+10*x^3*y^2+10*x^2
*y^3+5*x*y^4+y^5
```

## Two-Dimensional Expression Output

The `print` command prints Maple expressions in a two-dimensional notation. Depending on the version of Maple and the user interface, this notation is either the standard math notation that appears in text books and other typeset mathematical documents, or an approximation of standard math notation using only text characters.

The `print` command is called as follows.

```
print( expressionSequence )
```

The *expressionSequence* consists of one or more Maple expressions. Maple prints each expression, in turn, with commas separating them.

The output produced by `print` is always sent to the `default` output stream. You can use the `writeto` and `appendto` commands, described later, to temporarily redirect the `default` output stream to a file.

Several `interface` parameters affect the output of `print`. They are set using the syntax

```
interface( parameter = value )
```

They include:

`prettyprint` This selects the type of output that `print` is to produce.

- If you set `prettyprint` to 0, `print` produces the same output as `lprint`.

- If you set `prettyprint` to 1, `print` produces a simulated math notation using only text characters.
- If you set `prettyprint` to 2, and the version of Maple you are running is capable of it, `print` produces output using standard math notation.
- The default setting of `prettyprint` is 2.

`indentamount` This specifies the number of spaces that Maple uses to indent the continuation of expressions that are too large to fit on a single line. This parameter takes effect only when you set `prettyprint` (see previous definition) to 1, or when Maple is printing procedures. The default setting of `indentamount` is 4.

`labelling` **or** `labeling` You can set this to `true` or `false`, indicating whether Maple should use labels to represent common subexpressions in large expressions. Labels can make large expressions easier to read and comprehend. The default setting of `labelling` is `true`.

`labelwidth` This indicates the size that a subexpression must have for Maple to consider it for labeling (if `labelling` is `true`). The size is the approximate width, in characters, of the expression when printed with `print` and `prettyprint = 1`.

`screenwidth` This indicates the width of the screen in characters. When `prettyprint` is 0 or 1, Maple uses this width to decide when to wrap long expressions. When `prettyprint` is 2, the user interface uses pixels instead of characters, and determines the width automatically.

`verboseproc` Use this parameter when printing Maple procedures.

- If you set `verboseproc` to 1, Maple prints only user defined procedures; Maple shows system defined procedures in a simplified form giving only the arguments, and possibly a brief description of the procedure.
- If you set `verboseproc` to 2, Maple prints all procedures in full.
- If you set `verboseproc` to 3, Maple prints all procedures in full, and prints the contents of a procedure's remember table in the form of Maple comments after the procedure.

When you use Maple interactively, it automatically displays each computed result. The format of this display is the same as if you used the `print` command. Therefore, all the `interface` parameters that affect the `print` command also affect the display of results.

**Example** The following command-line example illustrates `print` output, and how `prettyprint`, `indentamount`, and `screenwidth` affect it.

```
> print(expand((x+y)^6));
```

$$x^6 + 6\,x^5\,y + 15\,x^4\,y^2 + 20\,x^3\,y^3 + 15\,x^2\,y^4 + 6\,x\,y^5 + y^6$$

```
> interface(prettyprint=1);
> print(expand((x+y)^6));

 6       5           4  2          3  3          2  4          5
x  + 6 x  y + 15 x  y  + 20 x  y  + 15 x  y  + 6 x y

        6
   + y

> interface(screenwidth=35);
> print(expand((x+y)^6));

 6       5        4  2       3  3
x  + 6 x  y + 15 x  y  + 20 x  y

             2  4        5     6
    + 15 x  y  + 6 x y  + y

> interface(indentamount=1);
> print(expand((x+y)^6));

 6       5         4  2        3  3
x  + 6 x  y + 15 x  y  + 20 x  y

         2  4       5    6
  + 15 x  y  + 6 x y  + y

> interface(prettyprint=0);
> print(expand((x+y)^6));

x^6+6*x^5*y+15*x^4*y^2+20*x^3*y^3+
15*x^2*y^4+6*x*y^5+y^6
```

## Writing Maple Strings to a File

The writeline command writes one or more Maple strings to a file. Each string appears on a separate line. Call the writeline command as follows.

```
writeline( fileIdentifier, stringSequence )
```

The *fileIdentifier* is the name or description of the file to which Maple is to write, and *stringSequence* is the sequence of strings that writeline should write. If you omit the *stringSequence*, then writeline writes a blank line to the file.

## Writing Bytes to a File

The writebytes command writes one or more individual characters or bytes to a file. You can specify the bytes either as a string or a list of integers.

The following syntax calls the writebytes command.

```
writebytes( fileIdentifier, bytes )
```

The *fileIdentifier* is the name or descriptor of the file to which writebytes is writing. The *bytes* argument specifies the bytes to write. This can be either a string or a list of integers. If you call writebytes with a filename, and that file is not open, Maple opens it in WRITE mode. If you specify the *bytes* as a string, Maple opens the file as a TEXT file; if you specify the *bytes* as a list of integers, Maple opens the file as a BINARY file.

**Example** The following example defines a Maple procedure which reads an entire file and copies it to a new file using writebytes.

```
> CopyFile := proc( sourceFile::string, destFile::string )
>     writebytes(destFile, readbytes(sourceFile, infinity));
> end proc:
```

## Formatted Output

The fprintf and printf commands write objects to a file, using a specified format.

Call the fprintf and printf commands as follows.

```
fprintf( fileIdentifier, format, expressionSequence )
printf( format, expressionSequence )
```

The *fileIdentifier* is the name or descriptor of the file to which Maple is to write. A call to printf is equivalent to a call to fprintf with default as the *fileIdentifier*. If you call `fprintf` with a filename, and that file is not yet open, Maples opens it in `WRITE` mode as a `TEXT` file.

The *format* specifies how Maple is to write the elements of the *expressionSequence*. This Maple string consists of a sequence of formatting specifications, possibly separated by other characters. Each format specification has the following syntax, where the brackets indicate optional components.

```
%[flags][width][.precision][modifiers]code
```

The "%" symbol begins the format specification. One or more of the following flags can optionally follow the "%" symbol:

+ A signed numeric value is output with a leading "+" or "-" sign, as appropriate.

- The output is left-justified instead of right-justified.

**blank** A signed numeric value is output with either a leading "-" or a leading blank, depending on whether the value is negative or non-negative.

`0` The output is padded on the left (between the sign and the first digit) with zeroes. If you also specify a "-", the "0" is ignored.

**{}** The braces enclose a set of detailed formatting options for printing an `rtable`. These are described in more detail in the help page `?rtable_printf`.

The optional *width* indicates the minimum number of characters to output for this field. If the formatted value has fewer characters, Maple pads it with blanks on the left (or on the right, if you specify "-").

The optional *precision* specifies the number of digits that appear after the decimal point for floating-point formats, or the maximum field width for string formats.

You can specify both *width* or *precision* as "*", in which case Maple takes the *width* or *precision* from the argument list. The *width* or *precision* argument(s) must appear, in that order, before the argument that is being output. A negative *width* argument is equivalent to the appearance of the "-" flag.

The optional *modifiers* are used to indicate the type of the value to be printed:

**l or L** The letters `l` and `L` are supported for compatibility with the C `printf` function, and indicate that a "long int" or "long long" is to be formatted. In Maple, these flags have no effect.

**zc or Z** One of these flags can precede any of the numeric formats, namely `d`, `o`, `x`, `e`, `f`, or `g`, indicating that a complex value is to be formatted. Each of the real and imaginary parts of the complex value are formatted using the specified format, with the `z` or `Z` elided. The `z` format prints the real part, followed by the character specified by `c`, followed by the imaginary part. The `Z` format prints the value in the form `x+yi`, where `x` is the real part, `y` is the imaginary part, and `i` is the current setting of `interface(imaginaryunit)`. If `y` is negative, a "-" is output instead of a "+". If a supplied value is not complex, it is treated as a complex value with a zero imaginary part.

The *code* indicates the type of object that Maple is to write. The *code* can be one of the following.

**d** Formats the object as a signed decimal integer.

**o** Formats the object as an unsigned octal (base 8) integer.

**x or X** Formats the object as an unsigned hexadecimal (base 16) integer. Maple represents the digits corresponding to the decimal numbers 10 through 15 by the letters "`A`" through "`F`" if you use "`X`", or "`a`" through "`f`" if you use "`x`".

**e or E** Formats the object as a floating-point number in scientific notation. One digit will appear before the decimal point, and *precision* digits will appear after the decimal point (six digits if you do not specify a *precision*). This is followed by the letter "`e`" or "`E`", and a signed integer specifying a power of 10. The power of 10 will have a sign and at least three digits, with leading zeroes added if necessary.

If the value being formatted is infinity, -infinity, or undefined, the output is "Inf", "-Inf", or "NaN" respectively.

**f** Formats the object as a fixed-point number. The number of digits specified by the *precision* will appear after the decimal point.

If the value being formatted is infinity, -infinity, or undefined, the output is "Inf", "-Inf", or "NaN" respectively.

**g or G** Formats the object using "`d`", "`e`" (or "`E`" if you specified "`G`"), or "`f`" format, depending on its value. If the formatted value does not contain a decimal point, Maple uses "`d`" format. If the value is less than $10^{-4}$ or greater than $10^{precision}$, Maple uses "`e`" (or "`E`") format. Otherwise, Maple uses "`f`" format.

If the value being formatted is infinity, -infinity, or undefined, the output is "Inf", "-Inf", or "NaN" respectively.

`y` **or** `Y` The floating-point object is formatted in byte-order-independent IEEE hex dump format (16 characters wide). At least 16 characters are always output, regardless of the specified width. The precision is ignored. The digits corresponding to the decimal numbers 10 through 15 are represented by the letters "`A`" through "`F`" if uppercase `Y` was specified, or "`a`" through "`f`" if lowercase `y` was specified.

`c` Outputs the object, which must be a Maple string containing exactly one character, as a single character.

`s` Outputs the object, which must be a Maple string of at least *width* characters (if specified) and at most *precision* characters (if specified).

`a` **or** `A` Outputs the object, which can be any Maple object, in correct Maple syntax. Maple outputs at least *width* characters (if specified) and at most *precision* characters (if specified). *Note:* Truncating a Maple expression by specifying a *precision* can result in an incomplete or syntactically incorrect Maple expression in the output.

The "`%a`" and "`%A`" formats are identical, except that "`%A`" omits any quotes that would normally appear around Maple symbols that require them.

`q` **or** `Q` These are similar to "`%a`" or "`%A`", except that "`%q`" or "`%Q`" ignores all remaining arguments and print them as an expression sequence, with each element formatted in "`%a`" or "`%A`" format respectively. No additional format specifiers can appear after "`%q`" or "`%Q`", since there are no arguments to format.

`m` The object, which can be any Maple object, is output in the Maple `.m` file format. Maple outputs at least *width* characters (if specified), and at most *precision* characters (if specified). *Note:* Truncating a Maple `.m` format expression by specifying a *precision* can result in an incomplete or incorrect Maple expression in the output.

`%` A percent symbol is output verbatim.

Maple outputs characters that are in *format* but not within a format specification verbatim.

All the formats apply to Arrays (type `Array`), Matrices (type `Matrix`), Vectors (type `Vector`), and hfarrays (type `hfarray`), all of which are objects of type `rtable`.

- If no rtable-specific formatting options are specified (via the {...} option, refer to `?rtable_printf`), the `%a`, `%A`, `%m`, and `%M` format codes print a representation of the rtable structure itself. For example, the format code `%a` prints a `Matrix`, `Vector`, or `Array` call.

- If no additional rtable-specific formatting options are specified for a format code *other than* `%a`, `%A`, `%m`, and `%M`, or if an empty rtable option sequence (that is, just {}) is specified for *any* format code, the following default formatting is applied:

  One-dimensional objects are formatted as one long line, with the elements separated by at least one space.

  Objects of `N` dimensions, where $N > 1$, are formatted as a sequence of $(N-1)$-dimensional objects separated by $N-2$ blank lines. Therefore, two-dimensional objects are formatted in the obvious way, three-dimensional objects are formatted as a series of two-dimensional objects separated by blank lines, and so on.

- Any of the floating-point formats can accept integer, rational, or floating-point objects; Maple converts the objects to floating-point values, and then outputs them appropriately.

- The `fprintf` and `printf` commands do *not* automatically start a new line at the end of the output. If you require a new line, the *format* string must contain a new line character, "\n". Output from `fprintf` and `printf` is *not* subject to line wrapping at `interface(screenwidth)` characters.

- The "%o", "%x", and "%X" formats use the underlying implementation that the hardware vendor provides. As a result, output of octal and hexadecimal values is subject to the restrictions of the operating system.

## Writing Tabular Data

The `writedata` command writes tabular data to `TEXT` files. In many cases, this is more convenient than writing an output procedure by using a loop and the `fprintf` command.

Call the `writedata` command in the following manner.

```
writedata( fileIdentifier, data, dataType, defaultProc )
```

The *fileIdentifier* is the name or descriptor of the file to which `writedata` writes the data.

If you call `writedata` with a filename, and that file is not yet open, Maple opens it in `WRITE` mode as a `TEXT` file. Furthermore, if you call `writedata` with a filename, the file automatically closes when `writedata` returns.

The *data* must be a vector, matrix, list, or list of lists.[1]

- If the *data* is a vector or list of values, `writedata` writes each value to the file on a separate line.
- If the *data* is a matrix or a list of lists of values, `writedata` writes each row or sublist to the file on a separate line, with tab characters separating the individual values.

The *dataType* is optional, and specifies whether `writedata` is to write the values as integers, floating-point values (the default), or strings.

- If you specify `integer`, the values must be numeric, and `writedata` writes them as integers (Maple truncates rational and floating-point values to integers).
- If you specify `float`, the values must be numeric, and `writedata` writes them as floating-point values (Maple converts integer and rational values to floating-point).
- If you specify `string`, the values must be strings.
- When writing matrices or lists of lists, you can specify the *dataType* as a list of data types, one corresponding to each column in the output.

The optional *defaultProc* argument specifies a procedure that `writedata` calls if a data value does not conform to the *dataType* you specified (for example, if `writedata` encounters a non-numeric value when the *dataType* is `float`). Maple passes the file descriptor corresponding to the *fileIdentifier*, along with the non-conforming value, as an argument to

[1]For information about how to read and write rtable-based Matrices and Vectors, refer to `?ImportMatrix` and `?ImportVector`.

the *defaultProc*. The default *defaultProc* simply generates the error, `Bad data found`. A more useful *defaultProc* might be the following.

```
> UsefulDefaultProc := proc(f,x) fprintf(f,"%a",x) end proc:
```

This procedure is generic. It can write any value to the file.

**Example** The following example computes a 5 by 5 Hilbert matrix, and writes its floating-point representation to a file.

```
> writedata("hilbertFile.txt",linalg[hilbert](5)):
```

Examining the file shows:

```
1           .5          .3333333333 .25         .2
.5          .3333333333 .25         .2          .1666666667
.3333333333 .25         .2          .1666666667 .1428571429
.25         .2          .1666666667 .1428571429 .125
.2          .1666666667 .1428571429 .125        .1111111111
```

## Flushing a Buffered File

I/O buffering may result in a delay between when you request a write operation and when Maple physically writes the data to the file. This capitalizes on the greater efficiency of performing one large write instead of several smaller ones.

Normally, the I/O library chooses when to write to a file automatically. In some situations, however, you want to ensure that the data you write is inserted into the file. For example, in UNIX, a common procedure is to run a command, such as `tail -f` *fileName*, in another window to monitor the information as Maple is writing it. For cases such as these, the Maple I/O library provides the `fflush` command.

Call the `fflush` command using the following syntax.

```
fflush( fileIdentifier )
```

The *fileIdentifier* is the name or descriptor of the file whose buffer Maple is to flush. When you call `fflush`, Maple writes all information that is in the buffer, but not yet in the physical file, to the file. Typically, a program would call `fflush` whenever something significant is written (for example, a complete intermediate result or a few lines of output).

Note that you do not need to use `fflush`; anything you write to a file is physically written before you close the file. The `fflush` command simply forces Maple to write data on demand, so that you can monitor the progress of a file.

### Redirecting the default Output Stream

The `writeto` and `appendto` commands redirect the `default` output stream to a file. This means that any operations that write to the `default` stream write to the file you specify instead.

You can call the `writeto` and `appendto` commands as follows.

```
writeto( fileName )
appendto( fileName )
```

The *fileName* argument specifies the name of the file to which Maple is to redirect the output. If you call `writeto`, Maple truncates the file if it exists, and writes subsequent output to the file. The `appendto` command appends to the end of the file if the file exists. If the file you specify is open (for example, it is in use by other file I/O operations), Maple generates an error.

The special *fileName* `terminal` (specified as a name, not a string) causes Maple to send subsequent `default` output to the original `default` output stream (the one that was in effect when you started Maple). The calls `writeto(terminal)` and `appendto(terminal)` are equivalent.

**Recommendation** Issuing a `writeto` or `appendto` call directly from the Maple prompt is not recommended. When `writeto` or `appendto` is in effect, Maple also writes any error messages that can result from subsequent operations to the file. Therefore, you cannot see what is happening. Generally, use the `writeto` and `appendto` commands within procedures or files of Maple commands that the `read` command is reading.

## 3.7 Conversion Commands

### Conversion between Strings and Lists of Integers

The `readbytes` and `writebytes` commands described in sections 3.5 and 3.6 can work with either Maple strings or lists of integers. You can use the `convert` command to convert between these two formats as follows.

```
convert( string, bytes )
convert( integerList, bytes )
```

If you pass `convert(...,bytes)` a string, it returns a list of integers; if you pass it a list of integers, it returns a string.

Due to the way strings are implemented in Maple, the character corresponding to the byte-value 0 cannot appear in a string. Therefore, if *integerList* contains a zero, `convert` returns a string of only those characters corresponding to the integers preceding the occurrence of 0 in the list.

Conversion between strings and lists of integers is useful when Maple must interpret parts of a stream of bytes as a character string, while it must interpret other parts as individual bytes.

In the following example, Maple converts a string to a list of integers. Then, it converts the same list, but with one entry changed to 0, back to a string. Notice that the string is truncated at the location of the 0.

```
> convert("Test String",bytes);
```

$$[84, 101, 115, 116, 32, 83, 116, 114, 105, 110, 103]$$

```
> convert([84,101,115,116,0,83,116,114,105,110,103],bytes);
```

"Test"

## Parsing Maple Expressions and Statements

The `parse` command converts a string of valid Maple input to the corresponding Maple expression. The expression is simplified, but not evaluated.

Use the `parse` command as follows.

```
parse( string, options )
```

The *string* argument is the string to be parsed. It must describe a Maple expression (or statement, see the following definition) by using the Maple language syntax.

You can supply one or more *options* to the `parse` command:

`statement` This indicates that `parse` is to accept statements in addition to expressions. However, since Maple automatically evaluates statements, `parse` evaluates the *string* if you specify `statement`.

`nosemicolon` Normally, `parse` supplies a terminating semicolon, ";" if the string does not end in a semicolon or a colon, ":". If you specify `nosemicolon`, this does not happen, and Maple generates an `unexpected end of input` error if the string is incomplete. The readstat command, which uses readline and parse, makes use of this facility to allow multi-line inputs.

If the *string* passed to parse contains a syntax error, parse generates an error (which you can trap with traperror) of the following form.

```
incorrect syntax in parse:
        errorDescription (errorLocation)
```

The *errorDescription* describes the nature of the error (for example, '+' unexpected, or unexpected end of input). The *errorLocation* gives the approximate character position within the string at which Maple detected the error.

When you call parse from the Maple prompt, Maple displays the parsed result depending on whether the call to parse ends in a semicolon or a colon. The *string* passed to parse does not require a trailing semicolon or a colon. If included, it is ignored.

```
> parse("a+2+b+3");
```

$$a + 5 + b$$

```
> parse("sin(3.0)"):
> %;
```

$$0.1411200081$$

## Formatted Conversion to and from Strings

The sprintf and sscanf commands are similar to fprintf/printf and fscanf/scanf, except that they read from or write to Maple strings instead of files.

Call the sprintf command using the following syntax.

```
sprintf( format, expressionSequence )
```

The *format* specifies how Maple is to format the elements of the *expressionSequence.* This Maple string consists of a sequence of formatting specifications, possibly separated by other characters. For more information, see **3.6 Formatted Output** on page 210.

The sprintf command returns a string containing the formatted result.

Call the sscanf command as follows.

```
sscanf( sourceString, format )
```

The *sourceString* provides the input for scanning. The *format* specifies how Maple is to parse the input. A sequence of conversion specifications (and possibly other anticipated characters) consist of this Maple string. For information on the *format*, see **Formatted Input** on page 198. The `sscanf` command returns a list of the scanned objects, just as `fscanf` and `scanf` do.

The following example illustrates `sprintf` and `sscanf` by converting a floating-point number and two algebraic expressions into a floating-point format, Maple syntax, and Maple `.m` format, respectively. This string is then parsed into the corresponding objects using `sscanf`.

```
> s := sprintf("%4.2f %a %m",evalf(Pi),sin(3),cos(3));
```

$$s := \text{“3.14 sin(3) -\%\$cosG6\#““\$”}$$

```
> sscanf(s,"%f %a %m");
```

$$[3.14, \sin(3), \cos(3)]$$

**Information:** For information on translating Maple expressions into other programming languages, see **6.1 Code Generation**.

## 3.8 Notes to C Programmers

If you have experience programming in the C or C++ programming languages, many of the I/O commands described in this chapter seem familiar. The Maple I/O library design purposely emulates the C standard I/O library.

In general, the Maple I/O commands work in a similar manner to their C counterparts. The differences that arise are the result of differences between the Maple and C languages, and how you use them. For example, in the C library, you must pass the `sprintf` function a buffer into which it writes the result. In Maple, strings are objects that you can pass as easily as numbers, so the `sprintf` command simply returns a string that is sufficiently long to hold the result. This method is both easier to work with and less error prone, as it removes the danger of writing past the end of a fixed length buffer.

Similarly, the `fscanf`, `scanf`, and `sscanf` commands return a list of the parsed results instead of requiring you to pass references to variables. This method is also less error prone, as it removes any danger of passing the wrong type of variable or one of insufficient size.

Other differences include the use of a single command, `filepos`, to perform the work of two C functions, `ftell` and `fseek`. You can do this in Maple because functions can take a variable number of arguments.

In general, if you have C or C++ programming experience, you should have little trouble using the Maple I/O library.

## 3.9 Conclusion

This chapter presented the details of importing and exporting data and code to and from Maple. While this book teaches fundamental concepts and provides a pedagogical introduction to topics, the Maple help system provides the details on each command and feature. It explains such things as the options and syntax of Maple commands and serves as a resource for use of the Maple interface. For more information on a command, enter `?command_name` at the Maple prompt.

# 4 Numerical Programming in Maple

## Floating-Point Calculations

The focus of this chapter is on how to perform floating-point calculations in Maple. You can select from the following.

- Software floating-point calculations of arbitrary precision – other than speed, independent of your computer
- Hardware floating-point arithematic – precision determined by the architecture of your computer, but offers exceptional speed

## In This Chapter

- Basics of the `evalf` Command
- Hardware Floating-Point Numbers
- Foating-Point Models in Maple
- Extending the `evalf` Command
- Using the `Matlab` Package

## Why Use Numerical Computations

Representation and manipulation of expressions in symbolic mode, in terms of variables, functions, and exact constants, is a powerful feature of the Maple system. Practical scientific computation also demands floating-point calculations which represent quantities by approximate numerical values.

Typically, numerical computations are used for one of three reasons.

1. Not all problems have analytical or symbolic solutions. For example, there are many forms of partial differential equations, but only a small subset have known closed-form solutions. Despite this, it is usually possible to find numerical solutions.

2. The analytic solution that Maple returns to a problem may be very large or complex. To understand the behavior of these expressions, compute a floating-point approximation.

3. In some cases, it is wasteful to compute an exact answer. Computing an analytic solution is not necessary if only an approximation is needed. For example, to plot a solution, an approximation accurate to the resolution of the plotting device is sufficient.

## 4.1 The Basics of `evalf`

The `evalf` command is the primary tool in Maple for performing floating-point calculations. It causes Maple to evaluate in software floating-point mode. The Maple software floating-point arithmetic has an $n$-digit machine floating-point model as its basis, but allows computations at arbitrary precision. The environment variable `Digits`, which has an initial setting of 10, determines the default number of digits for calculations.

```
> evalf(Pi);
```

$$3.141592654$$

You can alter the number of digits either by changing the value of `Digits`, or by specifying the number as an index to `evalf`. Note that when you specify the number of digits as an index to `evalf`, the default, `Digits`, remains unchanged.

```
> Digits := 20:
> evalf(Pi);
```

$$3.1415926535897932385$$

```
> evalf[200](Pi);
```

$$3.14159265358979323846264338327950288419\backslash$$
$$7169399375105820974944592307816406286\backslash$$
$$2089986280348253421170679821480865132\backslash$$
$$8230664709384460955058223172535940812\backslash$$
$$8481117450284102701938521105559644622\backslash$$
$$9489549303820$$

```
> evalf(sqrt(2));
```

$$1.4142135623730950488$$

```
> Digits := 10:
```

The number of digits you specify is the number of *decimal* digits that Maple uses during calculations. Specifying a larger number of digits is likely to give you a more accurate answer, and the maximum value of `Digits` is sufficiently large to be considered infinite for practical purposes. Unlike most hardware implementations of floating-point arithmetic, Maple stores and performs software operations on floating-point numbers in base 10.

**Accuracy** All floating-point computations are preferred in *finite precision*, with intermediate results generally being rounded to `Digits` precision. As such, it is possible for round-off errors to accumulate in long computations. Maple ensures that the result of any *single* floating-point arithmetic operation ($+$, $-$, $*$, $/$, or $\sqrt{\ }$) is fully accurate. Further, many of the basic functions in Maple, such as the trigonometric functions and their inverses, the exponential and logarithm functions, and some of the other standards special functions for mathematics, are accurate to within `.6` *units of last place* (ulps), meaning that if the `Digits + 1st` digit of the true result is a 4, Maple may round it up, or if it is a 6, Maple may round it down. Most mathematical functions in Maple, including numerical integration, achieve this accuracy on nearly all inputs.

Some definite integrals have no closed form solution in terms of standard mathematical functions. You can use `evalf` to obtain an answer via numerical integration.

```
> r := Int(exp(x^3), x=0..1);
```

$$r := \int_0^1 e^{(x^3)}\, dx$$

```
> value(r);
```

$$\int_0^1 e^{(x^3)}\, dx$$

```
> evalf(r);
```

$$1.341904418$$

In other cases, Maple can find an exact solution, but the form of the exact solution is almost incomprehensible. The following function Beta is a special function that appears in mathematical literature.

```
> q := Int( x^99 * (1-x)^199 / Beta(100, 200), x=0..1/5 );
```

$$q := \int_0^{1/5} \frac{x^{99}\,(1-x)^{199}}{B(100,\,200)}\, dx$$

```
> value(q);
```

$$\begin{array}{l}
278522905457805211792552486504343059984\backslash \\
038498009096903421704176220527155238 97\backslash \\
761906828166964420518416902474524718 18\backslash \\
797202945961766386779717574634134906 44\backslash \\
257275018611014357501573520181129894 92\backslash \\
972548449 \Big/ 21774128091037151646 8873\backslash \\
849715521159343849617672516710310132 43\backslash \\
122411486103082625144755525240513230 83\backslash \\
132387178403327502493606037826303413 76\backslash \\
825373673833460831833461652286611335 71\backslash \\
762601621483528326205933656911850124 66\backslash \\
147181896006639730419830500271656525 95\backslash \\
684264269948471337556838989257812500 00\backslash \\
0\dfrac{1}{B(100,\,200)}
\end{array}$$

```
> evalf(q);
```

$$0.3546007367\,10^{-7}$$

The two previous examples use the `Int` command rather than `int` for the integration. If you use `int`, Maple first tries to integrate the expression symbolically. Thus, when evaluating the following commands, Maple determines a symbolic answer and then converts it to a floating-point approximation, rather than performing direct numerical integration.

```
> evalf( int(x^99 * (1-x)^199 / Beta(100, 200), x=0..1/5) );
```

$$0.3546007367\,10^{-7}$$

When performing numerical calculations, do *not* use commands like `int`, `limit`, and `sum` that evaluate their arguments symbolically.

In general, results from `evalf(Int(...))` , `evalf(Sum(...))` , and `evalf(Limit(...))`, are more accurate than results obtained from the corresponding `evalf(int(...))`, `evalf(sum(...))`, and `evalf(limit(...))` operations. Generally, symbolic evaluation can be suppressed by using unevaluation quotes. For example, `evalf(sin(Pi/3)) = evalf(1/2 * 3^(1/2))` while `evalf('sin'(Pi/3))` computes a floating-point approximation to `sin(evalf(Pi/3))`.

## 4.2 Hardware Floating-Point Numbers

Maple offers an alternative to software floating-point numbers: computer hardware floating-point arithmetic. Hardware floating-point calculations are typically much faster than software floating-point calculations. However, hardware floating-point arithmetic accuracy depends on your computer, and you cannot increase the precision.

The `evalhf` command evaluates an expression using hardware floating-point arithmetic.

```
> evalhf( 1/3 );
```

$$0.333333333333333314$$

```
> evalhf( Pi );
```

$$3.14159265358979312$$

Generally, computers perform hardware floating-point arithmetic using a certain number of binary digits. The special construct, `evalhf(Digits)`, approximates the corresponding number of decimal digits.

```
> d := evalhf(Digits);
```

$$d := 15.$$

Therefore, `evalhf` and `evalf` return similar results if `evalf` uses a setting of `Digits` that is close to `evalhf(Digits)`. Maple usually displays two or three digits more than the value of `evalhf(Digits)` specifies. When you perform hardware floating-point calculations, Maple must convert all the base-10 software floating-point numbers to base-2 hardware floating-point numbers, and then convert the result back to base 10. The extra decimal digits allow Maple to reproduce the binary number precisely if you use it again in a subsequent hardware floating-point calculation.

```
> expr := ln( 2 / Pi * ( exp(2)-1 ) );
```

$$expr := \ln(2\,\frac{e^2 - 1}{\pi})$$

```
> evalhf( expr );
```

$$1.40300383684168617$$

```
> evalf[round(d)]( expr );
```

$$1.40300383684169$$

The results that `evalhf` returns, even including for `evalhf(Digits)`, are not affected by the value of `Digits`.

```
> Digits := 4658;
```

$$Digits := 4658$$

```
> evalhf( expr );
```

$$1.40300383684168617$$

```
> evalhf(Digits);
```

$$15.$$

```
> Digits := 10;
```

$$Digits := 10$$

You can use the `evalhf(Digits)` construct to determine whether hardware floating-point arithmetic provides sufficient precision in a particular application. If `Digits` is less than `evalhf(Digits)`, then you can take advantage of the faster hardware floating-point calculations. Otherwise, you should use software floating-point arithmetic to perform the calculation, with sufficient digits. The following `evaluate` procedure takes an *unevaluated* parameter, `expr`. Without the `uneval` declaration, Maple would evaluate `expr` symbolically before invoking `evaluate`.

```
> evaluate := proc(expr::uneval)
>    if Digits < evalhf(Digits) then
>       evalf(evalhf(expr));
>    else
>       evalf(expr);
>    end if;
> end proc:
```

The `evalhf` command evaluates many Maple functions, but not all. For example, you cannot evaluate an integral using hardware floating-point arithmetic.

```
> evaluate( Int(exp(x^3), x=0..1) );

Error, (in evaluate) unable to evaluate function 'Int'
in evalhf
```

You can improve the `evaluate` procedure so that it traps such errors and tries to evaluate the expression using software floating-point numbers instead.

```
> evaluate := proc(expr::uneval)
>    local result;
>    if Digits < evalhf(Digits) then
>       try
>          return evalf(evalhf(expr));
>       catch:
>       end try;
>    else
>       evalf(expr);
>    end if;
```

```
> end proc:
```

```
> evaluate( Int(exp(x^3), x=0..1) );
```

The `evaluate` procedure provides a model of how to write procedures that use hardware floating-point arithmetic whenever possible.

## Newton's Method

This section illustrates how to take advantage of hardware floating-point arithmetic to calculate successive approximations using Newton's method. You can use Newton's method to find numerical solutions to equations. As section 1.2 describes, if $x_n$ is an approximate solution to the equation $f(x) = 0$, then $x_{n+1}$, given by the following formula, is typically a better approximation.

$$x_{n+1} = x_n - \frac{f(x_n)}{f'(x_n)}$$

**Example** The `iterate` procedure takes a function, `f`, its derivative, `df`, and an initial approximate solution, `x0`, as input to the equation $f(x) = 0$. The `iteration` procedure calculates at most `N` successive Newton iterations until the difference between the new approximation and the previous one is small. The `iterate` procedure prints the sequence of approximations to show successive approximations.

```
> iterate := proc( f::procedure, df::procedure,
>                  x0::numeric, N::posint )
>    local xold, xnew;
>    xold := x0;
>    xnew := evalf( xold - f(xold)/df(xold) );
>    to  N-1 while abs(xnew-xold) > 10^(1-Digits) do
>       xold := xnew;
>       print(xold);
>       xnew := evalf( xold - f(xold)/df(xold) );
>    end do;
>    xnew;
> end proc:
```

The following procedure calculates the derivative of $f$ and passes all the necessary information to `iterate`.

```
> Newton := proc( f::procedure, x0::numeric, N::posint )
>    local df;
>    df := D(f);
>    print(x0);
>    iterate(f, df, x0, N);
> end proc:
```

Use Newton to solve the equation $x^2 - 2 = 0$.

```
> f := x -> x^2 - 2;
```

$$f := x \to x^2 - 2$$

```
> Newton(f, 1.5, 15);
```

$$1.5$$

$$1.416666667$$

$$1.414215686$$

$$1.414213562$$

$$1.414213562$$

**Example** This version of Newton uses hardware floating-point arithmetic if possible. Since iterate only tries to find a solution to an accuracy of 10^(1-Digits), Newton uses evalf to round the result of the hardware floating-point computation to an appropriate number of digits.

```
> Newton := proc( f::procedure, x0::numeric, N::posint )
>    local df, result;
>    df := D(f);
>    print(x0);
>    if Digits < evalhf(Digits) then
>       try
>          return evalf(evalhf(iterate(f, df, x0, N)));
>       catch:
>       end try;
>    else
>       iterate(f, df, x0, N);
>    end if;
> end proc:
```

Newton uses hardware floating-point arithmetic for the iterations and rounds the result to software precision. Hardware floating-point numbers have more digits than the software floating-point numbers, given the present setting of Digits.

```
> Newton(f, 1.5, 15);
```

$$1.5$$

$$1.41666666666666674$$

$$1.41421568627450988$$

$$1.41421356237468987$$

$$1.41421356237309514$$

$$1.414213562$$

`Newton` must use software floating-point arithmetic to find a root of the following Bessel function.

```
> F := z -> BesselJ(1, z);
```

$$F := z \to \mathrm{BesselJ}(1,\, z)$$

```
> Newton(F, 4, 15);
```

$$4$$

Software arithmetic is used because `evalhf` does not recognize `BesselJ` and the symbolic code for `BesselJ` uses the `type` command and remember tables, which `evalhf` does not allow.

```
> evalhf( BesselJ(1, 4) );
Error, unable to evaluate expression to hardware floats
```

Using a `try-catch` block as in the previous `Newton` procedure, allows the procedure to work when `evalhf` fails.

The previous `Newton` procedure prints many digits when it is trying to find a ten-digit approximation. The reason is that the `print` command is located inside the `iterate` procedure which is inside a call to `evalhf`, where all numbers are hardware floating-point numbers, and print as such.

## Computing with Arrays of Numbers

Use the `evalhf` command for calculations with numbers. The only structured Maple objects allowed in a call to `evalhf` are arrays of numbers, either table-based arrays or rtable-based Arrays. If an array has unassigned entries, `evalhf` initializes them to zero.

**Example** The following procedure calculates the polynomial $2+5x+4x^2$.

```
> p := proc(x)
>    local a, i;
>    a := array(0..2);
>    a[0] := 2;
>    a[1] := 5;
>    a[2] := 4;
>    sum( a[i]*x^i, i=0..2 );
> end proc:
```

```
> p(x);
```

$$2 + 5\,x + 4\,x^2$$

If you intend to enclose `p` in a call to `evalhf`, you cannot define the local array `a` using `array(1..3, [2,5,4])` because lists are not supported in `evalhf`. You can, however, enclose `p` in a call to `evalhf` if the parameter `x` is a number.

```
> evalhf(p(5.6));
```

$$155.439999999999997$$

You can also pass an array of numbers as a parameter inside a call to `evalhf`.

**Example** The following procedure calculates the determinant of a $2 \times 2$ matrix. The `(2,2)` entry in the array `a` is unassigned.

```
> det := proc(a::array(2))
>    a[1,1] * a[2,2] - a[1,2] * a[2,1];
> end proc:
```

```
> a := array( [[2/3, 3/4], [4/9]] );
```

$$a := \begin{bmatrix} \frac{2}{3} & \frac{3}{4} \\ \frac{4}{9} & a_{2,2} \end{bmatrix}$$

```
> det(a);
```

$$\frac{2}{3}a_{2,2} - \frac{1}{3}$$

If you call det from inside a call to evalhf, Maple uses the value 0 for the unassigned entry, a[2,2].

```
> evalhf( det(a) );
```

$$-0.333333333333333314$$

evalhf passes arrays by value, so the (2,2) entry of a is still unassigned.

```
> a[2,2];
```

$$a_{2,2}$$

If you want evalhf to modify an array that you pass as a parameter to a procedure, you must enclose the name of the array in a var construct. The var construct is special to evalhf and is necessary only if you want evalhf to modify an array of numbers that is accessible at the session level.

```
> evalhf( det( var(a) ) );
```

$$-0.333333333333333314$$

Now a is an array of floating-point numbers.

```
> eval(a);
```

$$\begin{bmatrix} 0.666666666666666629, & 0.750000000000000000 \\ 0.444444444444444420, & 0. \end{bmatrix}$$

The evalhf command always returns a single floating-point number, but the var construct allows you to calculate a whole array of numbers with one call to evalhf. **5.7 Generating Grids of Points** illustrates the use of var to calculate a grid of function values for plotting.

You can also create arrays of hardware floating-point values directly with the Array command. Proper use of this command can save significant amounts of time, especially in plotting routines, which rely heavily on arrays of floating-point values. For details and examples, refer to `?Array`, `?Matrix`, and `?Vector`.

## 4.3 Floating-Point Models in Maple

Maple can represent symbolic constants, such as $\pi$ and $\gamma$, exact integers and rational numbers, such as 37 and 3/4, and *approximations* to numeric values, using its *floating-point* system. Numbers in this system are represented by pairs of integers, `(m,e)`. The first integer is called the `significand` or `mantissa`. The second integer is called the `exponent`. The number represented is

$$m \times 10^e.$$

Examples of floating-point numbers in Maple are 3.1415, 1.0, −0.0007, 1.0$e$0, and 2$e$1234567. The last two are examples of floating-point numbers entered in *scientific notation*: the `"e"` separates the mantissa and exponent of the number. Such numbers can also be used to represent complex numbers (as can exact integers and rationals), for example, $1.0 + 2.7 * I$.

In some contexts, Maple distinguishes between *software floats* and *hardware floats*. The `evalhf` evaluator (discussed in section 4.2), for example, works with hardware floats, and Maple can construct certain kinds of matrices and vectors with hardware float entries. Generally, however, Maple works with software floats to perform approximate (but usually very accurate) numerical calculations.

Floating-point number systems are *approximations* to the mathematical set of real (and complex) numbers, and hence necessarily have limitations. Most importantly, such systems have limited range (there are largest and smallest representable numbers) and limited precision (the set of representable floating-point numbers is finite). One very important feature of the Maple software floating-point system is that you control the precision: you can specify the precision Maple uses for floating-point computations.

Some of the specific details of these computation systems are provided in the next few sections.

### Software Floats

Maple software floating-point computations are performed in base 10. The precision of a computation is determined by the setting of `Digits`. The maximum exponent, minimum exponent, and maximum value for

Digits are machine wordsize dependent. You can obtain the values for these limits from the Maple_floats command.

This software floating-point system is designed as a natural extension of the industry standard for hardware floating-point computation, known as IEEE 754. Thus, there are representations for infinity and undefined (what IEEE 754 calls a "NaN", meaning "Not a Number"). Complex numbers are represented by using the standard x + I*y format.

One important feature of this system is that the floating-point representation of zero, 0., retains its arithmetic sign in computations. That is, Maple distinguishes between +0. and -0. when necessary. In most situations, this difference is irrelevant, but when dealing with functions such as ln(x), which have a discontinuity across the negative real axis, preserving the sign of the imaginary part of a number on the negative real axis is important.

For more intricate applications, Maple implements extensions of the IEEE 754 notion of a numeric event, and provides facilities for monitoring events and their associated status flags. To learn more about this system, refer to ?numerics.

## Roundoff Error

When you perform floating-point arithmetic, whether using software or hardware floats, you are using *approximate* numbers rather than precise real numbers or expressions. Maple can work with exact (symbolic) expressions. The difference between an exact real number and its floating-point approximation is called the *roundoff error*. For example, suppose you request a floating-point representation of $\pi$.

```
> pi := evalf(Pi);
```

$$\pi := 3.141592654$$

Maple rounds the precise value $\pi$ to ten significant digits because Digits is set to its default value of 10. You can approximate the roundoff error above by temporarily increasing the value of Digits to 15.

```
> evalf[15](Pi - pi);
```

$$-0.41021\,10^{-9}$$

Roundoff errors arise from the representation of input data, and as a result of performing arithmetic operations. Each time you perform an arithmetic operation on two floating-point numbers, the infinitely-precise result is generally not representable in the floating-point number system and therefore the computed result also has an associated roundoff error.

For example, suppose you multiply two ten-digit numbers with `Digits = 10`. The result can have nineteen or twenty digits, but Maple stores only the first ten digits.

```
> 1234567890 * 1937128552;
```

$$2391516709101395280$$

```
> evalf(1234567890) * evalf(1937128552);
```

$$0.2391516709\,10^{19}$$

Whenever you apply one of the four basic arithmetic operations (addition, subtraction, multiplication, division, or square root) to two floating-point numbers, the result is the correctly rounded representation of the infinitely precise result, unless overflow or underflow occurs. Of course, Maple may need to compute an extra digit or two behind the scenes to ensure that the answer is correct.

Even so, sometimes a surprising amount of error can accumulate, particularly when subtracting two numbers which are of similar magnitude. In the following calculation, the accurate sum of $x$, $y$, and $z$ is $y = 3.141592654$.

```
> x := evalf(987654321);
```

$$x := 0.987654321\,10^{9}$$

```
> y := evalf(Pi);
```

$$y := 3.141592654$$

```
> z := -x;
```

$$z := -0.987654321\,10^{9}$$

```
> x + y + z;
```

$$3.1$$

This is known as *catastrophic cancellation*. During the subtraction the eight leading digits cancel out, leaving only two significant digits in the result.

One advantage of Maple software floats, in contrast to fixed-precision floating-point numbers systems, is that the user can increase the precision to reduce roundoff errors. For example, increasing `Digits` to 20 dramatically improves the result.

```
> Digits := 20;
```

$$Digits := 20$$

```
> x + y + z;
```

$$3.141592654$$

Employ standard numerical analysis techniques to avoid large errors accumulating in calculations. Often, reordering the operations leads to a more accurate final result. For example, when computing a sum, add the numbers with the smallest magnitudes first.

## 4.4 Extending the `evalf` Command

The `evalf` command can evaluate many functions and constants, such as `sin` and `Pi`. You can also define custom functions or constants, and extend `evalf` by adding information about how to compute such functions or constants.

### Defining New Constants

You can define a new constant and write procedures that manipulate this constant symbolically. You can then write a procedure that calculates a floating-point approximation of the constant to any number of digits. If you assign the procedure a name of the form `` `evalf/constant/name` ``, Maple invokes the procedure when you use `evalf` to evaluate an expression containing the constant, *name*.

**Example** Let the name `MyConst` represent the following infinite series:

$$MyConst = \sum_{i=1}^{\infty} \frac{(-1)^i \pi^i}{2^i i!}$$

You can calculate approximations to the series in many ways; the following procedure is one implementation. Note that if $a_i$ is the $i$th term in the sum, then $a_{i+1} = -a_i(\pi/2)/i$ gives the next term.

- You can calculate an approximation to the series by adding terms until the Maple model for software floating-point numbers cannot distinguish successive partial sums.
- Using numerical analysis, you can prove that this algorithm calculates an approximation of `MyConst` accurate to the number of digits specified by `Digits`, if you use two extra digits inside the algorithm.

The following procedure increments `Digits` by two and uses `evalf` to round the result to the proper number of digits before returning. The procedure does not have to reset the value of `Digits` because `Digits` is an environment variable, which is automatically reset after executing the procedure.

```
> `evalf/constant/MyConst` := proc()
>    local i, term, halfpi, s, old_s;
>    Digits := Digits + 2;
>    halfpi := evalf(Pi/2);
>    old_s := 1;
>    term := 1.0;
>    s := 0;
>    for i from 1 while s <> old_s do
>       term := -term * halfpi / i;
>       old_s := s;
>       s := s + term;
>    end do;
>    evalf[Digits-2](s);
> end proc:
```

When you invoke `evalf` on an expression containing `MyConst`, Maple invokes `` `evalf/constants/MyConst` `` to calculate an approximate value.

```
> evalf(MyConst);
```

$$-0.7921204237$$

```
> evalf[40](MyConst);
```

$$-0.7921204236492380914530443801650212299661$$

You can express the particular constant, `MyConst`, in closed form and, in this case, you can use the closed-form formula to calculate approximations to `MyConst` more efficiently.

```
> Sum( (-1)^i * Pi^i / 2^i / i!, i=1..infinity );
```

$$\sum_{i=1}^{\infty} \frac{(-1)^i \pi^i}{2^i\, i!}$$

```
> value(%);
```

$$\frac{1 - e^{(1/2\,\pi)}}{e^{(1/2\,\pi)}}$$

```
> expand(%);
```

$$\frac{1}{\sqrt{e^{\pi}}} - 1$$

```
> evalf(%);
```

$$-0.7921204237$$

## Defining New Functions

If you define new functions, you can write procedures that calculate numerical approximations to the function values. When you invoke `evalf` on an expression containing an unevaluated call to a function $F$, Maple calls the procedure `` `evalf/F` `` if such a procedure exists.

Consider the function $x \mapsto (x - \sin(x))/x^3$.

```
> MyFcn := x -> (x - sin(x)) / x^3;
```

$$MyFcn := x \to \frac{x - \sin(x)}{x^3}$$

This function is not defined at $x = 0$, but you can extend it as a continuous function by placing the limiting value in the `MyFcn` remember table.

```
> MyFcn(0) := limit( MyFcn(x), x=0 );
```

$$\mathrm{MyFcn}(0) := \frac{1}{6}$$

For small values of $x$, $\sin(x)$ is almost equal to $x$, so the subtraction $x - \sin(x)$ in the definition of MyFcn can lead to inaccuracies due to catastrophic cancellation. When you evaluate v below to ten digits, only the first two are correct.

```
> v := 'MyFcn'( 0.000195 );
```

$$v := \mathrm{MyFcn}(0.000195)$$

```
> evalf(v);
```

$$0.1618368482$$

```
> evalf(v, 2*Digits);
```

$$0.16666666634973617222$$

If you depend on accurate numerical approximations of MyFcn, you must write a custom procedure to compute them. You could write such a procedure by exploiting the series expansion of MyFcn.

```
> series( MyFcn(x), x=0, 11 );
```

$$\frac{1}{6} - \frac{1}{120}x^2 + \frac{1}{5040}x^4 - \frac{1}{362880}x^6 + \mathrm{O}(x^8)$$

The general term in the series is

$$a_i = (-1)^i \frac{x^{2i}}{(2i+3)!}, \qquad i \geq 0.$$

Note that $a_i = -a_{i-1}x^2/((2i+2)(2i+3))$.

- For small values of $x$, you can then calculate an approximation to MyFcn(x) by adding terms until the Maple model for software floating-point numbers cannot distinguish successive partial sums.
- For larger values of $x$, catastrophic cancellation is not a problem, so you can use evalf to evaluate the expression.
- Using numerical analysis, you can prove that this algorithm calculates an approximation of the function value accurate to the number of digits specified by Digits, if you use three extra digits inside the algorithm.

The following procedure increments Digits by three and uses evalf to round the result to the proper number of digits before returning.

```
> `evalf/MyFcn` := proc(xx::algebraic)
>    local x, term, s, old_s, xsqr, i;
>    x := evalf(xx);
>    Digits := Digits+3;
>    if type(x, numeric) and abs(x)<0.1 then
>       xsqr := x^2;
>       term := evalf(1/6);
>       s := term;
>       old_s := 0;
>       for i from 1 while s <> old_s do
>          term := -term * xsqr / ((2*i+2)*(2*i+3));
>          old_s := s;
>          s := s + term;
>       end do;
>    else
>       s := evalf( (x-sin(x))/x^3 );
>    end if;
>    eval[Digits-3](s);
> end proc:
```

When you invoke evalf on an expression containing an unevaluated call to MyFcn, Maple invokes `evalf/MyFcn`.

```
> evalf( 'MyFcn'(0.000195) );
```

$$0.1666666663498$$

Recode the symbolic version of MyFcn so that it takes advantage of `evalf/MyFcn` if the argument is a floating-point number.

```
> MyFcn := proc(x::algebraic)
>    if type(x, float) then
>       evalf('MyFcn'(x));
>    else
>       (x - sin(x)) / x^3;
>    end if;
> end proc:
```

The evalf command automatically looks for `evalf/MyFcn` when used in the evalf(`MyFcn`) syntax.

```
> MyFcn(0) := limit( MyFcn(x), x=0 );
```

$$\text{MyFcn}(0) := \frac{1}{6}$$

Now you can properly evaluate `MyFcn` with numeric as well as symbolic arguments.

```
> MyFcn(x);
```

$$\frac{x - \sin(x)}{x^3}$$

```
> MyFcn(0.099999999);
```

$$0.1665833531735$$

```
> MyFcn(0.1);
```

$$0.1665833531700$$

**1.5 Extending Maple** describes how to extend many other Maple commands.

## 4.5 Using the Matlab Package

Another way to accomplish numerical computations in Maple is to use the `Matlab` package, which provides access to several MATLAB® built-in functions. Note: You must have a copy of MATLAB properly installed on your computer. The mathematical functions provided are:

- `chol`: Cholesky factorization
- `defined`: test whether variable exists
- `det`: determinant
- `dimensions`: compute dimensions of matrix
- `eig`: eigenvalues and eigenvectors
- `evalM`: evaluate expression
- `fft`: discrete Fourier transforms
- `getvar`: get numeric array or matrix
- `inv`: matrix inverse

- `lu`: LU decomposition
- `ode45`: solve ordinary differential equation
- `qr`: QR orthogonal-triangular decomposition
- `size`: compute size of matrix
- `square`: determine whether matrix is square
- `transpose`: matrix transposition

Some support and utility commands are provided. MATLAB converts all Maple structures to its representation of hardware floating-point arrays before it performs any computations. The results are usually Arrays with data type float[8] (that is, hardware float entries). For more information, refer to `?Array` and `?Matrix`.

For more information on all these commands and the `Matlab` package in general, refer to `?Matlab`. To learn how to start the MATLAB application from a Maple session, refer to `?Matlab[openlink]`.

## 4.6 Conclusion

With numerical techniques, you can solve equations which are otherwise unsolvable, investigate the properties of complicated solutions, and quickly obtain numerical estimates.

Symbolic calculations give precise representations, but in some cases can be expensive to compute even with a tool as powerful as Maple. At the other extreme, hardware floating-point arithmetic allows you fast computation directly from Maple. This involves, however, limited accuracy. Software floating-point offers a balance. As well as sometimes being much faster than symbolic calculations, you also have the option to control the precision of your calculations, thus exerting control over errors.

Software floating-point calculations and representations mimic the IEEE 754 standard representation closely, except for the great advantage of arbitrary precision. The similarity with this popular standard allows you to readily apply accumulation of error and numerical analysis principles contained in numerous texts and papers.

# 5 Programming with Maple Graphics

## Maple Plots

Maple has a wide range of packages and procedures for generating 2-D and 3-D plots. These include:

- The `plot` and `plot3d` procedures for generating basic 2-D and 3-D plots, respectively
- The `plots` package for generating specialized plots, such as vector field plots or contour plots
- The `plottools` package for generating graphical objects for inclusion in plots

In addition to those listed above, many other Maple packages, such as `DEtools`, `Student`, and `stats`, include specialized procedures for plotting in specific contexts.

These procedures require as arguments information that allows the numerical plot data values to be computed. They also accept options that set attributes such as colour, shading, and axes style.

## Creating Plotting Procedures

The purpose of this chapter is to present some of the Maple plotting procedures, describe the structure of their output, and describe ways in which you can use them to create custom procedures. This chapter includes basic information about argument conventions, default settings, and option processing.

## In This Chapter

- Basic Plotting Procedures

- Programming with Plotting Library Procedures
- Maple Plot Data Structures
- Programming with Plot Data Structures
- Programming with the `plottools` Package
- Vector Field Plots
- Generating Grids of Points
- Animation
- Programming with Color

## 5.1 Basic Plotting Procedures

This section illustrates:

- Typical calling sequences of plotting procedures
- Properties that are common to plotting procedures
- Using operators or procedures versus expressions in the independent variables to define plots
- Specifying optional information

Many Maple plotting procedures, including `plot`, `plot3d`, and some commands in the `plots` package, accept input in one of two forms: expressions in one or two **independent variables**, or expressions involving **procedures and operators**. For example, the input can be the expression $a^2b - b^3 + 1$ in variables $a$ and $b$, or the expression $p + q$, where $p$ and $q$ are procedures.

The following command generates a 3-D plot of the surface defined by $\sin(x)\sin(y)$. The independent variables are $x$ and $y$.

```
> plot3d(sin(x)*sin(y), x=0..4*Pi, y=-2*Pi..2*Pi);
```

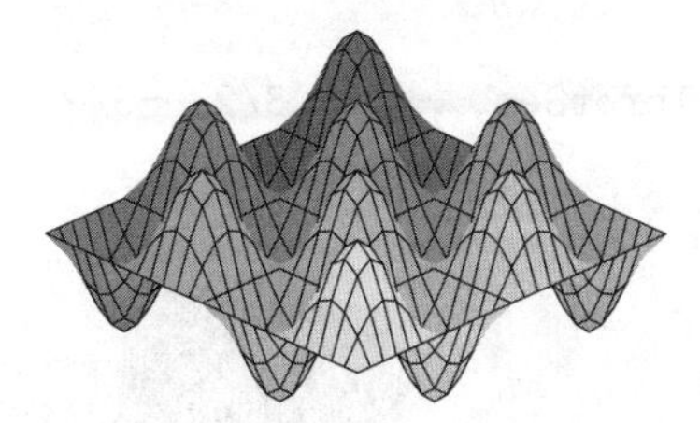

You can plot the same surface by first defining two procedures that each take two arguments:

```
> p := (x, y) -> sin(x):  q := (x, y) -> sin(y):
```

and then providing $p*q$ as the first argument to the `plot3d` command:

```
> plot3d(p * q, 0..4*Pi, -2*Pi..2*Pi);
```

In the first example, the `plot3d` procedure recognizes that the first argument is an expression in $x$ and $y$ because the second and third arguments have the forms `x=`*`range`* and `y=`*`range`*. In the second example, the second and third arguments are simply ranges and contain no variable names.

Working with expressions in independent variables is simple, but in many cases, procedures and operators provide a better mechanism for defining plots. We use the term *operator form* to refer to the form of the calling sequence that accepts procedures and operators.

**Example 1** The following procedure accepts a complex starting point $c = x + iy$ and computes the required number of iterations (to a maximum of 10) for the sequence $z_{n+1} = z_n^2 + c$ to exit the disk of radius 2.

```
> mandelbrotSet := proc(x, y)
>     local z, m;
>     z := evalf(x + y*I);
>     m := 0;
>     to 10 while abs(z) < 2 do
>         z := z^2 + (x+y*I);
>         m := m + 1;
>     end do:
>     m;
> end proc:
```

You can use the procedure to compute a 3-D Mandelbrot set on a $50 \times 50$ grid.

```
> plot3d(mandelbrotSet, -3/2..3/2, -3/2..3/2, grid=[50,50]);
```

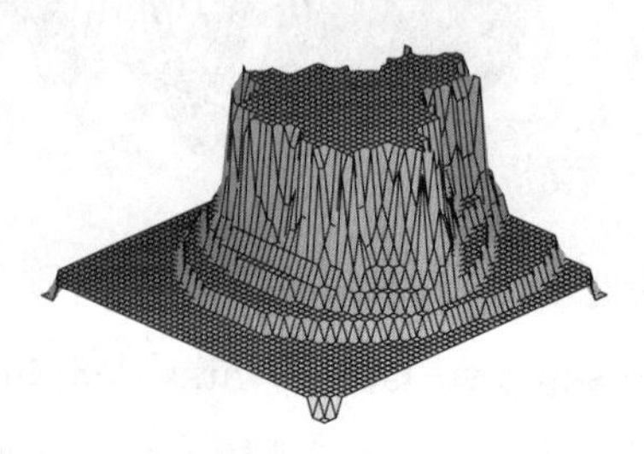

## Altering a Plot

After you issue a plotting command, the result is displayed on the default plotting device (in the worksheet, generally, the current window). You can use the tools available in the worksheet interface to interactively alter the plot characteristics, such as drawing style, axes style, and orientation. You can also specify this information using optional arguments to `plot3d`.

```
> plot3d(sin(x)*sin(y), x=-2*Pi..2*Pi, y=-2*Pi..2*Pi,
>         style=patchnogrid, axes=frame);
```

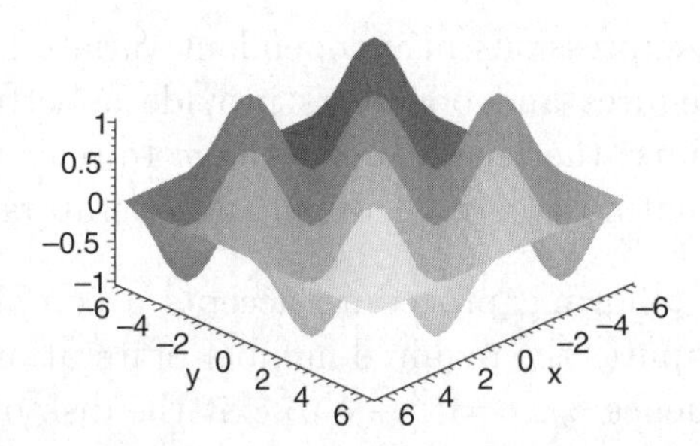


```
> plot3d(mandelbrotSet, -1.5..1.5, -1.5..1.5, grid=[50,50],
>         style=wireframe, orientation=[143,31]);
```

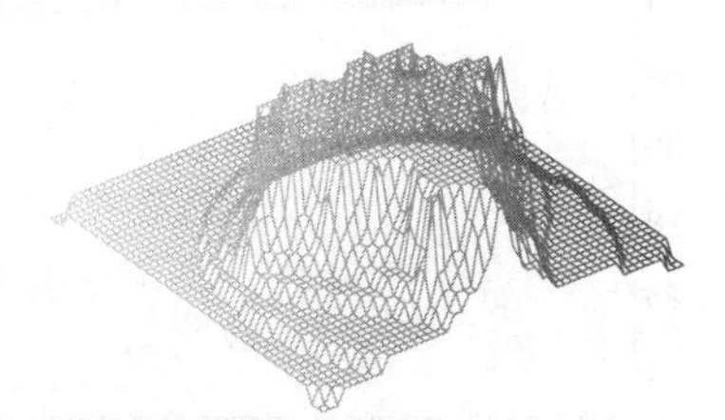

Most Maple plotting procedures accept optional arguments in the form *name*=*option*. Some of these options, such as the **grid** option used in previous examples, affect the numerical data generated by the plotting commands. You can use other options to specify visual information such as shading, line style, and coloring. For a description of all options available for 2-D and 3-D plotting, refer to `?plot/options` and `?plot3d/options`.

It is recommended that any plotting procedure you create allow users to specify a similar set of options. When writing programs that call existing Maple plotting procedures, simply pass the optional arguments directly to the Maple procedures.

## 5.2 Programming with Plotting Library Procedures

This section gives examples of programming with Maple plotting procedures.

### Plotting a Loop

Consider the problem of plotting a loop from a list of data.

```
> L1 := [[5,29], [11,23], [11,36], [9,35]];
```

$$L1 := [[5, 29], [11, 23], [11, 36], [9, 35]]$$

The `plot` command draws lines between the listed points.

```
> plot(L1);
```

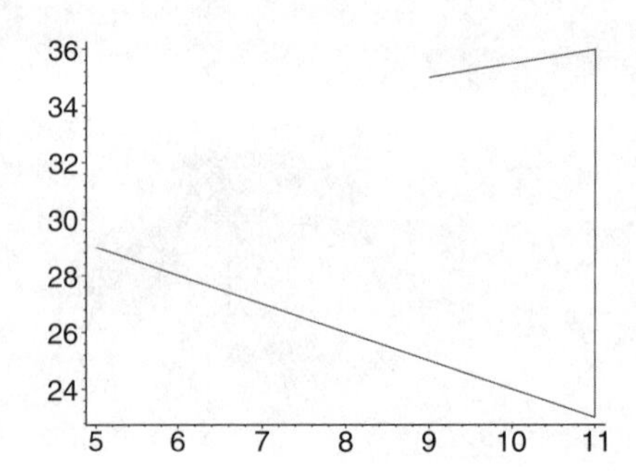


To draw a line from the last point to the first point, append the first point in L1 to the end of L1.

```
> L2 := [op(L1), L1[1]];
```

$$L2 := [[5, 29], [11, 23], [11, 36], [9, 35], [5, 29]]$$

```
> plot(L2);
```

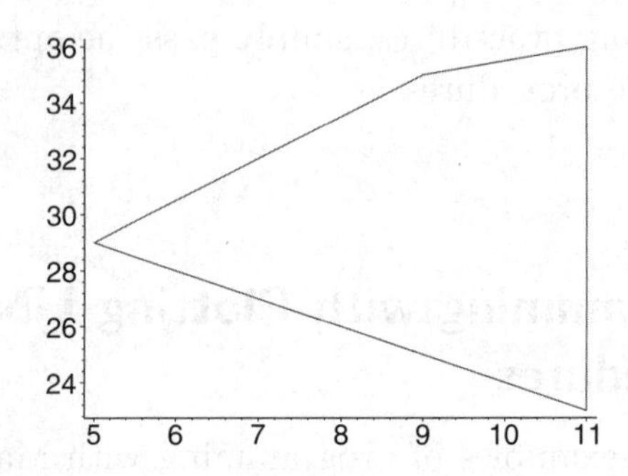


**Example 1** The procedure `loopplot` automates the previous technique.

```
> loopplot := proc(L)
>     plot([op(L), L[1]]);
> end proc;
```

$$loopplot := \mathbf{proc}(L)\,\mathrm{plot}([\mathrm{op}(L),\, L_1])\ \mathbf{end\ proc}$$

The `loopplot` procedure has two shortcomings.

- It should verify that the input, `L`, is a list of points, where each point is a list of two constants. That is, it should verify that `L` is of type `list([constant, constant])`.

- It should accept appropriate plotting options and pass them to the `plot` procedure.

**Example 2** Inside a procedure, `args` is the sequence of arguments passed to the procedure, and `nargs` is the number of arguments. Thus, `args[2..nargs]` is the sequence of options passed to `loopplot`. The `loopplot` procedure should pass all but its first argument, `L`, directly to `plot`.

```
> loopplot := proc(L::list([constant, constant]))
>     plot([op(L), L[1]], args[2..nargs]);
> end proc:
```

This version of `loopplot` gives an informative error message if you try to specify improper arguments. It also accepts plotting options.

```
> loopplot([[1, 2], [a, b]]);
```

```
Error, invalid input: loopplot expects its 1st
argument, L, to be of type list([constant, constant]),
but received [[1, 2], [a, b]]
```

```
> loopplot(L1, thickness=10);
```

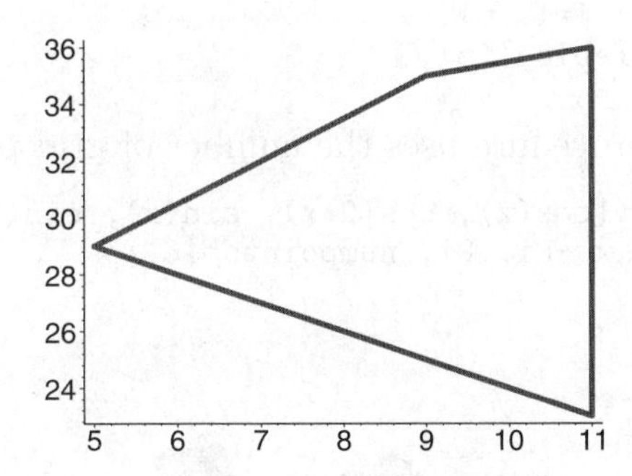


## Exercise

1. Improve the `loopplot` procedure so that it accepts the empty list as input.

## A Ribbon Plot Procedure

This section illustrates the creation of a `ribbonplot` procedure to generate a 3-D plot from a list of expressions in two variables or from a list of procedures.

**Example 3** The ribbonplot procedure uses the plots[display] procedure to display the plots. The ribbonplot procedure explicitly calls the plots[display] procedure using its full name so that ribbonplot works when the short forms of the procedure names in the plots package are not loaded.

The examples in this section use the hasoption procedure to process options. The hasoption command determines whether a certain option is present. In the ribbonplot procedure, hasoption returns false if numpoints is not among the options listed in opts. If opts contains a numpoints option, then hasoption assigns the value of the numpoints option to n, and returns the remaining options in the fourth argument (in this case, modifying the value of the list opts).

```
> ribbonplot := proc( Flist, r1::name=range )
>    local i, m, p, y, n, opts;
>    opts := [args[3..nargs]];
>    if not hasoption(opts, 'numpoints', 'n', 'opts')
>    then n := 25 # default numpoints
>    end if;
>
>    m := nops(Flist);
>    # op(opts) is any additional options
>    p := seq(plot3d(Flist[i], r1, y=(i-1)..i,
>                    grid=[n, 2], op(opts)),
>          i=1..m);
>    plots[display](p);
> end proc:
```

The ribbonplot procedure uses the number of grid points specified.

```
> ribbonplot([cos(x), cos(2*x), sin(x), sin(2*x)],
>            x=-Pi..Pi, numpoints=16);
```

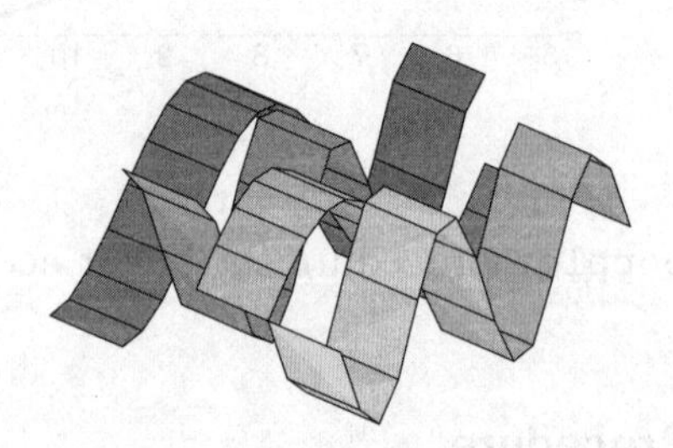

The input to ribbonplot must be a list of expressions. You can extend ribbonplot so that it also accepts a list of procedures. One difficulty with this extension is that you must create two-argument procedures from one-argument procedures, which was not required in **ribbonplot** in Example 3. To do this, create an auxiliary procedure, **extend**, that uses the **unapply** command.

```
> extend := proc(f)
>   local x,y;
>   unapply(f(x), x, y);
> end proc:
```

For example, the **extend** procedure converts the one-argument procedure representing the $R \to R$ mathematical function $x \mapsto \cos(2x)$ to a two-argument procedure.

```
> p := x -> cos(2*x):
> q := extend(p);
```

$$q := (x, y) \to \cos(2\,x)$$

**Example 4** The following is the new **ribbonplot** code.

```
> ribbonplot := proc(Flist, r1::{range, name=range})
>    local i, m, p, n, opts, newFlist;
>    opts := [args[3..nargs]];
>    if type(r1, range) then
>     # Operator-form input.
>       if not hasoption(opts, 'numpoints', 'n', 'opts')
>       then n := 25 # default numpoints
>       end if;
>       m := nops(Flist);
>     #  Provide operator-form input to plot3d.
>       p := seq(plot3d(extend(Flist[i]), r1, (i-1)..i,
>                  grid=[n,2], op(opts)),
>             i=1..m);
>       plots[display](p);
>    else
>     #  Expressions in variable lhs(r1). Convert each to a
>     #  procedure.
>       newFlist := map(unapply, Flist, lhs(r1));
>     #  Use lhs(r1) as the default x-axis label.
>       opts := ['labels'=[lhs(r1), "", ""],
>              args[3..nargs]];
>       ribbonplot(newFlist, rhs(r1), op(opts))
>    end if
> end proc:
```

The following is a ribbon plot of three functions.

```
> ribbonplot([cos, sin, cos + sin], -Pi..Pi);
```

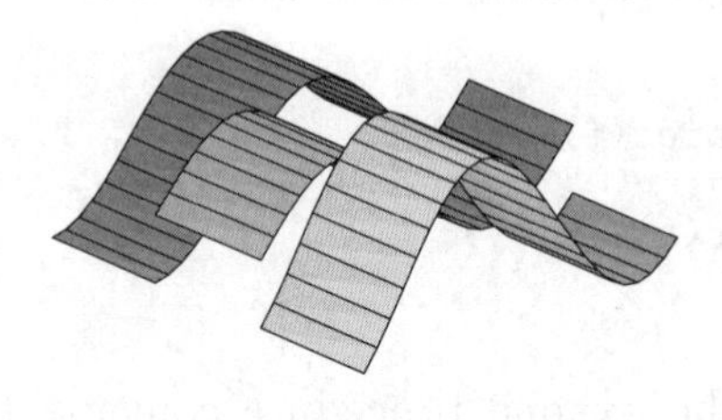

## 5.3 Maple Plot Data Structures

Maple generates plots by sending the user interface a PLOT or PLOT3D data structure, which is in fact an unevaluated function call. The information included inside these structures specifies the objects to plot. Every Maple plotting procedure creates such a structure. This process is described below and shown schematically in figure 5.1.

1. A Maple command produces a PLOT structure and passes it to the user interface.
2. In the user interface, Maple constructs primitive graphic objects based on the PLOT structure.
3. Maple then passes these objects to the chosen device driver for display.

**Figure 5.1** How plots are displayed

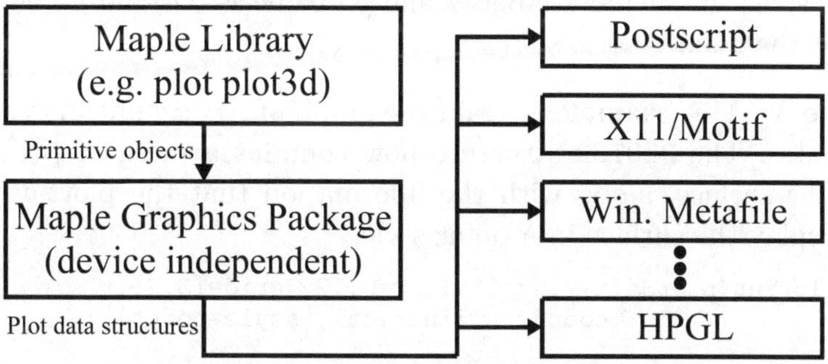

You can assign the plot data structures to variables, transform them into other structures, save them, or print them.

**Example 1** Use the lprint command to line-print a plot structure.

```
> lprint(plot(2*x+3, x=0..5, numpoints=3, adaptive=false));

PLOT(CURVES([[0., 3.], [2.61565849999999989, 8.2313170\
0000000066], [5., 13.]],COLOUR(RGB,1.0,0.,0.)),
AXESLABELS("x",""),VIEW(0. .. 5.,DEFAULT))
```

The previous plot command generates a PLOT data structure that includes the information for a single curve defined by three points. The curve is colored with RGB values $(1.0, 0, 0)$, which correspond to red. The plot has a horizontal axis running from 0 to 5. Maple, by default, determines the scale along the vertical axes using the information that you provide in the vertical components of the curve. The adaptive=false and numpoints=3 options turn off adaptive sampling and ensure that the curve consists of only three points.

**Example 2** This example is the graph of $z = xy$ over a $3 \times 4$ grid. The PLOT3D structure contains a grid of $z$ values over the rectangular region $[0, 1] \times [0, 2]$.

```
> lprint(plot3d(x*y, x=0..1, y=0..2, grid=[3,4]));

PLOT3D(GRID(0. .. 1.,0. .. 2.,Array(1 .. 3,1 .. 4,{(2,
2) = .333333333333333314, (2, 3) = .666666666666666629
, (2, 4) = 1., (3, 2) = .666666666666666629, (3, 3) =
1.33333333333333326, (3, 4) = 2.},datatype = float[8],
storage = rectangular,order = C_order)),AXESLABELS(x,y
,""))
```

The structure includes labels $x$ and $y$ for the $x$-axis and $y$-axis but no label for the $z$-axis.

**Example 3** This example is again the graph of $z = xy$ but in cylindrical coordinates. The PLOT3D structure now contains a mesh of points that define the surface, along with the information that the plotting device must display the surface in a point style.

```
> lprint(plot3d(x*y, x=0..1, y=0..2, grid=[3,2],
>             coords=cylindrical, style=point));
```

```
PLOT3D(MESH(Array(1 .. 3,1 .. 2,1 .. 3,{(1, 2, 3) = 2.
, (2, 2, 1) = .877582561890372758, (2, 2, 2) = .479425\
538604203006, (2, 2, 3) = 2., (3, 2, 1) = 1.0806046117\
3627952, (3, 2, 2) = 1.68294196961579300, (3, 2, 3) =
2.},datatype = float[8],storage = rectangular,order =
C_order)),STYLE(POINT))
```

Because the plot is not in Cartesian coordinates and there are no default labels, the PLOT3D structure does not contain an AXESLABELS structure.

## The PLOT Data Structure

You can construct and manipulate a plot data structure directly to create 2-D and 3-D plots. The data structure is an unevaluated PLOT or PLOT3D function call with arguments containing information that determines the objects that the plotting device displays. Maple evaluates the expression, for example,

```
> PLOT(CURVES([[0,0], [2,1]]));
```

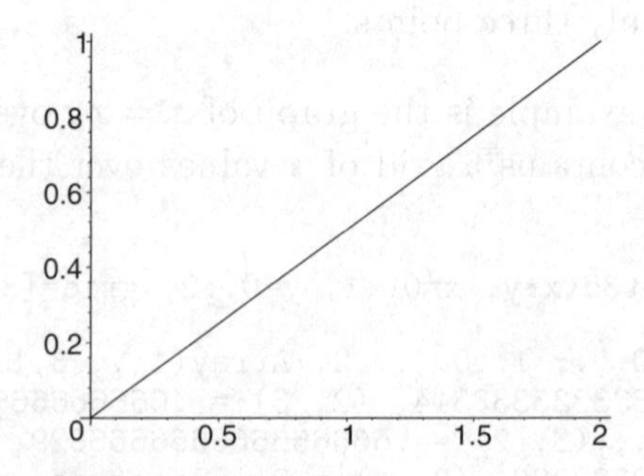


and passes it to the Maple interface, which determines that this is a plot data structure. The Maple interface then dismantles the contents and passes the information to a plot driver, which determines the graphical information that it renders to the plotting device. In the previous example PLOT structure, the result is a single line from the origin to the point $(2, 1)$. The CURVES data structure consists of one or more lists of points each representing a curve, along with optional arguments (for example, line style or line thickness information). Thus, the commands

```
> n := 200:
> points := [seq([2*cos(i*Pi/n), sin(i*Pi/n)], i=0..n)]:
> PLOT(CURVES(evalf(points)));
```

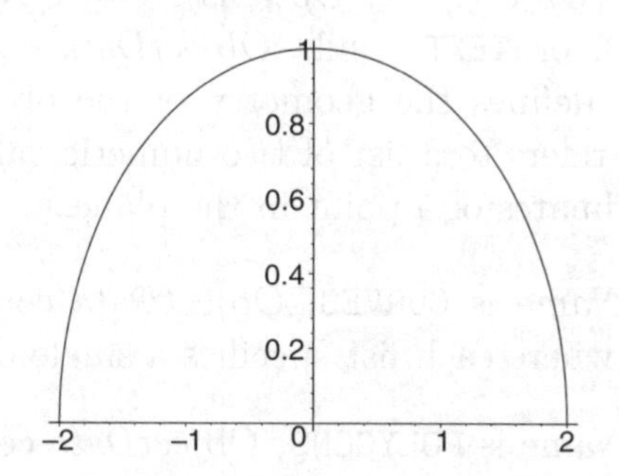


generate the plot of a sequence of $n + 1$ points in the plane. The points found inside the PLOT data structure must be numeric. If you omit the evalf statement, then non-numeric objects within the PLOT structure, such as $\sin(\pi/200)$, cause an error.

```
> PLOT(CURVES(points));
```

```
Plotting error, non-numeric vertex definition
```

```
> type(sin(Pi/n), numeric);
```

$$false$$

Hence, no plot is generated.

## Arguments Inside a PLOT Structure

A PLOT structure has the following form:

```
(Objects, Options)
```

where *Objects* is a sequence of one or more plot objects of the form *ObjectName*(*ObjectData*, *Options*) and *Options* is a sequence of zero or more plot options of the form *OptionName*(*OptionValue*).

**Note:** Plot options can appear as arguments of the PLOT structures or as arguments of plot object structures.

If a local option appears inside a plot object structure, it applies to only that object and overrides any value of a global option of the same name.

**Plot Object Structures** As shown previously, plot objects have the form *ObjectName*(*ObjectData*, *Options*). *ObjectName* can be CURVES, POLYGONS, POINTS, or TEXT, while *ObjectData* contains the basic numerical data that defines the geometry of the object. In the following description, *point* refers to a list of two numeric values, $[x, y]$, representing $x$- and $y$-coordinates of a point in the plane.

- When *ObjectName* is CURVES, *ObjectData* consists of one or more lists of points where each list specifies a single curve in the plane.
- When *ObjectName* is POLYGONS, *ObjectData* consists of one or more lists of points where each list specifies the vertices of a single polygon in the plane.
- When *ObjectName* is POINTS, *ObjectData* consists of one or more points.
- When *ObjectName* is TEXT, *ObjectData* consists of a point followed by a name representing the text string.

**Plot Option Structures** Plot options have the form *OptionName*(*OptionValue*). Examples of option structures are AXESTYLE(BOX), COLOR(RGB, 0.0, 1.0, 0.0), and VIEW(-4..4, -1..1). For a complete list of the plot option structures and the values each structure accepts, refer to ?plot/structure.

Some plot options **cannot** be specified as a local option within a plot object structure. For example, the AXESSTYLE option must be a global option, while a different COLOR option can be specified for each plot object.

**Example 4** This example demonstrates a simple way to generate a filled histogram of sixty-three values of the function $y = \sin(x)$ from 0 to 6.3, with each trapezoid colored individually by the HUE value corresponding to $y = |\cos(x)|$.

```
> p := i -> [[(i-1)/10, 0], [(i-1)/10, sin((i-1)/10)],
>            [i/10, sin(i/10)], [i/10, 0]]:
```

The function p(i) returns the vertices of the ith trapezoid in a list. For example, p(2) contains the vertices of the second trapezoid.

```
> p(2);
```

$$[[\frac{1}{10}, 0], [\frac{1}{10}, \sin(\frac{1}{10})], [\frac{1}{5}, \sin(\frac{1}{5})], [\frac{1}{5}, 0]]$$

Define the procedure $h$ to give the color of each trapezoid.

```
> h := i -> abs(cos(i/10)):
> PLOT(seq(POLYGONS(evalf(p(i)), COLOR(HUE, evalf(h(i)))),
>            i = 1..63));
```

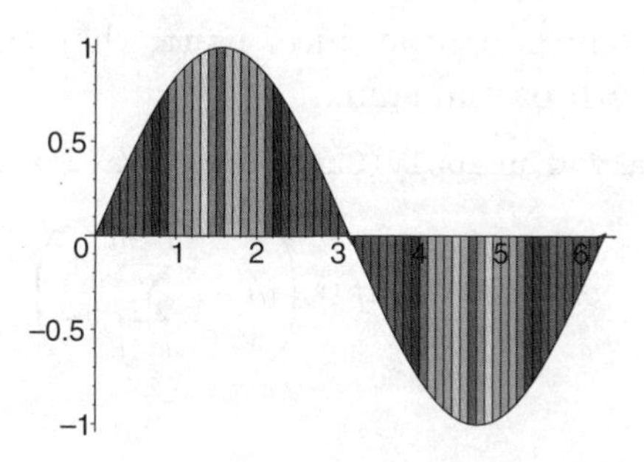


## A Sum Plot

You can create procedures that directly build PLOT data structures. For example, given an unevaluated sum, you can compute the partial sums and place the values in a CURVES structure.

```
> s := Sum(1/k^2, k=1..10);
```

$$s := \sum_{k=1}^{10} \frac{1}{k^2}$$

Use the typematch command to separate the unevaluated sum into its components.

```
> typematch(s, 'Sum'(term::algebraic,
>           n::name=a::integer..b::integer));
```

$$true$$

The typematch command assigns the parts of the sum to the given names.

```
> term, n, a, b;
```

$$\frac{1}{k^2},\ k,\ 1,\ 10$$

Now calculate the partial sums.

```
> sum(term, n=a..a+2);
```

$$\frac{49}{36}$$

The following defines a procedure, psum, that calculates a floating-point value of the $m$th partial sum.

```
> psum := evalf @ unapply(Sum(term, n=a..(a+m)), m);
```

$$psum := evalf@\left(m \to \sum_{k=1}^{1+m} \frac{1}{k^2}\right)$$

Now create the necessary list of points.

```
> points := [seq([[i,psum(i)], [i+1,psum(i)]],
>     i=1..(b-a+1))];
```

$$points := [[[1, 1.250000000], [2, 1.250000000]],$$
$$[[2, 1.361111111], [3, 1.361111111]],$$
$$[[3, 1.423611111], [4, 1.423611111]],$$
$$[[4, 1.463611111], [5, 1.463611111]],$$
$$[[5, 1.491388889], [6, 1.491388889]],$$
$$[[6, 1.511797052], [7, 1.511797052]],$$
$$[[7, 1.527422052], [8, 1.527422052]],$$
$$[[8, 1.539767731], [9, 1.539767731]],$$
$$[[9, 1.549767731], [10, 1.549767731]],$$
$$[[10, 1.558032194], [11, 1.558032194]]]$$

```
> points := map(op, points);
```

$$points := [[1, 1.250000000], [2, 1.250000000],$$
$$[2, 1.361111111], [3, 1.361111111], [3, 1.423611111],$$
$$[4, 1.423611111], [4, 1.463611111], [5, 1.463611111],$$
$$[5, 1.491388889], [6, 1.491388889], [6, 1.511797052],$$
$$[7, 1.511797052], [7, 1.527422052], [8, 1.527422052],$$
$$[8, 1.539767731], [9, 1.539767731], [9, 1.549767731],$$
$$[10, 1.549767731], [10, 1.558032194], [11, 1.558032194]]$$

This list has the correct form.

```
> PLOT(CURVES(points));
```

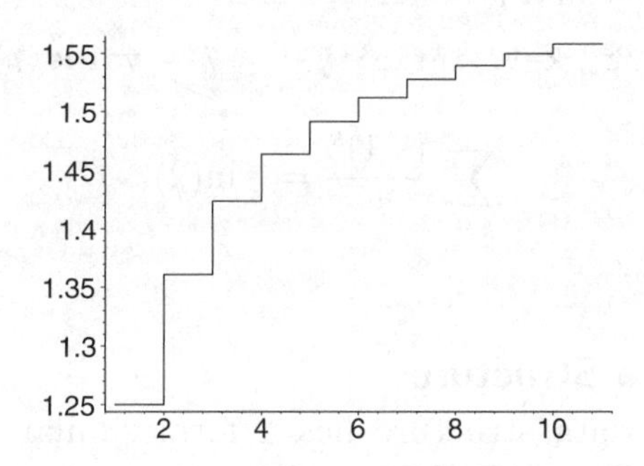


The sumplot procedure automates this technique.

```
> sumplot := proc(s)
>    local term, n, a, b, psum, m, points, i;
>    if typematch(s, 'Sum'(term::algebraic,
>          n::name=a::integer..b::integer)) then
>       psum := evalf @ unapply(Sum(term, n=a..(a+m)), m);
>       points := [seq([[i,psum(i)], [i+1,psum(i)]],
>          i=1..(b-a+1))];
>       points := map(op, points);
>       PLOT(CURVES(points));
>    else
>       error "expecting a Sum structure as input"
>    end if
> end proc:
```

The following is a sumplot of an alternating series.

```
> sumplot(Sum((-1)^k/k, k=1..25));
```

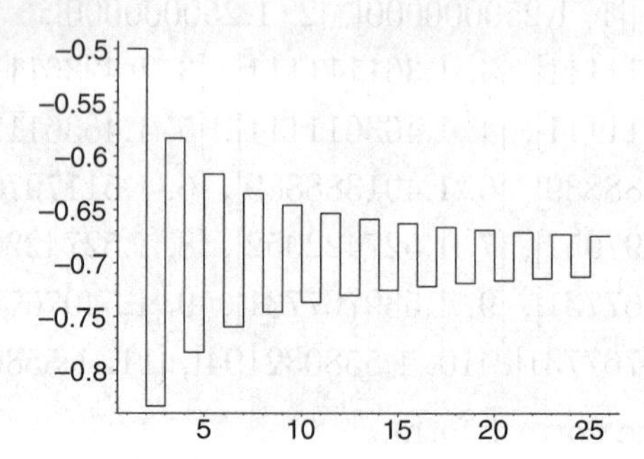


The limit of this sum is $-\ln 2$.

```
> Sum((-1)^k/k, k=1..infinity):   % = value(%);
```

$$\sum_{k=1}^{\infty} \frac{(-1)^k}{k} = -\ln(2)$$

## The PLOT3D Data Structure

The 3-D plotting data structure has a form similar to the PLOT data structure. The following Maple expression generates a 3-D plot of three lines and axes of type frame. Axes are generated using AXESSTYLE.

```
> PLOT3D(CURVES([[3, 3, 0], [0, 3, 1],
>                [3, 0, 1], [3, 3, 0]]),
>        AXESSTYLE(FRAME));
```

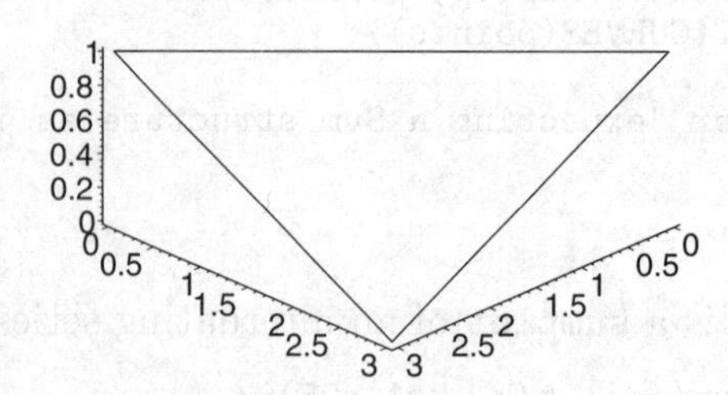


The following procedure creates the yellow sides of a box.

```
> yellowsides := proc(x, y, z, u)
>   # (x,y,0) = coordinates of a corner.
>   # z = height of box
>   # u = side length of box
```

```
>       POLYGONS(
>          [[x,y,0], [x+u,y,0], [x+u,y,z], [x,y,z]],
>          [[x,y,0], [x,y+u,0], [x,y+u,z], [x,y,z]],
>          [[x+u, y,0], [x+u,y+u,0], [x+u,y+u,z], [x+u,y,z]],
>          [[x+u, y+u,0], [x,y+u,0], [x,y+u,z], [x+u,y+u,z]],
>               COLOR(RGB,1,1,0));
> end proc:
```

The `redtop` procedure generates a red lid for the box.

```
> redtop := proc(x, y, z, u)
>    # (x,y,z) = coordinates of a corner.
>    # u = side length of square
>      POLYGONS([[x,y,z], [x+u,y,z], [x+u,y+u,z], [x,y+u,z]],
>               COLOR(RGB, 1, 0, 0));
>    end proc:
```

To display the sides and the top, place them in a `PLOT3D` structure.

```
> PLOT3D(yellowsides(1, 2, 3, 0.5),
>             redtop(1, 2, 3, 0.5),
>             STYLE(PATCH));
```

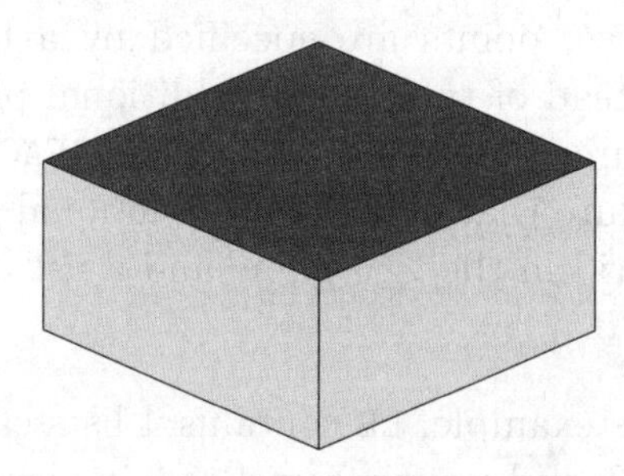

Using `yellowsides` and `redtop`, you can create a 3-D histogram plot. The following is the histogram corresponding to $z = 1/(x + y + 4)$, for $0 \leq x \leq 4$ and $0 \leq y \leq 4$.

```
> sides := seq(seq(yellowsides(i, j, 1/(i+j+4), 0.75),
>     j=0..4), i=0..4):
> tops := seq(seq(redtop( i, j, 1/(i+j+4), 0.75),
>     j=0..4), i=0..4):
```

Histograms display well in box-style axes.

```
> PLOT3D(sides, tops, STYLE(PATCH), AXESSTYLE(BOXED));
```

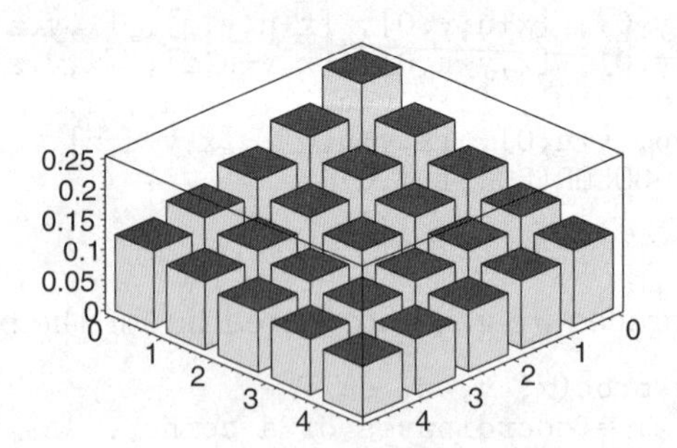


To create a `listbarchart3d` procedure which, for a given list of lists of heights, gives a 3-D bar chart for its output, modify the previous construction.

## Objects Inside a PLOT3D Data Structure

The format of a PLOT3D structure is similar to that of a PLOT structure. The allowable plot objects include all the objects that can appear in PLOT structures. Of course, points are specified by a list of three numerical values, $[x, y, z]$, instead of two. Three additional plot objects can appear in a PLOT3D structure: GRID, MESH, and ISOSURFACE.

GRID is a structure that describes a functional grid. It consists of two ranges defining a grid in the $x$–$y$ plane and a list of lists of $z$ values over this grid.

**Example 5** In this example, LL contains 4 lists each of length 3. Therefore, the grid is $4 \times 3$, and $x$ runs from 1 to 3 in increments of $2/3$, whereas $y$ runs from 1 to 2 in increments of $1/2$.

```
> LL := [[0,1,0], [1,1,1], [2,1,2], [3,0,1]]:
```

```
> PLOT3D(GRID(1..3, 1..2, LL), AXESLABELS(x,y,z),
>         ORIENTATION(135, 45), AXES(BOXED));
```

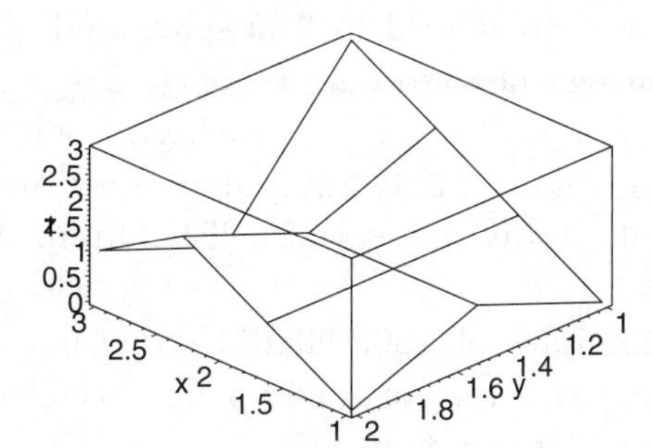


The MESH structure contains a list of lists of points, LL, describing a surface in 3-D space.

The MESH structure represents the quadrilaterals spanned by

$$LL_{i,j}, LL_{i,j+1}, LL_{i+1,j}, LL_{i+1,j+1}$$

for all meaningful values of $i$ and $j$.

**Example 6** In this example, LL contains 3 lists each of length 4, that is, twelve points defining six quadrilaterals.

```
> LL := [[[0,0,0], [1,0,0], [2,0,0], [3,0,0]],
>        [[0,1,0], [1,1,0], [2.1, 0.9, 0],
>                           [3.2, 0.7, 0]],
>        [[0,1,1], [1,1,1], [2.2, 0.6, 1],
>                           [3.5, 0.5, 1.1]]];
```

$$LL := [[[0, 0, 0], [1, 0, 0], [2, 0, 0], [3, 0, 0]],\\ [[0, 1, 0], [1, 1, 0], [2.1, 0.9, 0], [3.2, 0.7, 0]],\\ [[0, 1, 1], [1, 1, 1], [2.2, 0.6, 1], [3.5, 0.5, 1.1]]]$$

```
> PLOT3D(MESH(LL), AXESLABELS(x,y,z), AXES(BOXED),
>        ORIENTATION(-140, 45));
```

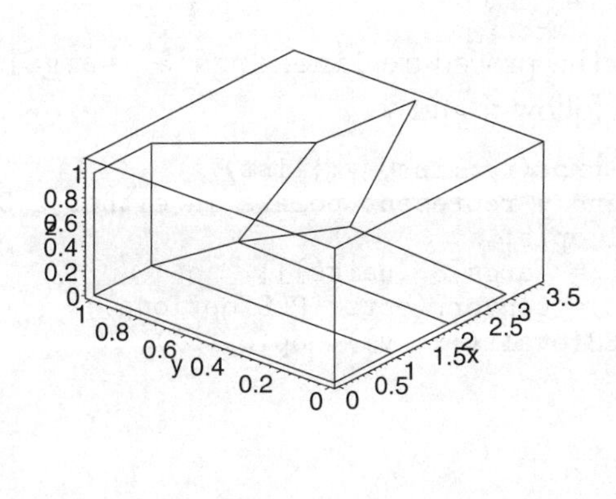

The ISOSURFACE structure contains samples of a mathematical function $f$ taken over a regular grid in 3-D space and is rendered as a 3-D surface approximating the zero surface of $f$. The data is a nested list containing values $[x, y, z, f(x, y, z)]$ for each grid point $(x, y, z)$.

The GRID, MESH, and ISOSURFACE structures allow the data to be provided in a Maple Array instead of a list. Often, Array data leads to faster processing.

For brevity, examples of ISOSURFACE structures and data in Array form are not presented here. For a complete specification of PLOT3D objects, refer to ?plot3d/structure.

All the options available for PLOT are also available for PLOT3D. There are additional 3-D options such as GRIDSTYLE, LIGHTMODEL, and AMBIENTLIGHT. For a complete list of options, refer to ?plot3d/structure.

## 5.4 Programming with Plot Data Structures

This section describes tools for programming at the PLOT and PLOT3D data structure level. Plotting data structures allows *direct* access to the Maple plotting facilities. The examples in section 5.3 showed the extent of the facilities' power. This section provides examples that describe how to program at this lower level.

### Writing Graphic Primitives

You can write procedures that allow you to work with plot objects at a more fundamental level. For example, the line and disk commands in the plottools package provide a model for programming primitives such as points, lines, curves, circles, rectangles, and arbitrary polygons in both two and three dimensions. In all cases, you can specify options, such as line or patch style and color, in the same format as in other plotting procedures in Maple.

**Example 1** In the procedure line, args[3..nargs] is the sequence of arguments that follow x and y.

```
> line := proc(x::list, y::list)
>     # x and y represent points in either 2-D or 3-D
>     local opts;
>     opts := [args[3..nargs]];
>     opts := convert(opts, PLOToptions);
>     CURVES(evalf([x, y]), op(opts));
> end proc:
```

The `convert(..., PLOToptions)` command converts user-level options to the format that `PLOT` requires.

```
> convert([axes=boxed, color=red], PLOToptions);
```

$$[\mathrm{AXESSTYLE}(BOX), \mathrm{COLOUR}(RGB, 1.00000000, 0., 0.)]$$

**Example 2** The `disk` procedure is similar to the `line` procedure in Example 1 except that you can specify the number of points that `disk` uses to generate the disk. Therefore, `disk` must handle the option `numpoints` separately.

```
> disk := proc(x::list, r::algebraic)
>   # draw a disk of radius r centered at x in 2-D.
>    local i, n, opts, vertices;
>    opts := [args[3..nargs]] ;
>    if not hasoption(opts, numpoints, n, 'opts')
>    then n := 50;
>    end if;
>    opts := convert(opts, PLOToptions);
>    vertices := seq(evalf([x[1] + r*cos(2*Pi*i/n),
>                               x[2] + r*sin(2*Pi*i/n)]),
>                        i = 0..n);
>    POLYGONS([vertices], op(opts));
> end proc:
```

To display two disks connected by a line, enter:

```
> with(plots):

Warning, the name changecoords has been redefined
```

```
> display(disk([-1, 0], 1/2, color=plum),
>         line([-1, 1/2], [1, 1/2]),
>         disk([1, 0], 1/2, thickness=3),
>         scaling=constrained);
```

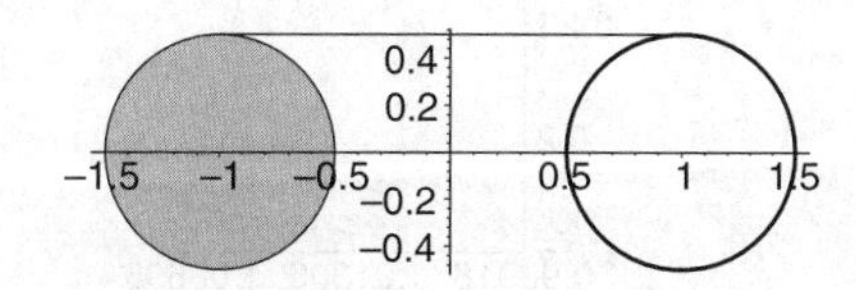

The options to the individual objects apply to only those objects.

## Plotting Gears

Example 3 shows how you can manipulate plotting data structures to embed 2-D plots into a 3-D setting.

**Example 3** The following procedure creates part of the boundary of a 2-D graph of a gear-like structure.

```
> outside := proc(a, r, n)
>   local p1, p2;
>     p1 := evalf([cos(a*Pi/n), sin(a*Pi/n)]);
>     p2 := evalf([cos((a+1)*Pi/n), sin((a+1)*Pi/n)]);
>     if r = 1 then p1, p2;
>     else p1, r*p1, r*p2, p2;
>     end if
> end proc:
```

For example:

```
> outside(Pi/4, 1.1, 16);
```

$$[0.9881327882, 0.1536020604],$$
$$[1.086946067, 0.1689622664],$$
$$[1.033097800, 0.3777683623],$$
$$[0.9391798182, 0.3434257839]$$

```
> PLOT(CURVES([%]), SCALING(CONSTRAINED));
```

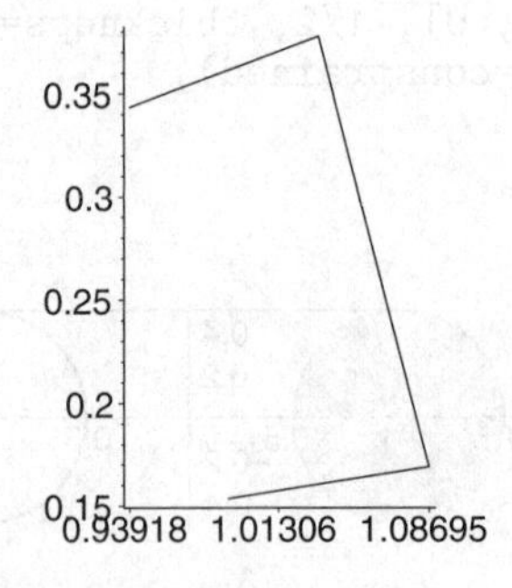

When you display the pieces together, you produce a gear. The option structure SCALING(CONSTRAINED), which corresponds to the option scaling=constrained, ensures that the gear appears circular.

```
> points := [seq(outside(2*a, 1.1, 16), a=0..16)]:
> PLOT(CURVES(points), AXESSTYLE(NONE), SCALING(CONSTRAINED));
```

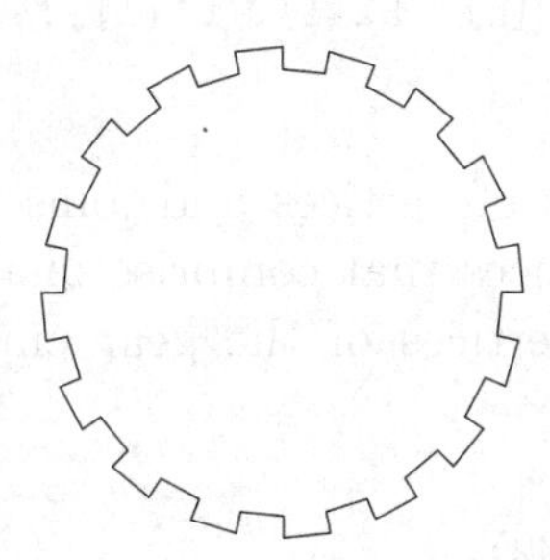

Fill this object using the POLYGONS object. Because Maple assumes that the polygons are convex, you must draw each wedge-shaped section of the gear as a triangular polygon.

```
> a := seq([[0, 0], outside(2*j, 1.1, 16)], j=0..15):
> b := seq([[0, 0], outside(2*j+1, 1, 16)], j=0..15):
> PLOT(POLYGONS(a,b), AXESSTYLE(NONE), SCALING(CONSTRAINED));
```

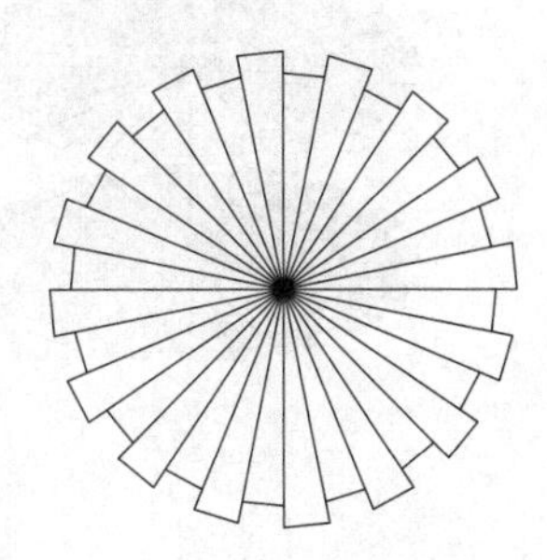

Adding STYLE(PATCHNOGRID) to the preceding structure and combining it with the curve from the first picture creates a filled gear-like structure. To embed this in three dimensions, at a thickness of $t$ units, use the utility procedures double:

```
> double := proc(L, t)
>    local u;
>    [seq([u[1], u[2], 0], u=L)],
>    [seq([u[1], u[2], t], u=L)];
> end proc:
```

which takes a list of vertices and creates two copies in 3-D space, the first at height 0 and the second at height $t$, and `border`:

```
> border := proc(L1, L2)
>    local i, n;
>    n := nops(L1);
>    seq([L1[i], L2[i], L2[i+1], L1[i+1]], i = 1..n-1),
>       [L1[n], L2[n], L2[1], L1[1]];
> end proc:
```

which accepts two lists of vertices and joins the corresponding vertices from each list into vertices that comprise quadrilaterals. You can create the top and bottom vertices of the gear embedded into 3-D space as follows.

```
> faces :=
> seq(double(p,1/2),
>     p=[seq([outside(2*a+1, 1.1, 16), [0,0]],
>            a=0..16),
>        seq([outside(2*a, 1,16), [0,0]], a=0..16)
>       ]):
```

The `faces` structure is a sequence of doubled outside values.

```
> PLOT3D( POLYGONS(faces));
```

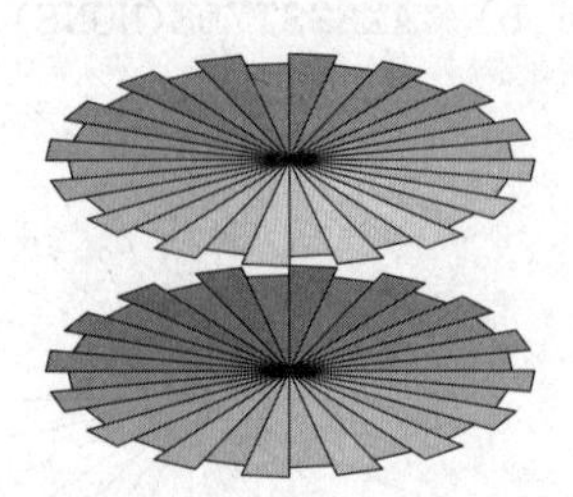

Similarly, the following are points on the outline of a gear.

```
> points := [seq(outside(2*a, 1.1, 16), a=0..16)]:
> PLOT(CURVES(points), AXESSTYLE(NONE), SCALING(CONSTRAINED));
```

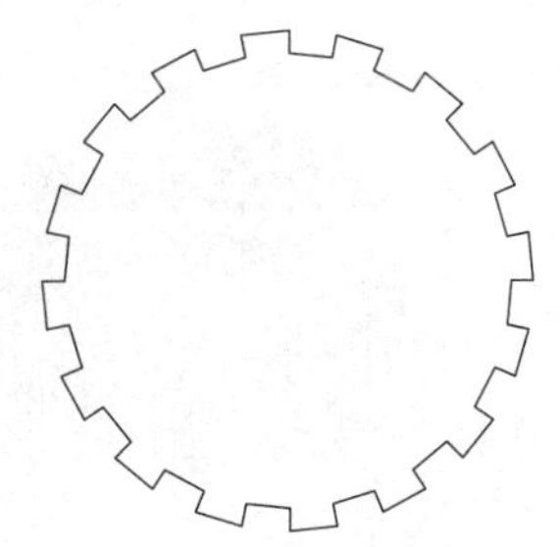

To create vertices of the polygons that comprise the border of the 3-D gear, double these points.

```
> bord := border(double([seq(outside(2*a+1, 1.1, 16),
>                               a=0..15)], 1/2)):
> PLOT3D(seq(POLYGONS(b), b=bord));
```

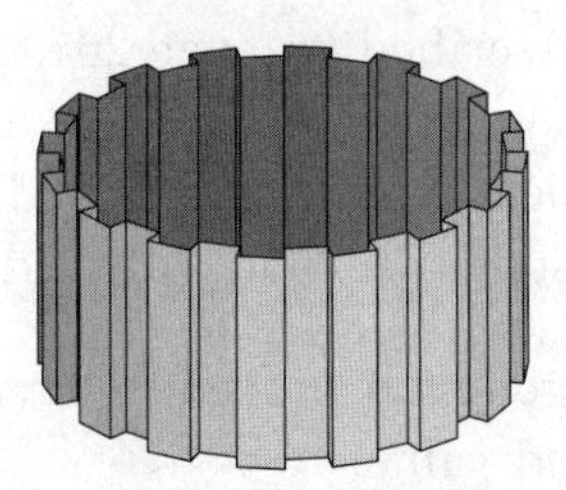

To display the gear, combine these two PLOT3D structures into a single structure. Use STYLE(PATCHNOGRID) as a local option to the top and bottom of the gear so that they do not appear as several triangles.

```
> PLOT3D(POLYGONS(faces, STYLE(PATCHNOGRID)),
>          seq(POLYGONS(b), b=bord),
>      STYLE(PATCH), SCALING(CONSTRAINED));
```

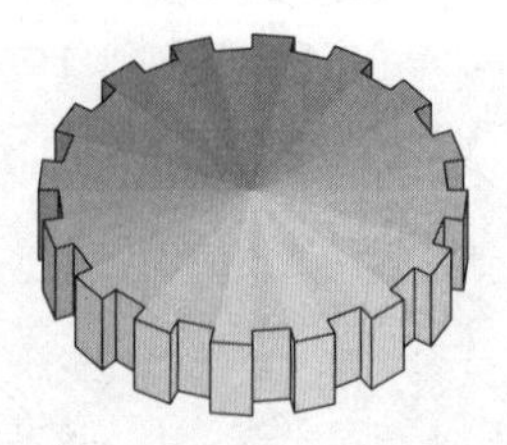

**Note:** The global STYLE(PATCH) and SCALING(CONSTRAINED) options apply to the whole PLOT3D structure, except where the local STYLE(PATCHNOGRID) option to the top and bottom of the gear overrides the global STYLE(PATCH) option.

## Polygon Meshes

MESH data structures, described on page 265, are generated when you use plot3d to draw parameterized surfaces. Example 4 converts a mesh of points to the set of vertices for the corresponding polygon. By using polygons instead of a MESH structure, you can modify the individual polygons.

**Example 4** The polygongrid procedure creates the vertices of a quadrangle at the $(i, j)$th grid value.

```
> polygongrid := proc(gridlist, i, j)
>    gridlist[j][i], gridlist[j][i+1],
>    gridlist[j+1][i+1], gridlist[j+1][i];
> end proc:
```

Use the makePolygongrid procedure to construct the appropriate polygons.

```
> makePolygongrid := proc(gridlist)
>    local m,n,i,j;
>    n := nops(gridlist);
>    m := nops(gridlist[1]);
>    POLYGONS(seq(seq([polygongrid(gridlist, i, j)],
>             i=1..m-1), j=1..n-1));
> end proc:
```

The following is a mesh of points in 2-D space.

```
> L := [seq([seq([i-1, j-1], i=1..3)], j=1..4)];
```

$$L := [[[0, 0], [1, 0], [2, 0]], [[0, 1], [1, 1], [2, 1]], [[0, 2], [1, 2], [2, 2]], [[0, 3], [1, 3], [2, 3]]]$$

The `makePolygongrid` procedure creates the `POLYGONS` structure corresponding to `L`.

```
> grid1 := makePolygongrid(L);
```

$$grid1 := \mathrm{POLYGONS}([[0, 0], [1, 0], [1, 1], [0, 1]], [[1, 0], [2, 0], [2, 1], [1, 1]], [[0, 1], [1, 1], [1, 2], [0, 2]], [[1, 1], [2, 1], [2, 2], [1, 2]], [[0, 2], [1, 2], [1, 3], [0, 3]], [[1, 2], [2, 2], [2, 3], [1, 3]])$$

Put the polygons inside a `PLOT` structure to display them.

```
> PLOT(grid1);
```

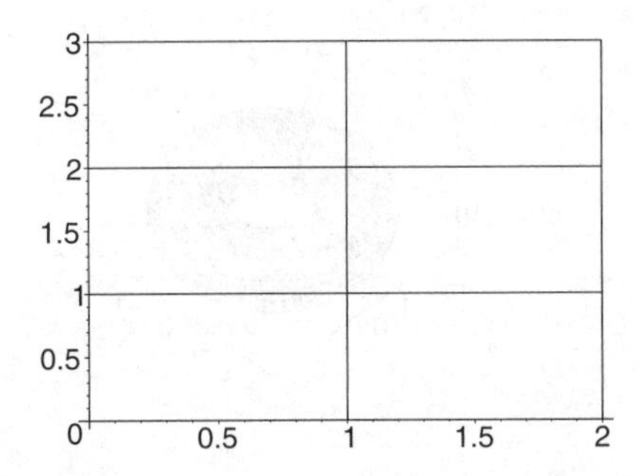


To convert `GRID` or `MESH` structures to polygons, you can also use the `convert(..., POLYGONS)` command. For more information, refer to `?convert/POLYGONS`. The `convert(..., POLYGONS)` command calls the procedure `` `convert/POLYGONS` `` which, in the case of a `MESH` structure, functions the same as the `makePolygongrid` procedure.

## 5.5 Programming with the plottools Package

While the plotting data structure allows direct access to all the functionality that the Maple plotting facilities provide, it does not allow you to specify colors (such as red or blue) in an intuitive way. It also does not allow you to use all the Maple representations of numeric data, such as $\pi$ or $\sqrt{2}$.

This section demonstrates how to work with basic graphic objects at a level higher than that of the plotting data structures. The `plottools` package provides commands for creating 2-D objects such as lines and disks, and 3-D objects such as spheres, tori, and polyhedra. For example, to draw a sphere of unit radius and a torus with a specified center using a patch rendering style and a frame axis style, enter:

```
> with(plots): with(plottools):

Warning, the name changecoords has been redefined
Warning, the name arrow has been redefined
```

```
> display(sphere([0, 0, 2]), torus([0, 0, 0]),
>         style=patch, axes=frame, scaling=constrained);
```

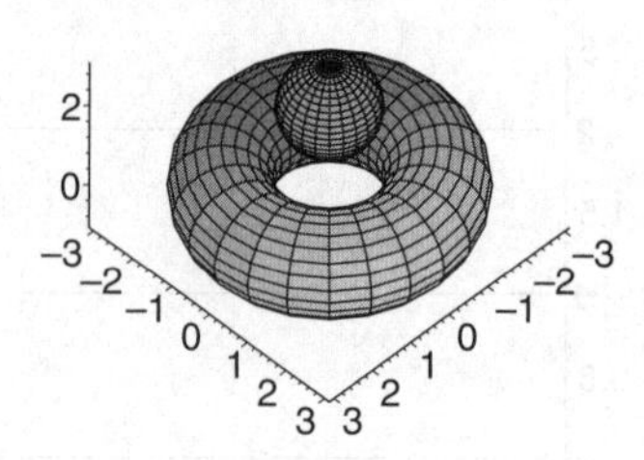


To rotate the plot or apply other transformations, use the procedures in the `plottools` package.

```
> rotate( %, Pi/4, -Pi/4, Pi/4 );
```

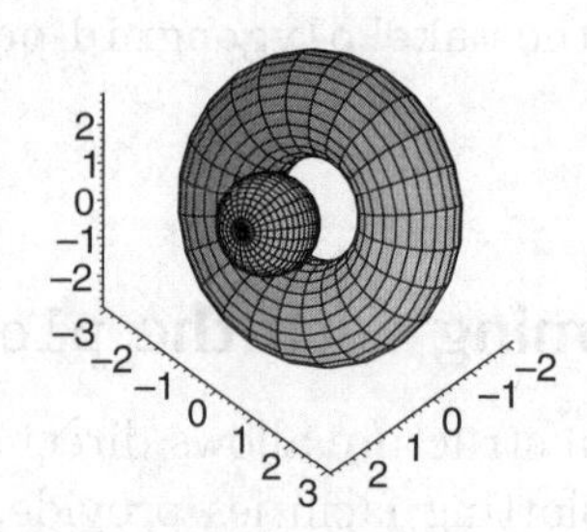

## A Pie Chart

You can write a plotting procedure to build a pie chart of a list of integer data. The **piechart** procedure uses the following **partialsum** procedure, which calculates the partial sums of a list of numbers up to a given term.

```
> partialsum := proc(d, i)
>    local j;
>    evalf(Sum(d[j], j=1..i))
> end proc:
```

The following is an example of a call to **partialsum**.

```
> partialsum([1, 2, 3, -6], 3);
```

$$6.$$

**Example 1** The **piechart** procedure:

- Computes the relative weights of the data along with the centers of each pie slice
- Uses a TEXT structure to place the data information at the center of each pie slice
- Uses the **pieslice** command from the **plottools** package to generate the pie slices
- Varies the colors of each slice by first defining a color procedure based on hue coloring

```
> piechart := proc(data::list(integer))
>    local b, c, i, n, x, y, total;
>
>    n := nops(data);
>    total := partialsum(data, n);
>    b := 0, seq(evalf(2*Pi*partialsum(data, i)/total),
>              i=1..n);
>    x := seq((cos(b[i])+cos(b[i+1]))/3, i=1..n):
>    y := seq((sin(b[i])+sin(b[i+1]))/3, i=1..n):
>    c := (i, n) -> COLOR(HUE, i/(n + 1)):
>    PLOT(seq(plottools[pieslice]([0, 0], 1,
>                b[i]..b[i+1], color=c(i, n)),
>            i=1..n),
>          seq(TEXT([x[i], y[i]], convert(data[i], name)),
>            i = 1..n),
>          AXESSTYLE(NONE), SCALING(CONSTRAINED));
> end proc:
```

The AXESSTYLE(NONE) option ensures that Maple does not draw any axes with the pie chart.

The following is a piechart with six slices.

```
> piechart([ 8, 10, 15, 10, 12, 16 ]);
```

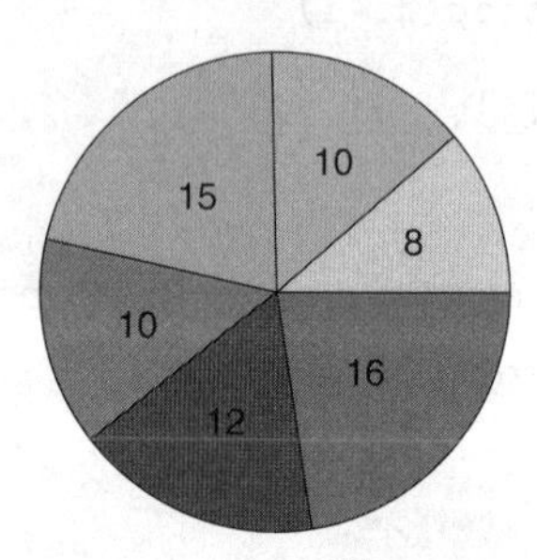


## A Dropshadow Procedure

You can use the existing procedures to create other types of plots that are not part of the Maple plotting library. For example, the following procedure computes the 3-D plot of a surface, $z = f(x, y)$, that has a dropshadow projection onto a plane located below the surface.

**Example 2** The procedure uses the contourplot, contourplot3d, and display commands from the plots package, and the transform command from the plottools package.

```
> dropshadowplot := proc(F::algebraic, r1::name=range,
>       r2::name=range, r3::name=range)
>    local minz, p2, p3, coption, opts, f, g, x, y;
>
>    # set the number of contours (default 8)
>    opts := [args[5..nargs]];
>    if not hasoption(opts, 'contours', coption, 'opts')
>    then coption := 8;
>    end if;
>
>    # determine the base of the plot axes
>    # from the third argument
>    minz := lhs(`if`(r3::range, r3, rhs(r3)));
>    minz := evalf(minz);
>
>
>    # create 2-D and 3-D contour plots for F.
>    p3 := plots[contourplot3d](F, r1, r2,
>             'contours'=coption, op(opts));
>    p2 := plots[contourplot](F, r1, r2,
>             'contours'=coption, op(opts));
>
```

```
>     # embed contour plot into R^3 via plottools[transform]
>     g := unapply([x,y,minz], x, y);
>     f := plottools[transform](g);
>     plots[display]([f(p2), p3]);
> end proc:
```

The `filled=true` option to `contourplot` and `contourplot3d` causes these two commands to fill the regions between the level curves with a color that indicates the level.

```
> expr := -5*x / (x^2+y^2+1);
```

$$expr := -5\,\frac{x}{x^2+y^2+1}$$

```
> dropshadowplot(expr, x=-3..3, y=-3..3, z=-4..3,
>     filled=true, contours=3, axes=frame);
```

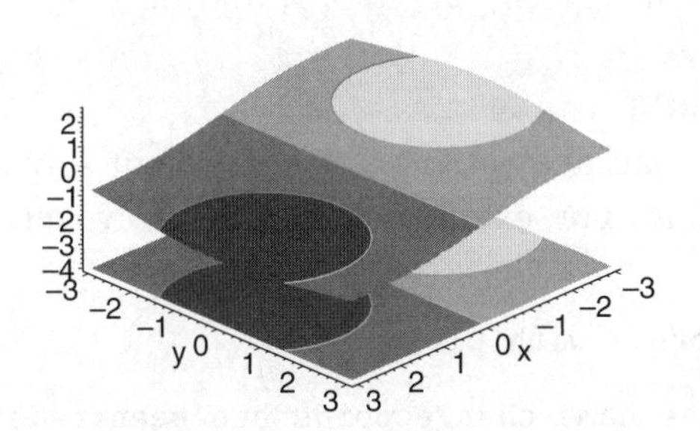


## Summary

- The first section of the `dropshadow` procedure determines if there is a `contours` option in the optional arguments (those after the fourth argument) by calling the `hasoption` procedure.
- The next section of `dropshadowplot` determines the $z$ value of the base. Note that it checks for input in operator form.
- The remaining sections create the correct plotting objects which represent the two types of contour plots.

The `dropshadowplot` procedure embeds the 2-D contour plot into 3-D space using the transformation

$$(x, y) \mapsto [x, y, minz]$$

from $R^2 \to R^3$. Finally, it displays the two plots in one 3-D plotting object.

**Note:** You can provide an alternate number of levels or specify the precise contour locations by using the `contours` option. Thus,

```
> dropshadowplot(expr, x=-3..3, y=-3..3, z=-4..3,
>                 filled=true, contours=[-2,-1,0,1,2]);
```

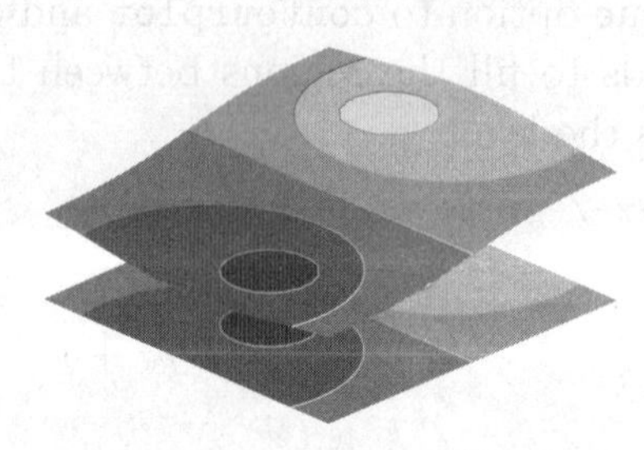

produces a plot similar to the one just generated, except that it produces 5 contours at levels $-2, -1, 0, 1$, and 2.

## Creating a Tiling

The `plottools` package provides a convenient environment for writing plotting programs. For example, you can draw circular arcs in a unit square.

```
> with(plots): with(plottools):
```

```
Warning, the name changecoords has been redefined
Warning, the name arrow has been redefined
```

```
> a := rectangle([0,0], [1,1]),
>      arc([0,0], 0.5, 0..Pi/2),
>      arc([1,1], 0.5, Pi..3*Pi/2):
> b := rectangle([1.5,0], [2.5,1]),
>      arc([1.5,1], 0.5, -Pi/2..0),
>      arc([2.5,0], 0.5, Pi/2..Pi):
```

You must use `display` from the `plots` package to show the objects that `rectangle` and `arc` create.

```
> display(a, b, axes=none, scaling=constrained);
```

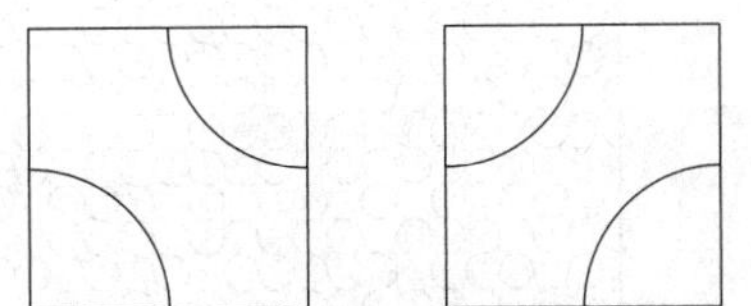

**Example 3** You can tile the plane with a and b type rectangles. The following procedure creates a $m \times n$ tiling using a procedure $g$ to determine when to use an a tile and when to use a b tile. The function $g$ returns either 0, to use an a tile, or 1, to use a b tile.

```
> tiling := proc(g, m, n)
>   local i, j, r, h, boundary, tiles;
>
>     # define an a tile
>     r[0] := plottools[arc]([0,0], 0.5, 0..Pi/2),
>             plottools[arc]([1,1], 0.5, Pi..3*Pi/2);
>     # define a b tile
>     r[1] := plottools[arc]([0,1], 0.5, -Pi/2..0),
>             plottools[arc]([1,0], 0.5, Pi/2..Pi);
>     boundary := plottools[curve]([[0,0], [0,n],
>                     [m,n], [m,0], [0,0]]);
>     tiles := seq(seq(seq(plottools[translate](h, i, j),
>                  h=r[g(i, j)]), i=0..m-1), j=0..n-1);
>     plots[display](tiles, boundary, args[4..nargs]);
> end proc:
```

**Example 4** Define the following procedure, which randomly returns either 0 or 1.

```
> oddeven := proc() rand() mod 2 end proc:
```

Create a $20 \times 10$ tiling (called a Truchet tiling) with no axes and constrained scaling.

```
> tiling(oddeven, 20, 10, scaling=constrained, axes=none);
```

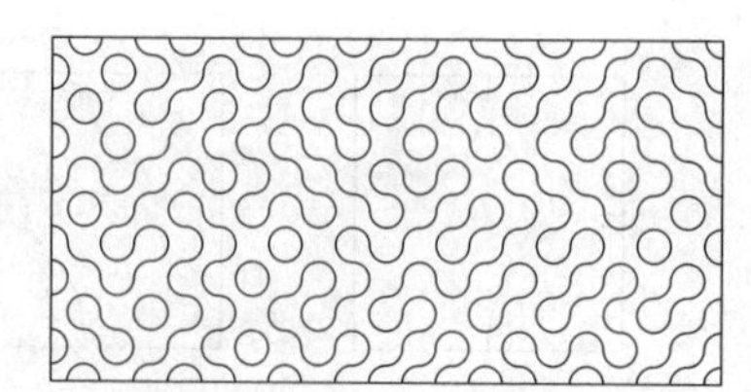

When you use the same procedure again, the random tiling is different.

```
> tiling(oddeven, 20, 10, scaling=constrained, axes=none);
```

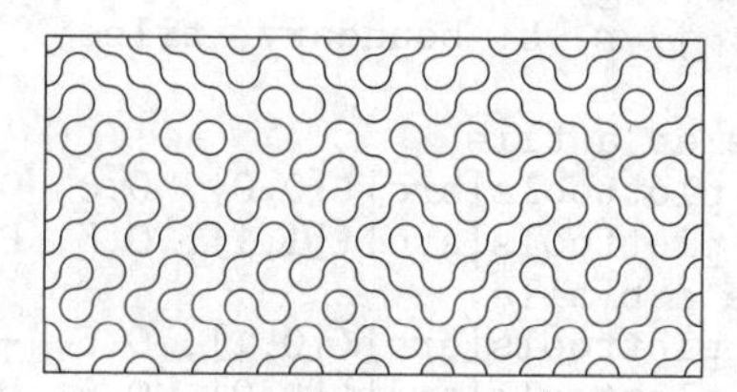

## A Smith Chart

You can use the commands in the plottools package to create graphs, such as a Smith Chart, which is used in microwave circuit analysis.

```
> smithChart := proc(r)
>     local i, a, b, c ;
>     a := PLOT(seq(plottools[arc]([-i*r/4,0], i*r/4, 0..Pi),
>                   i = 1..4 ),
>        plottools[arc]([0,r/2], r/2,
>                       Pi-arcsin(3/5)..3*Pi/2),
>        plottools[arc]([0,r], r, Pi..Pi+arcsin(15/17)),
>        plottools[arc]([0,2*r], 2*r,
>                       Pi+arcsin(3/5)..Pi+arcsin(63/65)),
>        plottools[arc]([0,4*r], 4*r,
>                       Pi+arcsin(15/17)..Pi+arcsin(63/65))
>              );
>     b := plottools[transform]((x, y) -> [x,-y])(a);
>     c := plottools[line]([ 0, 0], [ -2*r, 0]):
>     plots[display](a, b, c, axes = none,
>                    scaling = constrained, args[2..nargs]);
> end proc:
```

The following is a Smith Chart of radius 1.

```
> smithChart(1);
```

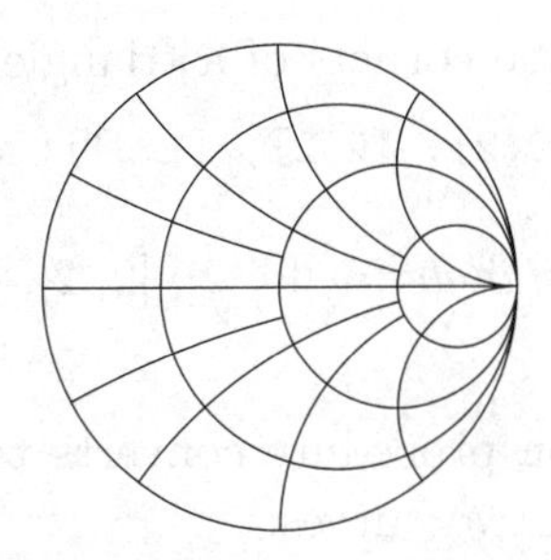

## Exercise

1. Make a Smith Chart by building appropriate circular arcs above the axes.
2. Create a copy reflected on the axis (using the `plottools[transform]` procedure).
3. Add a final horizontal line. The parameter $r$ denotes the radius of the largest circle.
4. Modify the `smithChart` procedure to add text to mark appropriate grid markers.

## Modifying Polygon Meshes

You can construct new plot tools that work like those in the `plottools` package.

**Example 5** Create a procedure that removes the inside of a single face of a polygon. Then, apply it to every face of a polygon.

```
> cutoutPolygon := proc(vlist::list, scale::numeric)
>     local i, center, outside, inside, n, edges, polys;
>
>     n := nops(vlist);
>     center := add(i, i=vlist) / n;
>     inside := seq(scale*(vlist[i]-center) + center, i=1..n);
>     outside := seq([inside[i], vlist[i], vlist[i+1],
>                      inside[i+1]],
>                     i=1..n-1):
>     polys := POLYGONS(outside,
>                   [inside[n], vlist[n], vlist[1], inside[1]],
>                   STYLE(PATCHNOGRID));
```

```
>     edges := CURVES([op(vlist), vlist[1]],
>                     [inside, inside[1]]);
>     polys, edges;
> end proc:
```

The following are the corners of a triangle.

```
> triangle := [[0,2], [2,2], [1,0]];
```

$$triangle := [[0, 2], [2, 2], [1, 0]]$$

The `cutoutPolygon` procedure converts `triangle` to three polygons (one for each side) and two curves.

```
> cutoutPolygon(triangle, 1/2);
```

$$\mathrm{POLYGONS}([[\frac{1}{2}, \frac{5}{3}], [0, 2], [2, 2], [\frac{3}{2}, \frac{5}{3}]],$$
$$[[\frac{3}{2}, \frac{5}{3}], [2, 2], [1, 0], [1, \frac{2}{3}]], [[1, \frac{2}{3}], [1, 0], [0, 2], [\frac{1}{2}, \frac{5}{3}]],$$
$$\mathrm{STYLE}(\mathit{PATCHNOGRID})), \mathrm{CURVES}($$
$$[[0, 2], [2, 2], [1, 0], [0, 2]], [[\frac{1}{2}, \frac{5}{3}], [\frac{3}{2}, \frac{5}{3}], [1, \frac{2}{3}], [\frac{1}{2}, \frac{5}{3}]])$$

Use the `plots[display]` command to show the triangle.

```
> plots[display](%, color=red);
```

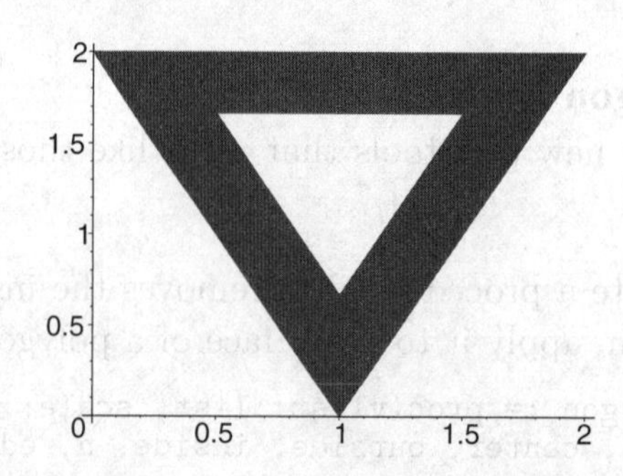


The following `cutout` procedure applies `cutoutPolygon` to every face of a polyhedron.

```
> cutout := proc(polyhedron, scale)
>    local v;
>    seq(cutoutPolygon(v, evalf(scale)), v=polyhedron);
> end proc:
```

The following command removes 3/4 of each face of a dodecahedron and displays the result.

```
> display(cutout(dodecahedron([1, 2, 3]), 3/4),
>         scaling=constrained);
```

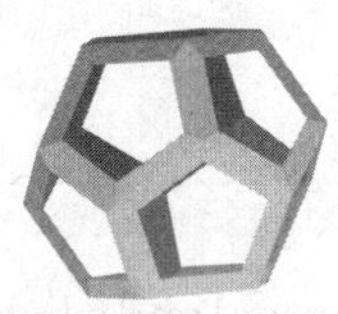

**Example 6** Raise or lower the barycenter of a polygon.

```
> stellateFace := proc(vlist::list, aspectRatio::numeric)
>    local apex, i, n;
>
>    n := nops(vlist);
>    apex :=  add(i, i = vlist) * aspectRatio / n;
>    POLYGONS(seq([apex, vlist[i], vlist[modp(i, n) + 1]],
>             i=1..n));
> end proc:
```

The following are the corners of a triangle in 3-D space.

```
> triangle := [[1,0,0], [0,1,0], [0,0,1]];
```

$$triangle := [[1, 0, 0], [0, 1, 0], [0, 0, 1]]$$

The `stellateFace` procedure creates three polygons, one for each side of the triangle.

```
> stellateFace(triangle, 1);
```

$$\mathrm{POLYGONS}([[\frac{1}{3}, \frac{1}{3}, \frac{1}{3}], [1, 0, 0], [0, 1, 0]],$$
$$[[\frac{1}{3}, \frac{1}{3}, \frac{1}{3}], [0, 1, 0], [0, 0, 1]], [[\frac{1}{3}, \frac{1}{3}, \frac{1}{3}], [0, 0, 1], [1, 0, 0]])$$

Because these polygons are 3-D objects, to display them, place the `POLYGONS` structure inside a `PLOT3D` structure.

```
> PLOT3D(%);
```

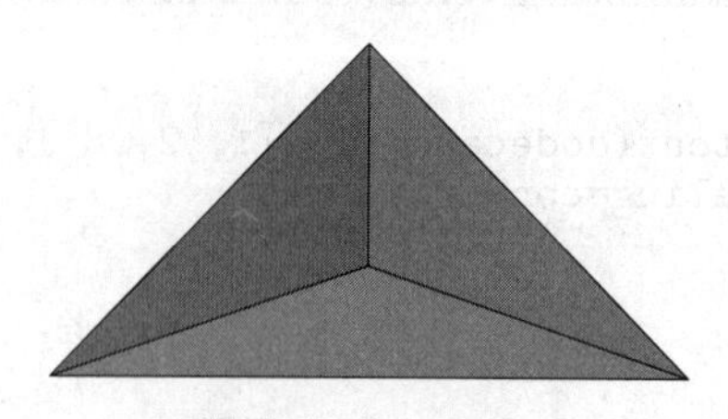

As in Example 5, you can extend the stellateFace procedure to act on arbitrary polyhedra with more than one face.

```
> stellate := proc(polyhedron, aspectRatio)
>    local v;
>    seq(stellateFace(v, evalf(aspectRatio)),
>          v=polyhedron);
> end proc:
```

The following commands construct and display a stellated dodecahedron.

```
> stellated := display(stellate(dodecahedron(), 3),
>             scaling=constrained):
> display(array([dodecahedron(), stellated]));
```

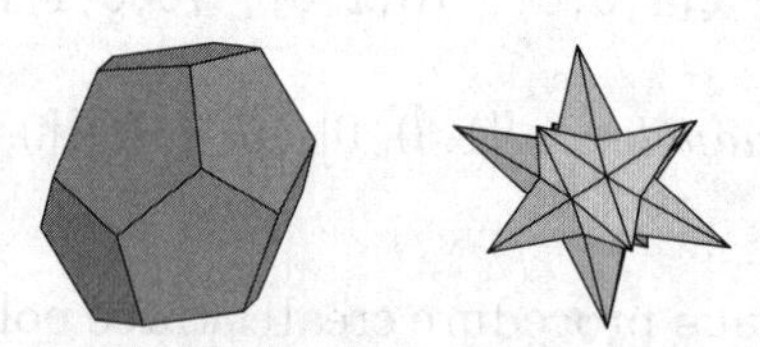

You can use the convert(..., POLYGONS) command to convert a GRID or MESH structure to the equivalent set of POLYGONS.

**Example 7** This example uses a version of the Klein bottle created from POLYGONS structures.

```
> kleinpoints := proc()
>    local bottom, middle, handle, top, p, q;
>
```

```
>     top := [(2.5 + 1.5*cos(v)) * cos(u),
>            (2.5 + 1.5*cos(v)) * sin(u), -2.5 * sin(v)]:
>     middle := [(2.5 + 1.5*cos(v)) * cos(u),
>            (2.5 + 1.5*cos(v)) * sin(u), 3*v - 6*Pi]:
>     handle := [2 - 2*cos(v) + sin(u), cos(u),
>            3*v - 6*Pi]:
>     bottom := [2 + (2+cos(u))*cos(v), sin(u),
>            -3*Pi + (2+cos(u)) * sin(v)]:
>     p := plot3d({bottom, middle, handle, top},
>            u=0..2*Pi, v=Pi..2*Pi, grid=[9,9]):
>     p := select(x -> op(0,x)=MESH, [op(p)]);
>     seq(convert(q , POLYGONS), q=p);
> end proc:
> display(kleinpoints(), style=patch,
>        scaling=constrained, orientation=[-110,71]);
```

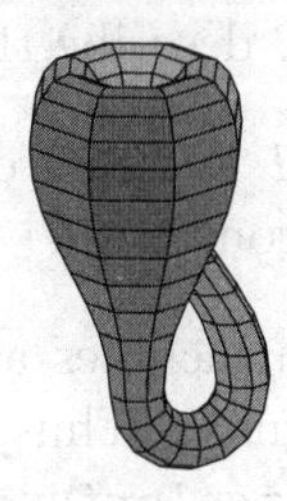

To alter the view of the Klein bottle, use polygon manipulation commands.

```
> display(seq( cutout(k, 3/4), k=kleinpoints()),
>        scaling=constrained);
```

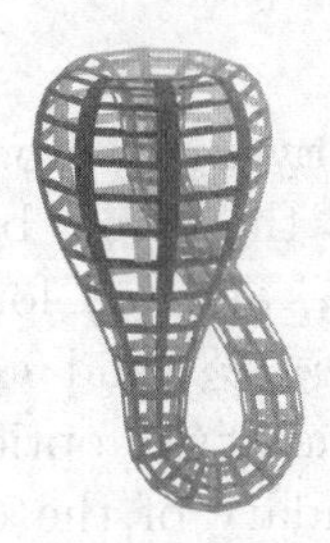

## 5.6 Vector Field Plots

This section describes how to plot a vector field of 2-D vectors in the plane. The examples illustrate the tools available for plot objects on grids in 2-D and 3-D space.

The goal is to create a procedure that plots a vector field and has the following syntax.

```
vectorfieldplot( F, r1, r2, options)
```

- The first argument, *F*, is a list of size two containing the expressions that specify the horizontal and vertical components of the vector field.
- The arguments *r1* and *r2* describe the domain grid of the vectors.
- The three arguments *F*, *r1*, and *r2* are similar in form to the arguments required for the `plot3d` command.
- The optional information includes any relevant plotting option that `plot` and `plot3d` recognize. Thus, options such as `grid=[m,n]`, `style=patch`, and `color=colorfunction` are valid.

### Drawing a Vector

The first step is to draw a vector. Let $[x, y]$ represent the starting point of the arrow and $[a, b]$ represent the components of the vector. Specify the shape of an arrow with three independent parameters, $t1$, $t2$, and $t3$, where $t1$ denotes the thickness of the arrow, $t2$ the thickness of the arrow head, and $t3$ the ratio of the length of the arrow head to the length of the arrow.

**Example 1** The following `myarrow` procedure constructs seven vertices of an arrow. It then builds the arrow by constructing two polygons: a triangle (spanned by $v_5$, $v_6$, and $v_7$) for the head of the arrow and a rectangle (spanned by $v_1$, $v_2$, $v_3$, and $v_4$) for the tail. It then removes boundary lines by setting the `style` option inside the polygon structure. It also constructs the boundary of the entire arrow via a closed curve through the vertices.

```
> myarrow := proc(point::list, vect::list, t1, t2, t3)
>    local a, b, i, x, y, L, Cos, Sin, v, locopts;
>
>    a := vect[1]; b := vect[2];
>    if has(vect, 'undefined') or (a=0 and b=0) then
>       return POLYGONS([]);
```

```
>     end if;
>     x := point[1]; y := point[2];
>     # L = length of arrow
>     L := evalf(sqrt(a^2 + b^2));
>     Cos := evalf(a / L);
>     Sin := evalf(b / L);
>     v[1] := [x + t1*Sin/2, y - t1*Cos/2];
>     v[2] := [x - t1*Sin/2, y + t1*Cos/2];
>     v[3] := [x - t1*Sin/2 - t3*Cos*L + a,
>              y + t1*Cos/2 - t3*Sin*L + b];
>     v[4] := [x + t1*Sin/2 - t3*Cos*L + a,
>              y - t1*Cos/2 - t3*Sin*L + b];
>     v[5] := [x - t2*Sin/2 - t3*Cos*L + a,
>              y + t2*Cos/2 - t3*Sin*L + b];
>     v[6] := [x + a, y + b];
>     v[7] := [x + t2*Sin/2 - t3*Cos*L + a,
>              y  - t2*Cos/2 - t3*Sin*L + b];
>     v := seq(evalf(v[i]), i= 1..7);
>
>     # convert optional arguments to PLOT data structure form
>     locopts := convert([style=patchnogrid, args[ 6..nargs ]],
>                        PLOToptions);
>     POLYGONS([v[1], v[2], v[3], v[4]],
>              [v[5], v[6], v[7]], op(locopts)),
>     CURVES([v[1], v[2], v[3], v[5], v[6],
>             v[7], v[4], v[1]]);
> end proc:
```

**Note:** Because each polygon must be convex, you must build the polygon structure for the arrow in two parts.

In the special case that the vector has both components equal to zero or an `undefined` component, such as a value resulting from a non-numeric value (for example, a complex value or a singularity point), the `myarrow` procedure returns a trivial polygon. The following are four arrows.

```
> arrow1 := PLOT(myarrow([0,0], [1,1], 0.2, 0.4, 1/3,
>                color=red)):
> arrow2 := PLOT(myarrow([0,0], [1,1], 0.1, 0.2, 1/3,
>                color=yellow)):
> arrow3 := PLOT(myarrow([0,0], [1,1], 0.2, 0.3, 1/2,
>                color=blue)):
> arrow4 := PLOT(myarrow([0,0], [1,1], 0.1, 0.5, 1/4,
>                color=green)):
```

The `display` command from the `plots` package can show an array of plots.

```
> with(plots):

Warning, the name changecoords has been redefined
```

```
> display(array([[arrow1, arrow2], [arrow3, arrow4]]),
>     scaling=constrained);
```

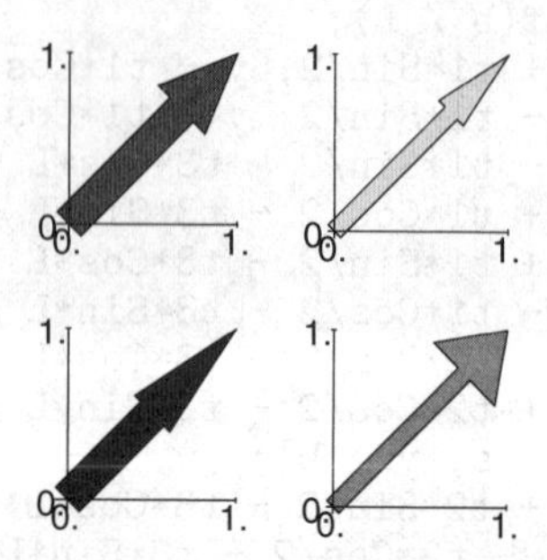


## Generating a Vector Plot Field

The remainder of this section presents a number of solutions to the programming problem of generating a vector field plot, each more powerful than its predecessors. The first and simplest solution requires the input be in operator form. This solution uses three utility procedures that process the domain information, generate a grid of function values, and place the information in a PLOT3D structure.

**Example 2** The procedure domaininfo determines the endpoints and increments for the grid. It takes as input the two ranges r1 and r2 and the two grid sizes $m$ and $n$, and returns the grid information as an expression sequence of four elements.

```
> domaininfo := proc(r1, r2, m, n)
>    lhs(r1), lhs(r2),
>    evalf((rhs(r1) - lhs(r1))/(m-1)),
>    evalf((rhs(r2) - lhs(r2))/(n-1));
> end proc:
```

The following example uses multiple assignments to assign the four values returned to separate variables.

```
> a, b, dx, dy := domaininfo(0..12, 20..100, 7, 9);
```

$$a, b, dx, dy := 0, 20, 2., 10.$$

Now a, b, dx, and dy have the following values.

```
> a, b, dx, dy;
```

0, 20, 2., 10.

**Example 3** To convert to a grid of numerical points, use the extensibility of the Maple `convert` command. The procedure `'convert/grid'` takes a procedure $f$ as input and applies it to the points in the grid which `r1`, `r2`, `m`, and `n` specify.

```
> 'convert/grid' := proc(f, r1, r2, m, n)
>   local a, b, i, j, dx, dy;
>     # obtain  information about domain
>     a,b,dx,dy := domaininfo(r1, r2, m, n);
>     # output grid of function values
>     [seq([seq(evalf(f(a + i*dx, b + j*dy)),
>        i=0..m-1)], j=0..n-1)];
> end proc:
```

Now apply the undefined name, $f$, to a grid as follows.

```
> convert(f, grid, 1..2, 4..6, 3, 2);
```

[[f(1., 4.), f(1.500000000, 4.), f(2.000000000, 4.)],
[f(1., 6.), f(1.500000000, 6.), f(2.000000000, 6.)]]

**Example 4** The final utility procedure determines the scaling that ensures that the arrows do not overlap. Then `generateplot` calls the `myarrow` procedure to draw the vectors.

**Note:** `generateplot` centers each arrow over its grid-point.

```
> generateplot := proc(vect1, vect2, m, n, a, b, dx, dy)
>     local i, j, L, xscale, yscale, mscale;
>
>     # Determine scaling factor.
>     L := max(seq(seq(vect1[j][i]^2 + vect2[j][i]^2,
>                 i=1..m), j=1..n));
>     xscale := evalf(dx/2/L^(1/2));
>     yscale := evalf(dy/2/L^(1/2));
>     mscale := max(xscale, yscale);
>
>     # Generate plot data structure.
>     # Each arrow is centered over its point.
>     PLOT(seq(seq(myarrow(
>         [a + (i-1)*dx - vect1[j][i]*xscale/2,
>          b + (j-1)*dy - vect2[j][i]*yscale/2],
>         [vect1[j][i]*xscale, vect2[j][i]*yscale],
>         mscale/4, mscale/2, 1/3), i=1..m), j=1..n));
>     # Thickness of tail = mscale/4
>     # Thickness of head = mscale/2
> end proc:
```

**Example 5** With these utility functions, you can write the `vectorfieldplot` command.

```
> vectorfieldplot := proc(F, r1, r2, m, n)
>    local vect1, vect2, a, b, dx, dy;
>
>    # Generate each component over the grid of points.
>    vect1 := convert(F[1], grid, r1, r2 ,m, n);
>    vect2 := convert(F[2], grid, r1, r2 ,m, n);
>
>    # Obtain the domain grid information from r1 and r2.
>    a,b,dx,dy := domaininfo(r1, r2, m, n);
>
>    # Generate the final plot structure.
>    generateplot(vect1, vect2, m, n, a, b, dx, dy)
> end proc:
```

Try the procedure on the vector field $(\cos(xy), \sin(xy))$.

```
> p := (x,y) -> cos(x*y): q := (x,y) -> sin(x*y):
> vectorfieldplot([p, q], 0..Pi, 0..Pi, 15, 20);
```

The `vectorfieldplot` code shows how to write a procedure that generates vector field plots based on alternative descriptions of the input.

**Example 6** You can create the `listvectorfieldplot` procedure, which accepts input consisting of a list of $m$ lists, each of which consists of $n$ lists with two elements. The pairs of elements specify the components of a vector. The domain grid is $1, \ldots, m$ in the horizontal direction and $1, \ldots, n$ in the vertical direction (as with the `plots[listplot3d]` command).

```
> listvectorfieldplot := proc(F)
>    local m, n, vect1, vect2;
>
>    n := nops(F);   m := nops(F[1]);
>    # Generate the 1st and 2nd components  of F.
>    vect1 := map(u -> map(v -> evalf(v[1]), u), F);
>    vect2 := map(u -> map(v -> evalf(v[2]), u), F);
>
```

```
>     # Generate the final plot structure.
>     generateplot(vect1, vect2, m, n, 1, 1, m-1, n-1)
> end proc:
```

The following is an example of a call to listvectorfieldplot.

```
> l := [[[1,1], [2,2], [3,3]],
>        [[1,6], [2,0], [5,1]]]:
> listvectorfieldplot(l);
```

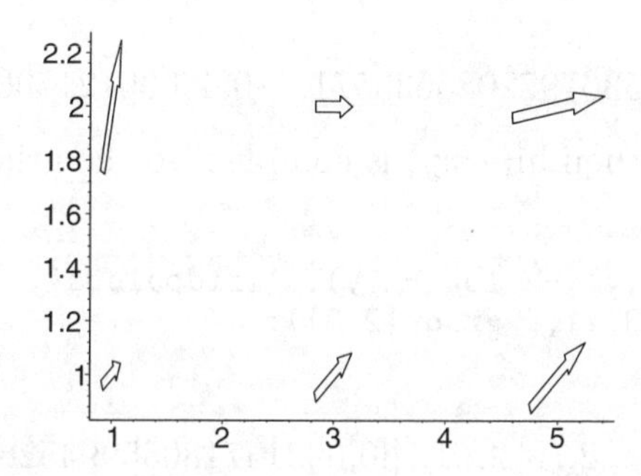


There are problems with the vectorfieldplot procedure.

- The procedure only works with operator form. You can solve this problem by converting expressions to procedures, and then recursively calling the vectorfieldplot procedure with the converted input (as in the ribbonplot procedure in section 5.2).
- The procedure only works with lists as input, not Arrays.

To overcome such problems, first convert all input procedures to procedures that generate only a numeric real value or the value undefined, the only type of data that can appear in a Maple plot data structure. It is recommended that you use the more efficient hardware floating-point calculations rather than software floating-point operations, whenever possible. For more information, see the examples in **5.7 Generating Grids of Points**.

Instead of writing a procedure for computing the grid, use the library function convert(..., gridpoints) which, in the case of a single input, generates a structure of the following form.

```
[ a.. b,  c.. d, [[z11, ... , z1n], ... ,
     [zm1 , ... , zmn]]]
```

It uses either expressions or procedures as input. The output gives the domain information `a..b` and `c..d` along with the `z` values of the input that it evaluates over the grid.

```
> convert(sin(x*y), 'gridpoints',
>     x=0..Pi, y=0..Pi, grid=[2, 3]);
```

$$[0...3.14159265358979, 0...3.14159265358979, [$$
$$[0., 0., 0.],$$
$$[0., -0.975367972083633571, -0.430301217000074065]]]$$

When $xy > 0$, then $\ln(-xy)$ is complex, so the grid contains the value `undefined`.

```
> convert((x,y) -> log(-x*y), 'gridpoints',
>     1..2, -2..1,  grid=[2,3]);
```

$$[1...2., -2...1., [[0.693147180559945286,$$
$$-0.693147180559945286, \mathit{undefined}],$$
$$[1.386294361, 0., \mathit{undefined}]]]$$

**Example 7** This version of the `vectorfieldplot` procedure accepts a number of options. In particular, it allows a `grid = [m,n]` option. To accomplish this, pass the options to `convert(..., gridpoints)`. The utility procedure `makevectors` handles the interface to `convert(..., gridpoints)`.

```
> makevectors := proc(F, r1, r2)
>    local v1, v2;
>
>    # Generate the numerical grid
>    # of components of the vectors.
>    v1 := convert(F[1], 'gridpoints', r1, r2,
>                  args[4 .. nargs]);
>    v2 := convert(F[2], 'gridpoints', r1, r2,
>                  args[4 .. nargs]);
>
>    # The domain information is contained in first
>    # two operands of v1. The function values in
>    # the 3rd components of v1 and v2.
>    [v1[1], v1[2], v1[3], v2[3]]
> end proc:
```

The new version of `vectorfieldplot` is:

```
> vectorfieldplot := proc(F, r1, r2)
>    local R1, R2, m, n, a, b, v1, v2, dx, dy, v;
>
>    v := makevectors(F, r1, r2, args[4..nargs]);
>    R1 := v[1];  R2 := v[2];  v1 := v[3];  v2 := v[4];
>
>    n := nops(v1); m := nops(v1[1]);
>    a, b, dx, dy := domaininfo(R1, R2, m, n);
>
>    generateplot(v1, v2, m, n, a, b, dx, dy);
> end proc:
```

Test this procedure.

```
> p := (x,y) -> cos(x*y):
> q := (x,y) -> sin(x*y):
> vectorfieldplot([p, q], 0..Pi, 0..Pi, grid=[3, 4]);
```

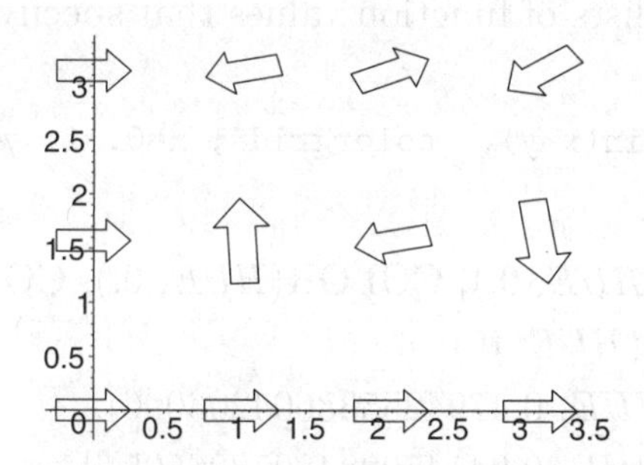


All the previous versions of **vectorfieldplot** scale all vectors by the same factor so that each vector fits into a single grid box. No overlapping of arrows occurred. However, the length of the arrows is dependent on the size of the grid boxes. This can produce graphs that have a large number of very small, almost indiscernible vectors. For example, the following plot of the gradient field of $F = \cos(xy)$ exhibits this behavior.

```
> vectorfieldplot([y*cos(x*y), x*sin(x*y)],
>     x=0..Pi, y=0..Pi, grid=[15,20]);
```

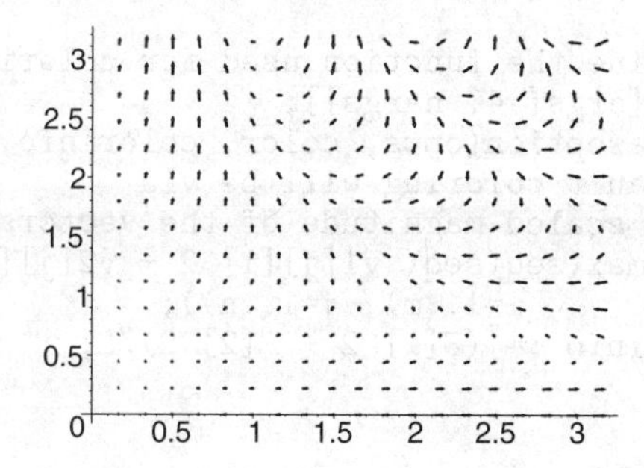

The final version of vectorfieldplot differs in that all the arrows have the same length—the color of each vector indicates its magnitude. First create a utility procedure that generates a grid of colors from the function values.

**Example 8** Utility Procedure

```
> `convert/colorgrid` := proc(colorFunction)
>    local colorinfo, i,j, m, n;
>
>    colorinfo := op(3, convert(colorFunction,
>        'gridpoints', args[2..nargs]));
>    map(x -> map(y -> COLOR(HUE, y), x), colorinfo);
> end proc:
```

This procedure uses the convert( ... , gridpoints) procedure to generate a list of lists of function values that specify the colors (using hue coloring).

```
> convert(sin(x*y), 'colorgrid', x=0..1, y=0..1, grid=[2,3]);
```

$$[[\mathrm{COLOR}(HUE, 0.), \mathrm{COLOR}(HUE, 0.), \mathrm{COLOR}(HUE, 0.)], [\mathrm{COLOR}(HUE, 0.), \mathrm{COLOR}(HUE, 0.479425538604203006), \mathrm{COLOR}(HUE, 0.841470984807896505)]]$$

**Example 9** The final version of the vectorfieldplot procedure is:

```
> vectorfieldplot := proc(F, r1, r2)
>    local v, m, n, a, b, dx, dy, opts, p, v1, v2,
>          L, i, j, norms, colorinfo,
>          xscale, yscale, mscale;
>
>    v := makevectors(F, r1, r2, args[4..nargs]);
>    v1 := v[3];  v2 := v[4];
>    n := nops(v1); m := nops(v1[1]);
>
>    a,b,dx,dy := domaininfo(v[1], v[2], m, n);
>
>   # Determine the function used for coloring the arrows.
>   opts := [args[ 4..nargs]];
>   if not hasoption(opts, color, colorinfo, 'opts') then
>      # Default coloring will be via
>      # the scaled magnitude of the vectors.
>      L := max(seq(seq( v1[j][i]^2 + v2[j][i]^2,
>                i=1..m), j=1..n));
>      colorinfo := (F[1]^2 + F[2]^2)/L;
>   end if;
>
```

```
>    # Generate the information needed to color the arrows.
>    colorinfo := convert(colorinfo, 'colorgrid',
>          r1, r2, op(opts));
>
>    # Get all the norms of the vectors using zip.
>    norms := zip((x,y) -> zip((u,v)->
>        if u=0 and v=0 then 1 else sqrt(u^2 + v^2) end if,
>           x, y), v1, v2);
>    #  Normalize v1 and v2 (again using zip).
>    v1 := zip((x,y) -> zip((u,v)-> u/v, x, y), v1, norms);
>
>    v2 := zip((x,y) -> zip((u,v)-> u/v, x, y), v2, norms);
>
>    # Generate scaling information and plot data structure.
>    xscale := dx/2.0;  yscale := dy/2.0;
>    mscale := max(xscale, yscale);
>
>    PLOT(seq(seq(myarrow(
>         [a + (i-1)*dx - v1[j][i]*xscale/2,
>          b + (j-1)*dy - v2[j][i]*yscale/2],
>         [v1[j][i]*xscale, v2[j][i]*yscale],
>         mscale/4, mscale/2, 1/3,
>          'color'=colorinfo[j][i]
>                    ), i=1..m), j=1..n));
> end proc:
```

This version produces the following plots.

```
> vectorfieldplot([y*cos(x*y), x*sin(x*y)],
>     x=0..Pi, y=0..Pi,grid=[15,20]);
```

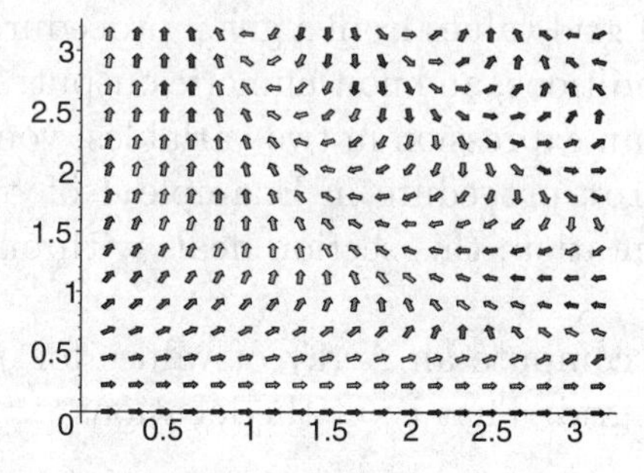


You can color the vectors via a function, such as $\sin(xy)$.

```
> vectorfieldplot([y*cos(x*y), x*sin(x*y)],
>     x=0..Pi, y=0..Pi, grid=[15,20], color=sin(x*y));
```

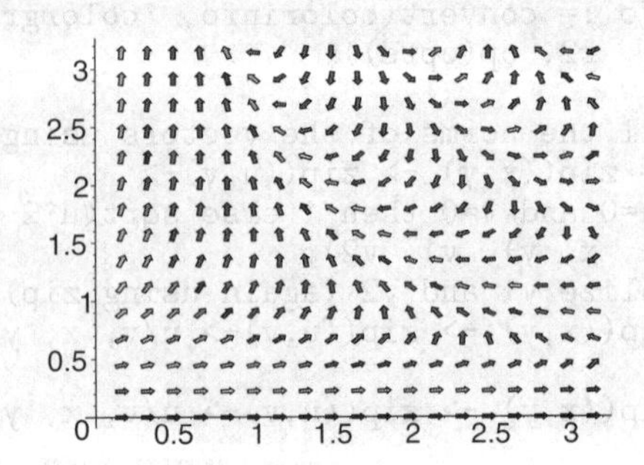


Other vector field routines can be derived from the preceding routines. For example, you can also write a complex vector field plot that takes complex number locations and complex number descriptions of vectors as input. Simply generate the grid of points in an alternate manner.

The `arrow` procedure, in the `plots` package, generates arrows and vectors. The `arrow` procedure is more versatile than the procedures described in this section.

## 5.7 Generating Grids of Points

Section 5.6 illustrated the steps involved in the simple operation of obtaining an Array of grid values from a given procedure. You must consider efficiency, error conditions, and non-numeric output. To handle the case in which the input is an expression in two variables, you can use the method from the `ribbonplot` procedure in Example 4 of section 5.2. Thus, for simplicity of presentation, this section deals with only operator form input.

The goal is to compute an Array of values for $f$ at each point on a $m \times n$ rectangular grid. That is, at the locations

$$x_i = a + (i-1)\delta_x \quad \text{and} \quad y_j = c + (j-1)\delta_y$$

where $\delta_x = (b-a)/(m-1)$ and $\delta_y = (d-c)/(n-1)$. Here $i$ and $j$ vary from 1 to $m$ and 1 to $n$, respectively. The final procedure that is created in this section (in Example 3) is similar to the `convert( ..., gridpoints)` library procedure, except that it produces an Array instead of a list of lists.

Consider the function $f\colon (x,y) \mapsto 1/\sin(xy)$. You need to evaluate $f$ over the $m \times n$ grid with the ranges $a..b$ and $c..d$.

```
> f := (x,y) -> 1/sin(x*y);
```

$$f := (x, y) \to \frac{1}{\sin(x\,y)}$$

**Example 1** The first step is to convert the function $f$ to a numeric procedure. Because Maple requires numeric values (rather than symbolic) for plots, convert $f$ to a procedure that returns numerical answers or the special value `undefined`.

```
> fnum := convert(f , numericproc);
```

$fnum :=$ **proc**$(x, y)$
**local** $r$;
**try** $r := \mathrm{evalhf}(\mathrm{f}(x, y))$ **catch** : **end try**;
**if not** $\mathrm{type}(r, \textit{'numeric'})$ **then**
**try** $r := \mathrm{evalf}(\mathrm{f}(x, y))$ **catch** : **end try**
**end if**;
'if'$(\mathrm{type}(r, \textit{'numeric'}), r, \textit{'undefined'})$
**end proc**

The `fnum` procedure, which is the result of this conversion, attempts to calculate the numerical values as efficiently as possible. Hardware floating-point arithmetic, although of limited precision, is more efficient than software floating-point and is frequently sufficient for plotting. Thus, the `fnum` procedure tries the `evalhf` function first. If `evalhf` generates an error or returns a non-numeric result, the `fnum` procedure attempts the calculation again by using software floating-point arithmetic and then calling `evalf`. Even this calculation is not always possible. For example, the function $f$ is undefined whenever $x = 0$ or $y = 0$. In such cases, the procedure `fnum` returns the name `undefined`. The Maple plot display routines recognize this special name.

At the point $(1, 1)$, the function $f$ has the value $1/\sin(1)$ and so `fnum` returns a numerical estimate.

```
> fnum(1,1);
```

$$1.18839510577812123$$

However, if you try to evaluate $f$ at $(0, 0)$, Maple returns that the function is undefined at these coordinates.

```
> fnum(0,0);
```

$$undefined$$

**Summary** Creating such a procedure is the first step in creating the grid of values. For efficiency, when possible, compute the function values and the grid points by using hardware floating-point arithmetic. In addition, it is recommended that you perform as much computation as possible in a single call to `evalhf`. For hardware floating-point arithmetic, Maple must first convert the expression to a series of commands involving hardware floating-point numbers, and then convert the results back to the Maple format for numbers. For more information on numerical calculations, see chapter 4.

**Example 2** The following procedure generates the coordinates of the grid in the form of an Array. Because the procedure plots surfaces, the Array is two dimensional. The procedure returns an Array `z` of function values.

```
> evalgrid := proc(F, z, a, b, c, d, m, n)
>    local i, j, dx, dy;
>
>    dx := (b-a)/m; dy := (d-c)/n;
>    for i to m do
>       for j to n do
>          z[i, j] := F(a+(i-1)*dx, c+(j-1)*dy);
>       end do;
>    end do;
> end proc:
```

This `evalgrid` procedure is purely symbolic and does not handle error conditions.

```
> A := Array(1..2, 1..2):
> evalgrid(f, 'A', 1, 2, 1, 2, 2, 2):
> A;
```

$$\begin{bmatrix} \frac{1}{\sin(1)} & \frac{1}{\sin(\frac{3}{2})} \\ \frac{1}{\sin(\frac{3}{2})} & \frac{1}{\sin(\frac{9}{4})} \end{bmatrix}$$

```
> evalgrid(f, 'A', 0, Pi, 0, Pi, 2, 2):
```

```
Error, (in f) numeric exception: division by zero
```

**Example 3** The gridpoints procedure uses the evalgrid procedure. The procedure accepts a procedure, two ranges, and the number of grid points to generate in each dimension. Like the procedure fnum which Maple generated from the previously defined procedure $f$, this routine attempts to create the grid using hardware floating-point arithmetic. Only if this fails, does gridpoints use software floating-point arithmetic.

```
> gridpoints := proc(f, r1, r2, m, n)
>     local u, x, y, z, a, b, c, d;
>
>     # Domain information:
>     a := lhs(r1); b := rhs(r1);
>     c := lhs(r2); d := rhs(r2);
>
>     if Digits <= evalhf(Digits) then
>        try
>           # Try to use hardware floats.
>           z := Array(1..m, 1..n, datatype=float[8]);
>           evalhf(evalgrid(f, z, a, b, c, d, m, n));
>        catch:
>           # Use software floats, first converting f to
>           # a software float function.
>           z := Array(1..m, 1..n);
>           evalgrid(convert(f, numericproc), z, a, b, c, d, m, n);
>        end try;
>     else
>        # Use software floats, first converting f to
>        # a software float function.
>        z := Array(1..m, 1..n);
>        evalgrid(convert(f, numericproc), z, a, b, c, d, m, n);
>     end if;
>     z;
> end proc:
```

**Testing the Procedures** The gridpoints procedure can use hardware floating-point arithmetic to calculate two of the numbers, but it must use software calculations in four cases where the function is undefined.

```
> gridpoints((x,y) -> 1/sin(x*y) , 0..3, 0..3, 2, 3);
```

$$[undefined\,,\ undefined\,,\ undefined]$$
$$[undefined\,,\ 1.00251130424672485\,,$$
$$7.08616739573718667]$$

In the following example, `gridpoints` can use hardware floating-point for all the calculations. Therefore, this calculation is faster, although the difference is not apparent unless you try a much larger example.

```
> gridpoints((x,y) -> sin(x*y),  0..3, 0..3, 2, 3);
```

$$[0., 0., 0.]$$
$$[0., 0.997494986604054445, 0.141120008059867213]$$

If you ask for more digits than hardware floating-point arithmetic can provide, then `gridpoints` uses software floating-point operations.

```
> Digits := 22:
> gridpoints((x,y) -> sin(x*y),  0..3,  0..3, 2, 3);
```

$$[0., 0., 0.]$$
$$[0., 0.9974949866040544309417,$$
$$0.1411200080598672221007]$$

```
> Digits := 10:
```

When hardware floating-point calculations are possible, the data is returned in an Array with `datatype=float[8]`, in which case you can display it by enclosing it in a `GRID` structure in a `PLOT3D` structure.

```
> PLOT3D(GRID(0..3, 0..3, gridpoints((x,y) -> sin(x*y), 0..3,
>          0..3, 10, 10)), AXES(BOXED));
```

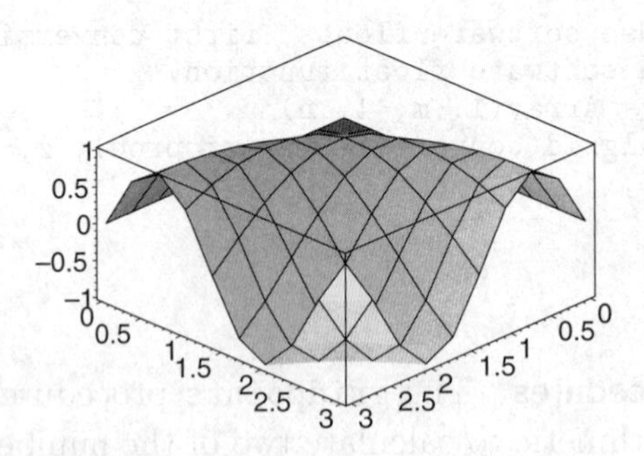


Otherwise, the data is returned in an Array with the default `datatype=anything`, which must be converted to an Array with `datatype=float[8]` before being placed inside a plot data structure.

## 5.8 Animation

Maple can generate animations in two or three dimensions. As with all Maple plotting facilities, such animations produce user-accessible data structures. Data structures of the following type represent animations.

```
PLOT( ANIMATE( ... ) )
```

or

```
PLOT3D( ANIMATE( ... ) )
```

Inside the ANIMATE function is a sequence of frames; each frame is a list of the same plotting objects that can appear in a single plotting structure. Every procedure that creates an animation builds such a sequence of frames. For example, print the output of such a procedure using the following Maple command (output not shown).

```
> lprint( plots[animate]( plot, [x*t, x=-1..1], t = 1..3,
>          numpoints=3, frames = 3 ) );
```

The function points is a parameterization of the curve $(x, y) = (1 + \cos(t\pi/180)^2, 1 + \cos(t\pi/180)\sin(t\pi/180))$.

```
> points := t -> evalf(
>         [ (1 + cos(t/180*Pi)) * cos(t/180*Pi ),
>           (1 + cos(t/180*Pi)) * sin(t/180*Pi ) ] ):
```

For example,

```
> points(2);
```

$$[1.998172852, 0.06977773357]$$

You can plot a sequence of points.

```
> PLOT( POINTS( seq( points(t), t=0..90 ) ) );
```

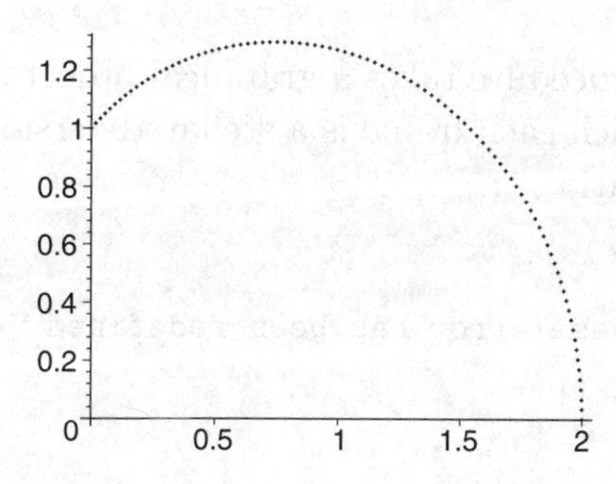

You can now make an animation. Make each frame consist of the polygon spanned by the origin, $(0, 0)$, and the sequence of points on the curve.

```
> frame := n -> [ POLYGONS([ [ 0, 0 ],
>                   seq( points(t), t = 0..60*n ) ],
>                   COLOR( RGB, 1.0/n, 1.0/n, 1.0/n ) ) ]:
```

The animation (not shown) consists of six frames.

```
> PLOT( ANIMATE( seq( frame(n), n = 1..6 ) ) );
```

## Animation in Static Form

The `display` command from the `plots` package can show an animation in static form.

```
> with(plots):
Warning, the name changecoords has been redefined
```

```
> display( PLOT(ANIMATE(seq(frame(n), n = 1..6))) );
```

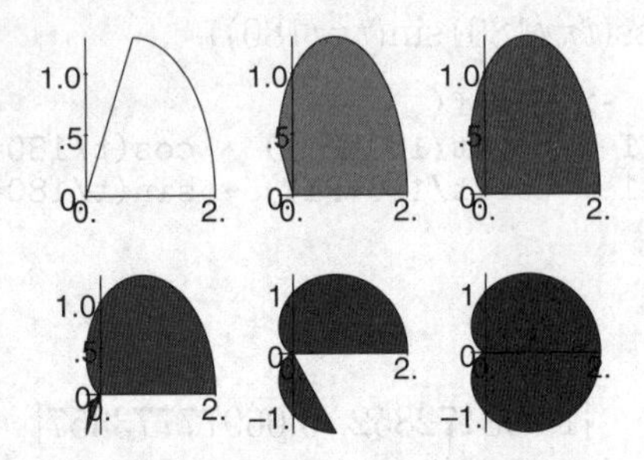

## Graphical Object as Input

The `varyAspect` procedure illustrates how a stellated surface varies with the aspect ratio.

**Example 1** The procedure takes a graphical object as input and creates an animation in which each frame is a stellated version of the object with a different aspect ratio.

```
> with(plottools):
Warning, the name arrow has been redefined
```

```
> varyAspect := proc( p )
>   local n, opts;
>   opts := convert( [ args[2..nargs] ], PLOT3Doptions );
>   PLOT3D( ANIMATE( seq( [ stellate( p, n/sqrt(2)) ],
>                         n=1..4 ) ),
>         op( opts ));
> end proc:
```

Try the procedure on a dodecahedron.

```
> varyAspect( dodecahedron(), scaling=constrained );
```

The static version is:

```
> display( varyAspect( dodecahedron(),
>                     scaling=constrained ) );
```

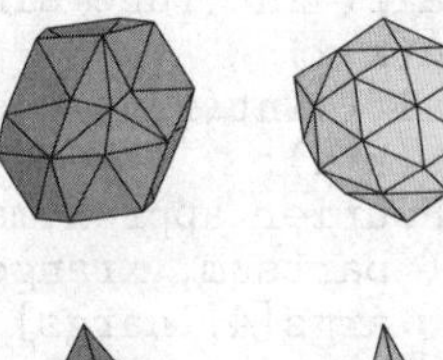

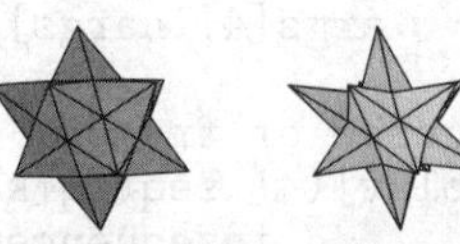

## Methods for Creating Animations

The Maple library provides two methods for creating animations: the `animate` command in the `plots` package and the `display` command with the `insequence = true` option. For example, you can show how a Fourier series approximates a function, $f$, on an interval $[a, b]$ by visualizing the function and successive approximations as the number of terms increase with each frame. You can derive the $n$th partial sum of the Fourier series by using $f_n(x) = c_0/2 + \sum_{k=1}^{n} c_k \cos(\frac{2\pi}{b-a}kx) + s_k \sin(\frac{2\pi}{b-a}kx)$, where

$$c_k = \frac{2}{b-a} \int_a^b f(x) \cos\left(\frac{2\pi}{b-a}kx\right) dx$$

and

$$s_k = \frac{2}{b-a} \int_a^b f(x) \sin\left(\frac{2\pi}{b-a}kx\right) dx.$$

**Example 2** The `fourierPicture` procedure first calculates and plots the $k$th Fourier approximation for $k$ up to $n$. Then `fourierPicture` generates an animation of these plots, and finally it adds a plot of the function as a backdrop.

```
> fourierPicture :=
> proc( func, xrange::name=range, n::posint)
>     local x, a, b, l, k, j, p, q, partsum;
>
>     a := lhs( rhs(xrange) );
>     b := rhs( rhs(xrange) );
>     l := b - a;
>     x := 2 * Pi * lhs(xrange) / l;
>
>     partsum := 1/l * evalf( Int( func, xrange) );
>     for k from 1 to n do
>        # Generate the terms of the Fourier series of func.
>        partsum := partsum
>           + 2/l * evalf( Int(func*sin(k*x), xrange) )
>                 * sin(k*x)
>           + 2/l * evalf( Int(func*cos(k*x), xrange) )
>                 * cos(k*x);
>        # Plot k-th Fourier approximation.
>        q[k] := plot( partsum, xrange, color=blue,
>                      args[4..nargs] );
>     end do;
>     # Generate sequence of frames.
>     q := plots[display]( [ seq( q[k], k=1..n ) ],
>                          insequence=true );
>     # Add the function plot, p, to each frame.
>     p := plot( func, xrange, color = red, args[4..nargs] );
>     plots[display]( [ q, p ] );
> end proc:
```

You can now use `fourierPicture` to plot, for example, the first six Fourier approximations of $e^x$.

```
> fourierPicture( exp(x), x=0..10, 6 ):
```

The static version is:

```
> display( fourierPicture( exp(x), x=0..10, 6 ) );
```

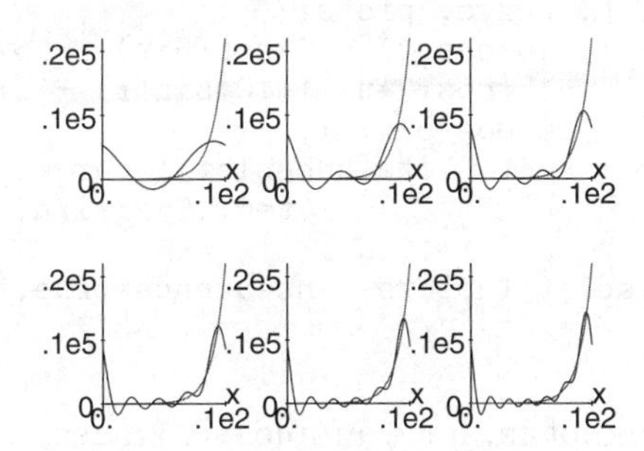


The following are the first six Fourier approximations of `x -> signum(x-1)`. Because the `signum` function is discontinuous, the `discont=true` option is required.

```
> fourierPicture( 2*signum(x-1), x=-2..3, 6,
>                  discont=true );
```

The static version is:

```
> display( fourierPicture( 2*signum(x-1), x=-2..3, 6,
>                  discont=true ) );
```

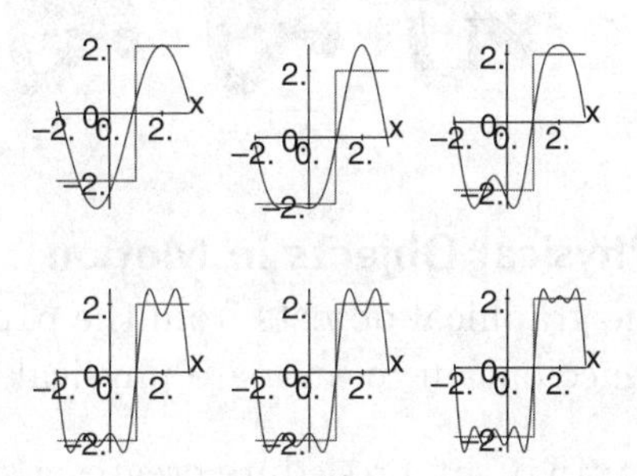


You can also create similar animations with other series approximations, such as Taylor, Padé, and Chebyshev–Padé, with the generalized series structures that Maple uses.

## Two and Three Dimensions

Animation sequences exist in both two and three dimensions.

**Example 3** The following procedure ties a trefoil knot by using the `tubeplot` function in the `plots` package.

```
> TieKnot := proc( n:: posint )
>    local i, t, curve, picts;
>    curve := [ -10*cos(t) - 2*cos(5*t) + 15*sin(2*t),
>               -15*cos(2*t) + 10*sin(t) - 2*sin(5*t),
>               10*cos(3*t) ]:
>    picts := [ seq( plots[tubeplot]( curve,
>                         t=0..2*Pi*i/n, radius=3),
>                   i=1..n ) ];
>    plots[display]( picts, insequence=true, style=patch);
> end proc:
```

You can tie the knot in, for example, six stages.

```
> TieKnot(6);
```

The static version is:

```
> display( TieKnot(6) );
```

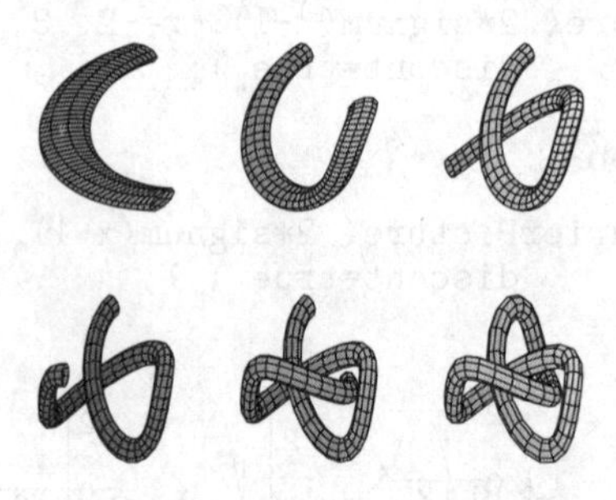

## Demonstrating Physical Objects in Motion

You can combine the graphical objects from the `plottools` package with the display in-sequence option to animate physical objects in motion.

**Example 4** The `springPlot` procedure creates a spring from a 3-D plot of a helix. The `springPlot` procedure also creates a box and a copy of this box. It moves one of the boxes to various locations depending on a value of $u$. For every $u$, locate these boxes above and below the spring. The `springPlot` procedure then makes a sphere and translates it to locations above the top box with the height varying with a parameter. It produces the entire animation by organizing a sequence of positions and showing them in sequence by using `display`.

```
> springPlot := proc( n )
>    local u, curve, springs, box, tops, bottoms,
>          helix, ball, balls;
>    curve := (u,v) -> spacecurve(
>          [cos(t), sin(t), 8*sin(u/v*Pi)*t/200],
>          t=0..20*Pi,
```

```
>           color=black, numpoints=200, thickness=3 ):
>     springs := display( [ seq(curve(u,n), u=1..n) ],
>                        insequence=true ):
>     box := cuboid( [-1,-1,0], [1,1,1], color=red ):
>     ball := sphere( [0,0,2], grid=[15, 15], color=blue ):
>     tops :=  display( [ seq(
>       translate( box, 0, 0, sin(u/n*Pi)*4*Pi/5 ),
>       u=1..n ) ], insequence=true ):
>     bottoms := display( [ seq( translate(box, 0, 0, -1),
>       u=1..n ) ], insequence=true ):
>     balls := display( [ seq( translate( ball, 0, 0,
>          4*sin( (u-1)/(n-1)*Pi ) + 8*sin(u/n*Pi)*Pi/10 ),
>          u=1..n ) ],  insequence=true ):
>     display( springs, tops, bottoms, balls,
>        style=patch, orientation=[45,76],
>        scaling=constrained );
> end proc:
```

The code in the `springPlot` procedure uses the short names of commands from the `plots` and `plottools` packages to improve readability. In general, it is recommended that you use long names. To use this version of the `springPlot` procedure, you must *first* load the `plots` and `plottools` packages.

```
> with(plots): with(plottools):
> springPlot(6);
> display( springPlot(6) );
```

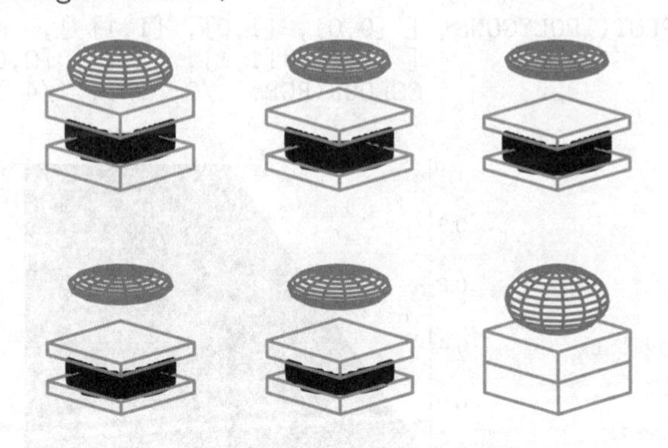

For information on the commands in the `plottools` package related to graphics procedures, see **5.5 Programming with the `plottools` Package**.

## 5.9 Programming with Color

You can color each type of object in plot data structures, and add colors to plotting routines. The `color` option allows you to use a:

- Solid color by specifying a name, RGB value, or HUE value
- Color function by specifying a Maple formula or function

Try the following commands (output not shown).

```
> plot3d( sin(x*y), x=-3..3, y=-3..3, color=red );
> plot3d( sin(x*y), x=-3..3, y=-3..3,
>    color=COLOUR(RGB, 0.3, 0.42, 0.1) );
```

```
> p := (x,y) -> sin(x*y):
> q := (x,y) -> if x < y then 1 else x - y end if:
```

```
> plot3d( p, -3..3, -3..3, color=q );
```

Although usually less convenient, you can also specify the color attributes at the lower level of graphics primitives. At the lowest level, you can color a graphical object by including a COLOUR function as one of the options inside the object.

```
> PLOT( POLYGONS( [ [0,0], [1,0], [1,1] ],
>                 [ [1,0], [1,1], [2,1], [2,0] ],
>                 COLOUR(RGB, 1/2, 1/3, 1/4 ) ) );
```

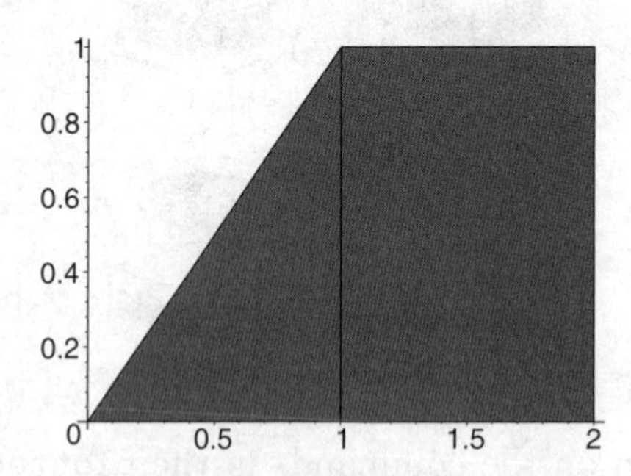


You can use different colors for each polygon by using

```
PLOT( POLYGONS( P1, ... , Pn ,
      COLOUR(RGB, p1, ..., pn)) )
```

or

```
PLOT( POLYGONS( P1, COLOUR(RGB, p1) ),    ... ,
      POLYGONS( Pn, COLOUR(RGB, pn)) )
```

For example, the following two PLOT structures represent the same picture of a red and a green triangle.

```
> PLOT( POLYGONS( [ [0,0], [1,1], [2,0] ],
>                 COLOUR( RGB, 1, 0, 0 ) ),
>       POLYGONS( [ [0,0], [1,1], [0,1] ],
>                 COLOUR( RGB, 0, 1, 0 ) ) );

> PLOT( POLYGONS( [ [0,0], [1,1], [2,0] ],
>                 [ [0,0], [1,1], [0,1] ],
>                 COLOUR( RGB, 1, 0, 0, 0, 1, 0 ) ) );
```

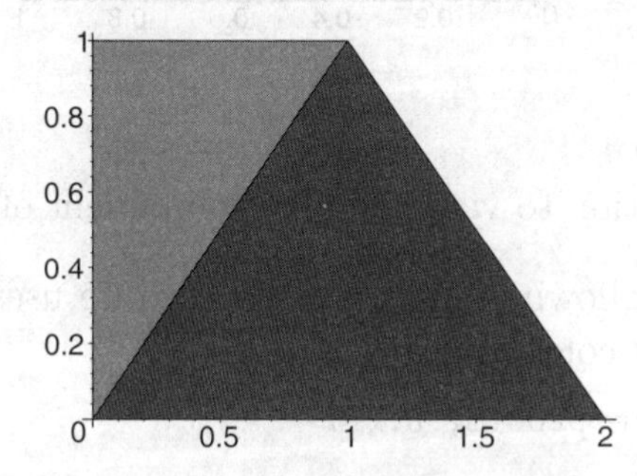


The three RGB values must be numbers between 0 and 1.

## Generating Color Tables

The following procedure generates an $m \times n$ color table of RGB values.

**Example 1** The colormap procedure returns a sequence of two elements: a POLYGONS structure and a TITLE.

```
> colormap := proc(m, n, B)
>    local i, j, points, colors, flatten;
>    # points = sequence of corners for rectangles
>    points :=  seq( seq( evalf(
>            [ [i/m, j/n], [(i+1)/m, j/n],
>              [(i+1)/m, (j+1)/n], [i/m, (j+1)/n] ]
>                  ), i=0..m-1 ), j=0..n-1 ):
>    # colors = listlist of RGB color values
>    colors :=  [seq( seq( [i/(m-1), j/(n-1), B],
>                  i=0..m-1 ), j=0..n-1 )] ;
>    # flatten turns the colors listlist into a sequence
>    flatten := a -> op( map(op, a) );
>    POLYGONS( points,
>              COLOUR(RGB, flatten(colors) ) ),
>    TITLE( cat( "Blue=", convert(B, string) ) );
```

```
> end proc:
```

The following is a $10 \times 10$ table of colors; the blue component is 0.

```
> PLOT( colormap(10, 10, 0) );
```

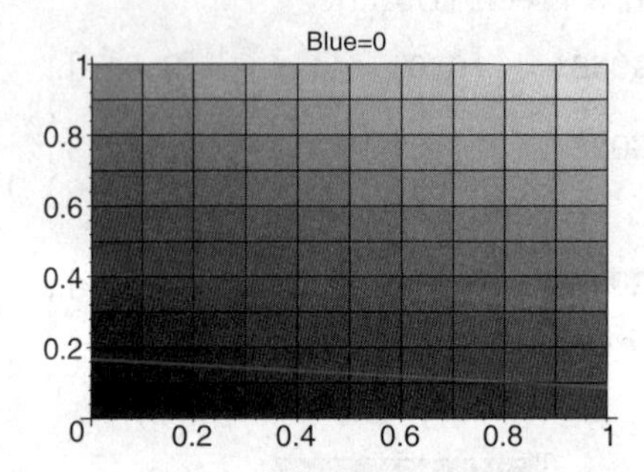


## Using Animation

You can use animation to vary the blue component of the previous table.

**Example 2** The following `colormaps` procedure uses animation to generate an $m \times n \times f$ color table.

```
> colormaps := proc(m, n, f)
>     local t;
>     PLOT( ANIMATE( seq( [ colormap(m, n, t/(f-1)) ],
>                        t=0..f-1 ) ),
>           AXESLABELS("Red", "Green") );
> end proc:
```

For example, the following function produces a $10 \times 10 \times 10$ color table (not shown).

```
> colormaps(10, 10, 10);
```

You can create a color scale for HUE coloring as follows.

```
> points := evalf( seq( [ [i/50, 0], [i/50, 1],
>                         [(i+1)/50, 1], [(i+1)/50, 0] ],
>                       i=0..49)):
```

```
> PLOT( POLYGONS(points, COLOUR(HUE, seq(i/50, i=0..49)) ),
>       AXESTICKS(DEFAULT, 0), STYLE(PATCHNOGRID) );
```

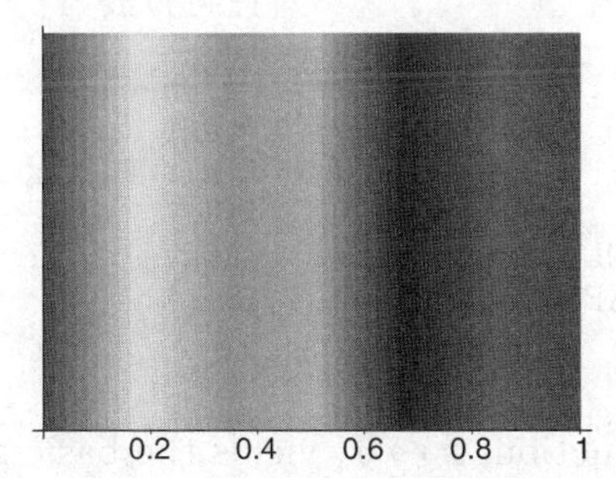


The AXESTICKS(DEFAULT, 0) specification eliminates the axes labeling along the vertical axis but leaves the default labeling along the horizontal axis.

You can create a colormapHue procedure that creates the color scale for any color function based on HUE coloring.

```
> colormapHue := proc(F, n)
>    local i, points;
>    points := seq( evalf( [ [i/n, 0], [i/n, 1],
>                            [(i+1)/n, 1], [(i+1)/n, 0] ]
>                          ), i=0..n-1 ):
>    PLOT( POLYGONS( points,
>            COLOUR(HUE, seq( evalf(F(i/n)), i=0.. n-1) )),
>          AXESTICKS(DEFAULT, 0), STYLE(PATCHNOGRID) );
> end proc:
```

The basis of this color scale is $y(x) = \sin(\pi x)/3$ for $0 \leq x \leq 40$.

```
> colormapHue( x -> sin(Pi*x)/3, 40);
```

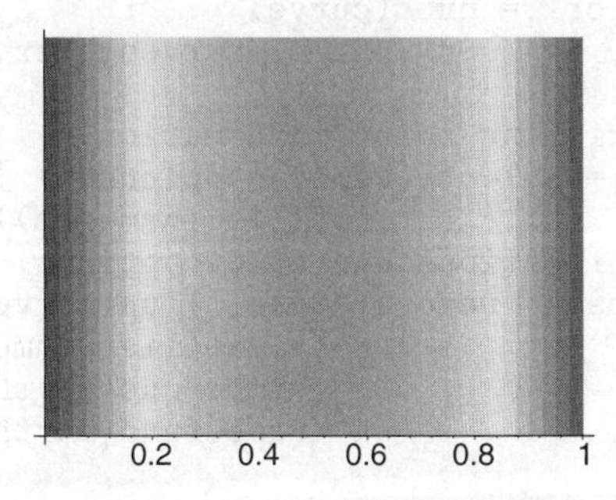


To create the grayscale coloring, use an arbitrary procedure, $F$, because gray levels have equal parts of red, green, and blue.

```
> colormapGraylevel := proc(F, n)
>    local i, flatten, points, grays;
```

```
>     points := seq( evalf([ [i/n, 0], [i/n, 1],
>                            [(i+1)/n, 1], [(i+1)/n, 0] ]),
>               i=0..n-1):
>     flatten := a -> op( map(op, a) );
>     grays := COLOUR(RGB, flatten(
>           [ seq( evalf([ F(i/n), F(i/n), F(i/n) ]),
>                 i=1.. n)]));
>     PLOT( POLYGONS(points, grays),
>           AXESTICKS(DEFAULT, 0) );
> end proc:
```

The identity function, $x \mapsto x$, yields the basic gray scale.

```
> colormapGraylevel( x->x, 20);
```

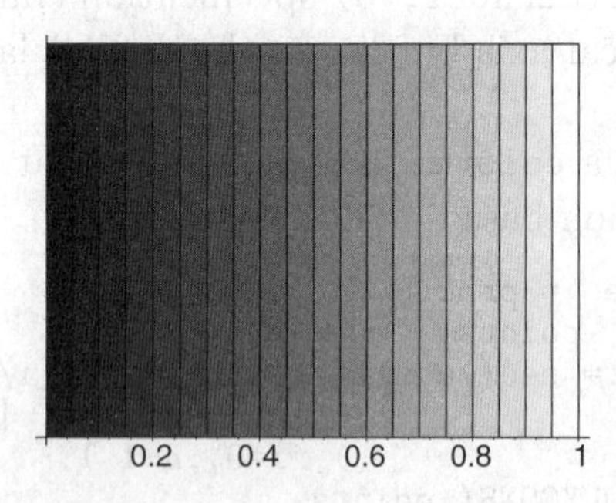


## Adding Color Information to Plots

You can add color information to an existing plot data structure.

**Example 3** The procedure `addCurvecolor` colors each curve in a `CURVES` function via the scaled $y$ coordinates.

```
> addCurvecolor := proc(curve)
>     local i, j, N, n , M, m, curves, curveopts, p, q;
>
>     # Get existing point information.
>     curves := select( type, [ op(curve) ],
>                       list(list(numeric)) );
>     # Get all options but color options.
>     curveopts := remove( type, [ op(curve) ],
>                          { list(list(numeric)),
>                            specfunc(anything, COLOR),
>                            specfunc(anything, COLOUR) } );
>
>     # Determine the scaling.
>     # M and m are the max and min of the y-coords.
>     n :=  nops( curves );
>     N := map( nops, curves );
>     M := [ seq( max( seq( curves[j][i][2],
>              i=1..N[j] ) ), j=1..n ) ];
>     m := [ seq( min( seq( curves[j][i][2],
```

```
>             i=1..N[j] ) ), j=1..n ) ];
>     # Build new curves adding HUE color.
>     seq( CURVES( seq( [curves[j][i], curves[j][i+1]],
>                   i=1..N[j]-1 ),
>               COLOUR(HUE, seq((curves[j][i][2]
>                               - m[j])/(M[j] - m[j]),
>                          i=1..N[j]-1)),
>               op(curveopts) ), j=1..n );
> end proc:
```

For example:

```
> c := CURVES( [ [0,0], [1,1], [2,2], [3,3] ],
>              [ [2,0], [2,1], [3,1] ] );
```

$$c := \mathrm{CURVES}([[0, 0], [1, 1], [2, 2], [3, 3]],\ [[2, 0], [2, 1], [3, 1]])$$

```
> addCurvecolor( c );
```

$$\mathrm{CURVES}([[0, 0], [1, 1]], [[1, 1], [2, 2]], [[2, 2], [3, 3]],\ \mathrm{COLOUR}(\mathit{HUE}, 0, \frac{1}{3}, \frac{2}{3})), \mathrm{CURVES}([[2, 0], [2, 1]],\ [[2, 1], [3, 1]], \mathrm{COLOUR}(\mathit{HUE}, 0, 1))$$

To apply the new coloring to a plot, map the addCurvecolor procedure over all the CURVES objects of an existing plot structure.

```
> addcolor := proc( aplot )
>     local recolor;
>     recolor := x -> if op(0,x)=CURVES then
>                         addCurvecolor(x)
>                     else x end if;
>     map( recolor, aplot );
> end proc:
```

Try addcolor on a plot of $\sin(x) + \cos(x)$.

```
> p := plot( sin(x) + cos(x), x=0..2*Pi,
>            linestyle=2, thickness=3 ):
> addcolor( p );
```

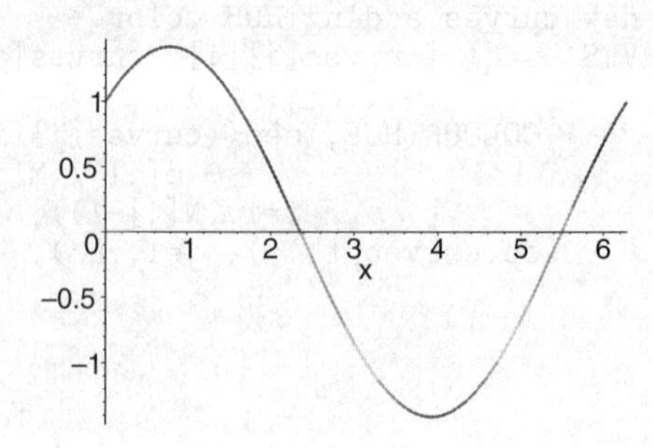


If you specify color for two curves in the same display, the two colorings are independent.

```
> q := plot( cos(2*x) + sin(x), x=0..2*Pi ):
> addcolor( plots[display](p, q) );
```

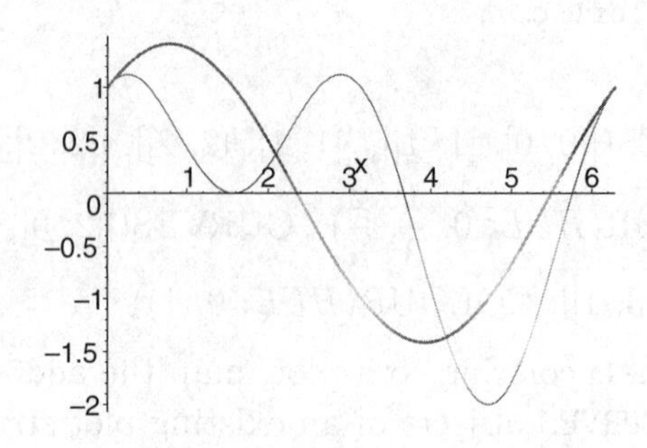


The addcolor procedure also works on 3-D space curves.

```
> spc := plots[spacecurve]( [ cos(t), sin(t), t ], t=0..8*Pi,
>                  numpoints=100, thickness=2, color=black ):
> addcolor( spc );
```

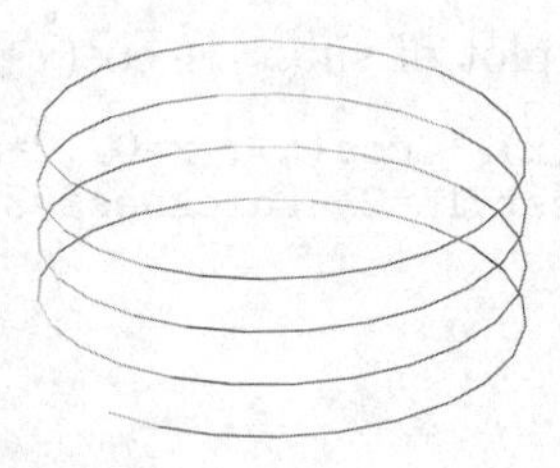

You can alter the coloring of an existing plot by using coloring functions. Coloring functions must be of the form $C_{Hue}: R^2 \rightarrow [0,1]$ (for Hue coloring) or of the form $C_{RGB}: R^2 \rightarrow [0,1] \times [0,1] \times [0,1]$ (for RGB coloring).

Example 3 uses the color function $C_{Hue}(x,y) = y/\max(y_i)$.

## Creating A Chess Board Plot

Example 4 shows how to make a chess board type grid with red and white squares in a 3-D plot.

**Note:** Do not simply assign a coloring function as an argument to `plot3d`. A coloring function, in such a case, provides colors for the vertices of the grid instead of the color patches.

**Example 4** You must first convert the grid or mesh to polygonal form. The remainder of the procedure assigns either a red or white color to a polygon, depending on which grid area it represents.

```
> chessplot3d := proc(f, r1, r2)
>     local m, n, i, j, plotgrid, p, opts, coloring, size;
>
>     # obtain grid size
>     # and generate the plotting data structure
>     if hasoption( [ args[4..nargs] ], grid, size) then
>        m := size[1];
>        n := size[2];
>     else  # defaults
>        m := 25;
>        n := 25;
>     end if;
>
>     p := plot3d( f, r1, r2, args[4..nargs] );
>
>     # convert grid data (first operand of p)
>     # into polygon data
>     plotgrid := op( convert( op(1, p), POLYGONS ) );
>     # make coloring function - alternating red and white
>     coloring := (i, j) -> if modp(i-j, 2)=0 then
>                                 convert(red, colorRGB)
>                           else
>                                 convert(white, colorRGB)
>                           end if;
>     # op(2..-1, p) is all the operands of p but the first
>     PLOT3D( seq( seq( POLYGONS( plotgrid[j + (i-1)*(n-1)],
>                                 coloring(i, j) ),
>                 i=1..m-1 ), j=1..n-1 ),
>            op(2..-1, p) );
> end proc:
```

The following is a chess board plot of $\sin(x)\sin(y)$.

```
> chessplot3d( sin(x)*sin(y), x=-Pi..Pi, y=-Pi..Pi,
>              style=patch, axes=frame );
```

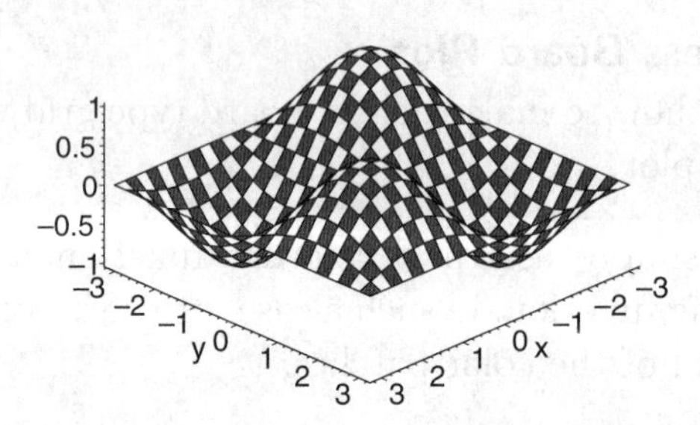


**Note:** The `chessplot3d` procedure works when the plot structure from `plot3d` is of `GRID` or `MESH` output type. The `MESH` output type is used for parametric surfaces or surfaces that use alternate coordinate systems, for example,

```
> chessplot3d( (4/3)^x*sin(y), x=-1..2*Pi, y=0..Pi,
>              coords=spherical, style=patch,
>              lightmodel=light4 );
```

## 5.10 Conclusion

In this chapter, you have learned how to make graphics procedures based on the `plot` and `plot3d` commands, as well as the commands found in the `plots` and `plottools` packages. However, for greater control, you must create `PLOT` and `PLOT3D` data structures directly; these are the primitive specifications of all Maple plots. Inside PLOT data structures, you can specify, for example, point, curve, and polygon objects. Inside PLOT3D data structures, you can specify the objects used in PLOT structures as well as, for example, grids of values and meshes of points. You have also learned how to handle plot options, create numerical plotting procedures, work with grids and meshes, manipulate plots and animations, and apply non-standard coloring to graphics.

# 6 Advanced Connectivity

## In This Chapter

- Code Generation
- External Calling: Using Compiled Code in Maple
- OpenMaple: Using Maple in Compiled Code

### Code Generation

The `CodeGeneration` package provides utilities for translating Maple code into other programming languages such as C, Fortran, Java, MATLAB, and Visual Basic®. The resulting code can be compiled and used independent of Maple.

### External Calling: Using Compiled Code in Maple

Compiled code can be seamlessly integrated into Maple. Maple can execute functions written in C, Fortran, or Java, passing parameters and returning values as if the external function were a native Maple procedure. Using compiled code truly extends the Maple kernel. The kernel extension must be reliable because it can affect the entire Maple program.

### OpenMaple: Using Maple in Compiled Code

Maple can be used by compiled C or C++ code using OpenMaple™. The OpenMaple Application Programming Interface (API) provides access to Maple algorithms and data structures.

## 6.1 Code Generation

### The CodeGeneration Package

Conversion of Maple code to other programming languages can be performed using the `CodeGeneration` package. Translators to several programming languages are available. For a complete list, refer to ?CodeGeneration. You can use the Maple symbolic environment to develop a numeric algorithm, and then translate it to another language for inclusion in an existing program or for faster execution. To perform a translation to one of the supported languages, use the `CodeGeneration` package function of the same name, or the context-sensitive menu options in the worksheet environment. You can also extend the predefined translators or create translators for other programming languages.

**Important:** You may be familiar with the `C` and `fortran` functions in the `codegen` package. It is recommended that you use the newer `CodeGeneration` package instead. However, the `codegen` package also contains a number of support functions not currently available in the `CodeGeneration` package, which can be used to preprocess the Maple input before translation with the `CodeGeneration` functions.

## Calling `CodeGeneration` Functions

Call the `CodeGeneration` functions using the following syntax, where $L$ is one of the supported languages, for example, `C`.

```
CodeGeneration[L]( expression, options )
```

The *expression* can take one of the following forms.

- A single algebraic expression: Maple generates a statement in the target language assigning this expression to a variable.
- A list of equations of the form *name=expression*: Maple interprets this as a sequence of assignment statements. Maple generates the equivalent sequence of assignment statements in the target language.
- A list, array, or rtable: Maple generates a statement or sequence of statements assigning the elements to an array in the target language.
- A Maple procedure or module: Maple generates an equivalent structure in the target language. For example, to translate a procedure to C, Maple generates a function along with any necessary directives for library inclusion. To translate a module to Java, Maple generates a Java class declaration with exports translated to public static methods and module locals translated to private static methods. For detailed information on translation to a specific language, refer to the help pages for that language, for example, `?CodeGeneration[C]` and `?CodeGeneration/General/CDetails`.

You can use many options with the `CodeGeneration` functions. For detailed information, refer to the `?CodeGenerationOptions` help page. Some of the more commonly used options follow.

- `optimize=value`: This option specifies whether optimization is performed. The default value is `false`. When the value is `true`, the `codegen[optimize]` function is used to optimize the Maple code before it is translated.

- `output=value`: This option specifies the form of the output. By default, formatted output is printed to the terminal. If a name (different from the name `string`) or a string is specified as the value, the result is appended to a file of that name. If the value is the name `string`, a string containing the result is returned. This string can then be assigned and manipulated.

- `reduceanalysis=value`: This option specifies whether a reduced form of type analysis is performed in the case that the Maple input is a list of equations representing a computation sequence. Using the default value, `reduceanalysis=false`, can reduce the number of type mismatches in the translated code. However, using the `reduceanalysis=true` option can significantly reduce the time and memory required for translation.

**Notes on Code Translation** Because the Maple language differs substantially from the target languages supported by `CodeGeneration`, the translation capabilities are limited, and the generated output may not be the exact equivalent of the input code. The `?CodeGenerationDetails` help page provides more information on the translation process and hints on how to take full advantage of the facilities. In addition, there are help pages containing notes relevant to specific languages. For details refer to the help pages for the corresponding language, for example, `?CodeGeneration/General/CDetails`.

## Translation Process

The `CodeGeneration` functions recognize only a subset of the Maple types. These are listed on the `?CodeGenerationDetails` help page. The Maple types are translated to appropriate types in the target language. Compatibility of types is checked before operations are translated, and type coercions are performed if necessary. The `CodeGeneration` functions attempt to deduce the type of any untyped variable. You can exercise greater control over type analysis and deduction by using the coercetypes, declare, deducetypes and defaulttype options, as described on the ?CodeGenerationOptions help page.

The CodeGeneration functions can translate a subset of the Maple functions. These are listed on the ?CodeGenerationDetails help page. Some functions are translated only to certain target languages. For more information about a specific language, refer to its detailed help page, for example, ?CodeGeneration/General/CDetails.

The return type of a procedure is deduced if you do not declare it. If more than one return statement is present, the types of all objects returned must be compatible in the target language. If a return statement contains a sequence of objects, the sequence is translated to an array. Implicit returns are recognized in some situatiions, but translations to explicit returns can be suppressed with the deducereturn=false option. When necessary, an automatically generated return variable is used to hold a return value.

Lists, Maple objects of type array, and rtables are translated to arrays in the target language. Type analysis and deduction capabilities with respect to arrays are very limited. It is recommended that you declare the type and ranges for all arrays. In some target languages, arrays are reindexed to begin at index 0.

**Example 1** The following example demonstrates the translation of a procedure to Java.

```
> f := proc(x)
>     local y;
>     y := ln(x)*exp(-x);
>     printf("The result is %f", y);
>   end proc:
> CodeGeneration[Java](f);
```

```
import java.lang.Math;

class CodeGenerationClass {
  public static void f (double x)
  {
    double y;
    y = Math.log(x) * Math.exp(-x);
    System.out.print("The result is " + y);
  }
}
```

**Example 2** The following example demonstrates the translation of a procedure to C. The defaulttype option sets the default type to integer, and the `output` option specifies that a string is returned. In this case, the output is assigned to the variable `s`.

```
> g := proc(x, y, z)
>     return x*y-y*z+x*z;
> end proc:
> s := CodeGeneration['C'](g, defaulttype=integer, output=string);
```

$$s := \text{“int g (int x, int y, int z)\textbackslash}$$
$$\{\backslash$$
$$\text{return(x * y - y * z + x * z);\textbackslash}$$
$$\}\backslash$$
$$\text{”}$$

**Example 3** The following example demonstrates the translation of a procedure to Fortran. Because Fortran 77 is case-insensitive, the variable `X` is renamed to avoid a conflict with the variable `x`.

```
> h := proc(X::numeric, x::Array(numeric, 5..7))
>     return X+x[5]+x[6]+x[7];
> end proc:
> CodeGeneration[Fortran](h);
```

```
Warning, The following variable name replacements were
made: [cg] = [X]
      doubleprecision function h (cg, x)
        doubleprecision cg
        doubleprecision x(5:7)
        h = cg + x(5) + x(6) + x(7)
        return
      end
```

**The Intermediate Code** All Maple input to `CodeGeneration` translators is processed and converted to an inert intermediate form known as the *intermediate code*. The intermediate code is the basic object upon which all `CodeGeneration` translators operate. For information about the intermediate code, refer to `?CodeGeneration/General/IntermediateCodeStructure`.

The names appearing in intermediate code expressions are members of the subpackage `CodeGeneration:-Names`.

Error and warning messages issued from `CodeGeneration` package functions sometimes refer to the intermediate form of the Maple expression that triggered the message.

When determining the cause of an error message or writing and debugging custom language definitions, it is recommended that you determine the intermediate form of a Maple expression input. In general you can determine the intermediate form with the CodeGeneration:-IntermediateCode translator. However, because some aspects of the intermediate code are specific to the language to which you are translating, it may help to see the intermediate code for a specific translator. This can be done by setting infolevel[CodeGeneration] to a value greater than 3 and performing a translation.

Example 4 shows the intermediate code for the expression $2x^2 - 1$. The first argument of the Scope structure is the name of a type table used internally during the translation process.

**Example 4** The following example shows the intermediate form of the expression $2x^2 - 1$.

```
> CodeGeneration[IntermediateCode](2*x^2-1);

Scope( nametab,
  StatementSequence(
    Assignment(GeneratedName("cg"), Sum(Product(Integer(2),
    Power(Name("x"), Integer(2))), Negation(Integer(1))))
  )
)
```

## Extending the CodeGeneration Translation Facilities

The CodeGeneration package is distributed with translators for several programming languages. In addition, you can define new translators to enable CodeGeneration to generate code for other languages. Tools for this task are available in the LanguageDefinition subpackage of CodeGeneration.

Custom translators can define a language in its entirety, or extend existing language definitions, overriding and extending only those language components that need to be changed.

To see a list of languages currently recognized by CodeGeneration, and thus available for extending, use the CodeGeneration:-LanguageDefinition:-ListLanguages command.

**The Printing Phase** As noted previously, the CodeGeneration package first processes the Maple input and translates it to an intermediate form. This is followed by the *printing* phase, which translates the intermediate form to a Maple string according to transformation rules specific to the target language.

For each name used in the intermediate form, there is a *print handler* procedure. During the printing phase, Maple traverses the intermediate form recursively. For each subexpression of the intermediate form, Maple calls the print handler associated with that class of expressions.

## Defining a Custom Translator

This section explains the process of defining a translator for a target language.

**Using a `Printer` Module** With each `CodeGeneration` language definition there is an associated Maple module, called a `Printer` module, which contains language-specific print handlers and data. A `Printer` module has a number of functions, which set and reference language-specific printing data.

There are two ways to obtain a `Printer` module. The `LanguageDefinition:-GenericPrinter()` returns a *generic* `Printer` module containing no language-specific data, and the `LanguageDefinition:-Get(language_name):-Printer` command returns a copy of the `Printer` module used for a previously defined language `language_name`.

The most frequently-used `Printer` package function is the `Print` command. Given a string, `Print` prints the string to a buffer. Given an intermediate-form expression, `Print` invokes the print handler appropriate for the expression. In this manner, `Print` recurses through the intermediate form until it is printed in its entirety to the buffer. At this point, translation is complete.

Table 6.1 lists important `Printer` functions. For a complete listing and more detailed information, refer to `?CodeGeneration/LanguageDefinition/Printer`.

**Example 5** This example illustrates how data is stored and retrieved from a `Printer` module.

```
> with(CodeGeneration:-LanguageDefinition):
> Printer := GenericPrinter();
```

**Table 6.1** Select `Printer` Functions

| | |
|---|---|
| `AddFunction` | Define a translation for a function name and type signature |
| `AddOperator` | Define a translation for a unary or binary operator |
| `AddPrintHandler` | Set a procedure to be the *print handler* for an intermediate form name |
| `GetFunction` | Get a translation for a function name and type signature |
| `GetOperator` | Get a translation for a unary or binary operator |
| `GetPrintHandler` | Get the current 'print handler' procedure for an intermediate form name |
| `Indent` | Indent a printed line when supplied as an argument to `Print` |
| `Print` | Print arguments to buffer |
| `PrintTarget` | Initiate printing of an intermediate form |

*Printer* := **module**()
**export** *PrintTarget*, *GetFunctionSignature*, *AddLibrary*,
*AddOperator*, *GetOperator*, *AddType*, *GetType*,
*AddPrintHandler*, *GetPrintHandler*,
*SetLanguageAttribute*, *ApplyLanguageAttribute*,
*GetLanguageAttribute*, *AddFunction*, *AddFunctions*,
*GetFunction*, *SetPrecedence*, *GetPrecedence*,
*GetIncludes*, *GetExpressionType*, *GetScopeName*,
*GetScopeStructure*, *Indent*, *PopIndentation*,
*PushIndentation*, *Endline*, *Linebreak*, *Print*,
*PrintBinary*, *PrintParentheses*, *PrintStatementBlock*,
*PrintDelimitedList*, *PrintUnary*;
...
**end module**

```
> Printer:-AddOperator( Addition = "+" );
```

"+"

```
> Printer:-AddFunction( "sin", [numeric]::numeric, "sine" );
```

["sine", {}]

```
> Printer:-GetOperator( Addition );
```

$$\text{“+”}$$

```
> Printer:-GetFunction( "sin", [numeric]::numeric );
```

$$[\text{“sine”}, \{\}]$$

Within a language definition, the `Printer` module associated with the language definition can be referenced by the name `Printer`. (**Note:** This applies for both language definition methods described in the next section.)

**Language Translator Definition** There are two distinct methods of defining a language translator for use by `CodeGeneration`: using the `LanguageDefinition:-Define` command and creating a language definition module.

For simple languages or small extensions of existing languages, use the `LanguageDefinition:-Define` method. To produce a translator that preprocesses or postprocesses the generated output, or makes frequent use of a utility function in translations, create a language definition module.

**Note:** The translators supplied with the `CodeGeneration` package, for example, C, VisualBasic, and Java, are implemented using language definition modules.

**Using the `Define` command** The `Define` command takes a series of function call arguments `f1`, `f2`, ... where the function names are, for example, `AddFunction`, `AddFunctions`, `AddOperator`, `AddPrintHandler`, `AddType`, and `SetLanguageAttribute`.

These function calls accept identical syntax and perform the same actions as the `Printer` functions of the same name. That is, they define print handlers and other data specific to the language translation you are defining. For more information on their purpose and accepted syntax, refer to `?CodeGeneration/LanguageDefinition/Printer`.

**Note:** The `Define` command automatically creates a `Printer` module for the language. You do not need to create one using `LanguageDefinition:-GenericPrinter` or `LanguageDefinition:-Get`.

**Example 6** This example illustrates a C translator, in which the translated code uses a specialized library function my_mult for multiplication instead of the built-in * operator.

```
> CodeGeneration:-LanguageDefinition:-Define("MyNewLanguage",
>     extend="C",
>     AddPrintHandler(
>         CodeGeneration:-Names:-Product = proc(x,y)
>             Printer:-Print("mymult(", args[1], ", ", args[2],
>                 ")");
>         end proc
>     )
> ):
```

**Note:** In the previous example, one of the arguments of the LanguageDefinition:-Define command is the function call AddPrintHandler, which takes a name and a procedure as arguments. This makes the supplied procedure responsible for *printing* any Product subexpression of the intermediate form. The call to Printer:-Print specifies that the translator uses the automatically-generated Printer module.

**Example 7** This example defines a language MyLanguage. It specifies, among other instructions, that the addition operation should be translated as plus, the multiplication operation as times, and the assignment operation as :=. Once defined, the translator is used to convert a simple Maple expression to MyLanguage.

```
> CodeGeneration:-LanguageDefinition:-Define("MyLanguage",
>     AddOperator(
>         CodeGeneration:-Names:-Addition        = "plus",
>         CodeGeneration:-Names:-Division        = "divided by",
>         CodeGeneration:-Names:-Multiplication = "times",
>         CodeGeneration:-Names:-Negation        = "-",
>         CodeGeneration:-Names:-Subtraction     = "minus"
>     ),
>     SetLanguageAttribute(
>         "Indent_Char" = " ", "Indent_Base"=2, "Indent_Increment"=2
>     ),
>     AddOperator( CodeGeneration:-Names:-Assignment = ":=" )
> );
> CodeGeneration:-Translate(-x+y*z, language="MyLanguage");

  cg0 := -x plus y times z;
```

**Example 8** This example extends the C translator to translate Maple print statements to C++-style cout commands.

```
> CodeGeneration:-LanguageDefinition:-Define("MyExtensionLanguage",
>    extend="C",
>    AddFunction( "print", anything::void,
>       proc(x)
>          Printer:-Print("cout << ");
>          Printer:-PrintDelimitedList([args], " << ");
>          Printer:-Print(" << endl");
>       end proc
>    )
> );
> p1 := proc() print("abcde") end proc:
> CodeGeneration:-Translate(p1, language="MyExtensionLanguage");
```

```
void p1 (void)
{
  cout << "abcde" << endl;
}
```

**Creating a Language Definition Module** A language definition module is a Maple module with exports PrintTarget and Printer. The module exports must satisfy the following criteria.

- Printer - A Printer module, that is, either a generic Printer module returned by CodeGeneration:-LanguageDefinition:-GenericPrinter or a Printer module obtained from another language definition module using LanguageDefinition:-Get("language_name"):-Printer.
- PrintTarget - Returns a string, the translated output. In most cases, PrintTarget simply calls Printer:-PrintTarget.

The body of the module definition must contain a sequence of calls to Printer functions that define language-specific data and utility procedures.

Once defined, a language definition module can be added to to the set of languages recognized by CodeGeneration by using the CodeGeneration:-LanguageDefinition:-Add command.

**Note:** When creating your language definition module, you must delay the evaluation of the module by using single quotes before adding it using LanguageDefinition:-Add. That is, the language definition module must be added as a module definition, not as a module.

**Example 9** This example adds a definition module. Note the use of delayed-evaluation quotes around the module definition.

```
> UppercaseFortran77 := 'module()
>     export Printer, PrintTarget;
>     Printer := eval(CodeGeneration:-LanguageDefinition:-Get(
>         "Fortran")):-Printer;
>     PrintTarget := proc(ic, digits, prec, func_prec, namelist)
>         Printer:-SetLanguageAttribute("Precision" = prec);
>         StringTools:-UpperCase(Printer:-PrintTarget(args));
>     end proc:
> end module':
> CodeGeneration:-LanguageDefinition:-Add("UppercaseFortran",
>     UppercaseFortran77);
```

**Using a New Translator** After adding the definition of the language using either the `LanguageDefinition:-Define` or `LanguageDefinition:-Add` commands, translate to the new language using the `CodeGeneration:-Translate` command.

**Example 10** This example demonstrates the use of a new translator. Compare the output of the `Fortran` command with that of the new translator.

```
> p1 := proc() sin(x+y*z)+trunc(x); end proc:
> CodeGeneration:-Fortran(p1);

      doubleprecision function p1 ()
        p1 = sin(x + y * z) + dble(int(aint(x)))
        return
      end

> CodeGeneration:-Translate(p1, language="UppercaseFortran");

      DOUBLEPRECISION FUNCTION P1 ()
        P1 = DSIN(X + Y * Z) + DBLE(INT(DINT(X)))
        RETURN
      END
```

## 6.2 External Calling: Using Compiled Code in Maple

The following three calling methods are presented in this section.

- Calling External Functions
- Generating Wrappers
- Customizing Wrappers

Any of the following three methods can be used to call an external function. Typically, method 1 is sufficient. Methods 2 and 3 can be used when more control over type conversions or greater access to Maple data structures is needed. Each method builds upon the previous one. When considering method 3, read about methods 1 and 2 first.

**Method 1: Calling External Functions** In most cases, compiled functions use only standard hardware types like integers, floating-point numbers, strings, pointers (to strings, integers, and floating-point numbers), matrices, and vectors. In these cases, the Maple software automatically translates between its internal representation and the hardware representation. This method is efficient and easy to use because it does not require the use of a compiler. This method of *directly calling* the external code allows the use of an external library without modification.

**Method 2: Generating Wrappers** Method 1 can use only standard data types. When dealing with complicated compound types or passing functions or records as parameters, a compiled *wrapper* is needed. Java and Fortran do not use these data structures; this method applies only to C routines. The wrapper performs the conversion between the Maple internal representation and the hardware representation. Maple automatically generates and compiles wrappers (based on your specifications) to interface with libraries of compiled code. Compared to directly calling the external function, you can use a more diverse set of external libraries. External calls that use these wrappers require a C compiler.

**Method 3: Customizing Wrappers** For flexibility beyond the other methods, an external API allows you to augment existing wrappers or write *custom wrappers*. You can write the wrapper in C or Fortran. This powerful method also allows direct access to Maple data structures from the wrapper.

### Calling Methods Summary

- Any of the methods(1 - 3) can be used to call a C function.
- Methods 1 or 3 can be used to call a Fortran function. Method 2 is not applicable to Fortran functions.

- Only method 1 is available for calling a Java method (Only static methods can be called).

### Method 1: Calling External Functions

To understand the Maple external calling facility, consider the following C code that adds two numbers and returns the result. Note that such a function would never be used because the Maple + operator exists, but working through this example demonstrates the steps required to use compiled code in Maple.

```
int add( int num1, int num2 )
{
    return num1+num2;
}
```

There are 3 basic steps required to call an external function.

**Step 1: DLL Creation** First, this function must be compiled into a Dynamic Link Library (Windows XXX.DLL), or Shared Library (UNIX libXXX.so or Macintosh XXX.dylib). For the rest of this chapter, the compiled library is referred to as a DLL. If the sources are downloaded from the internet or purchased, a DLL may already have been built. Otherwise, consult the compiler's documentation for help on how to build a DLL. When building the DLL, ensure that you *export* the function that Maple is intended to be able to call. In this case, the function name is *add*.

This is the only step that requires the user to have knowledge of a specific compiler. For the remaining steps, it does not matter if the function was written in C, Fortran, or Java.

For Maple, the external library functions must be compiled by using the `_stdcall` calling convention, which is the default under UNIX but must be specified when using most Windows compilers.

**Step 2: Function Specification** To make the appropriate argument conversions, Maple requires information about the function that it calls. At a minimum, Maple requires the following.

- Name of the function
- Type of parameters the function passes and returns
- Name of the DLL containing the function

The specification of the parameter types are independent of the compiler. The same specification can be used regardless of the language used to compile the DLL. The example uses the C type *int*. In Maple, this is specified as `integer[4]`. The 4 in the square brackets denotes the number of bytes used to represent the integer. Most C compilers use 4-byte *ints*, but some older compilers may use 2-byte *ints*. The Maple type specification supports both types of compiler integer sizes. For a map of the most common type relations, see Table 6.2 on page 336.

Since `num1` and `num2` are both *ints*, they can be specified as the following in Maple.

```
num1::integer[4]
num2::integer[4]
```

The return type does not have a name so the keyword `RETURN` is used.

```
RETURN::integer[4]
```

Using all of this information, the complete function can be defined by calling the Maple function `define_external`.

```
> myAdd := define_external(
>         'add',
>         'num1'::integer[4],
>         'num2'::integer[4],
>         'RETURN'::integer[4],
>         'LIB'="mylib.dll"
>     );
```

**Important:** Specify the function exactly, and ensure that the arguments are in the correct order. Failure to do this may result in strange behavior or program crashes when executing Step 3.

**Step 3: Function Invocation** Executing the `define_external` call for `myAdd` returns a Maple procedure that translates Maple types to hardware types that can work with an external function. This procedure can be used the same way as other Maple procedures.

```
> myAdd(1,2);
```

$$3$$

```
> a := 33:
> b := 22:
```

```
> myAdd(a,b);
```

$$55$$

```
> r:= myAdd(a,11);
```

$$r := 44$$

**Important:** Procedures generated in this manner contain run-time information and thus cannot be saved. The `define_external` command must be reissued after exiting or restarting Maple.

The following subsections provide additional information for Step 2, the function specification.

## External Definition

The `define_external` function constructs and returns another function which can be used to make the actual call. The `define_external` function is called as follows.

```
define_external( functionName, LANGUAGE, arg1::type1, ...,
                 argN::typeN, options, `LIB`=dllName)
define_external( functionName, `MAPLE`,
                 options, `LIB`=dllName )
```

- The *functionName* parameter specifies the name of the actual external function to be called. This name can be specified as a Maple string or name.

- The *LANGUAGE* parameter denotes the programming language used to compile the DLL. The default is C. Other recognized languages are JAVA and FORTRAN.

- The parameters *arg1* through *argN* describe the arguments of the function to be called. These should be specified in the order they appear in the documentation or source code for the external function, without regard to issues such as actual passing order (left to right versus right to left). The intent is that the Maple procedure `define_external` returns has the same calling sequence as the actual external function when used in the language for which it was written. The only exception is that one argument may be given the name `RETURN`. This specifies the type returned by the function rather than a parameter passed to the function. For more information about how each *argi* is specified, see the following **Type Specification** subsection.

- The *options* are used to specify argument passing conventions, libraries, or calling methods. For details, see the appropriate sections of this chapter.

- If instead of the *arg* parameters, the single word `MAPLE` is specified, the external function is assumed to accept the raw Maple data structures passed without conversion. This assumes that the wrapper has been manually generated and compiled into a DLL. Various support functions for writing such external functions are described in **Method 3: Customizing Wrappers** on page 350. Using `MAPLE` instead of specifying arguments is the basis of method 3.

- The name of the DLL containing the external function is specified by using the *LIB* option to `define_external`. The *dllName* is a string that specifies the filename of the library in which the function is to be found. The format of this name is highly system dependent. Likewise, whether a full pathname is required depends on the system. In general, the name should be in the same format as would be specified to a compiler on the same system. When calling a Java method, *dllName* is the name of the class containing the method.

## Type Specification

Step two of the introductory example indicated how to specify types using Maple notation. Maple uses its own notation to provide a generic well-defined interface for calling compiled code in any language.

The format of each *arg* parameter is as follows.

```
argumentIdentifier :: dataDescriptor
```

The return value description is also described by using a data descriptor, with the name `RETURN` as the *argumentIdentifier*. If the function returns no value, no `RETURN` parameter is specified. Also, if no parameters are passed, no argument identifiers are required.

**Table 6.2** Basic Type Translations

| Maple Data Descriptor | C Type | Fortran Type | Java Type |
|---|---|---|---|
| integer[1] | char | BYTE | byte |
| integer[2] | short | INTEGER*2 | short |
| integer[4] | int | INTEGER | int |
| | long[1] | INTEGER*4 | |
| integer[8] | long[1] | INTEGER*8 | long |
| | long long | INTEGER*8 | |
| float[4] | float | REAL | float |
| | | REAL*4 | |
| float[8] | double | DOUBLE PRECISION | double |
| | | REAL*8 | |
| char[1] | char | CHARACTER | char |
| boolean[1] | char | LOGICAL*1 | boolean |
| boolean[2] | short | LOGICAL*2 | |
| boolean[4] | int | LOGICAL | |
| | long | LOGICAL*4 | |
| boolean[8] | long | LOGICAL*8 | |
| | long long | LOGICAL*8 | |

[1] The C type *long* is typically (but not necessarily) 4-bytes on 32-bit machines and 8-bytes on 64-bit machines. Use the *sizeof* operator or consult your compiler manual to verify *sizeof(long)*.

## Scalar Data Formats

External libraries generally deal with scalar data supported directly by the underlying machine. All array, string, and structured formats are built up from these. The data descriptors used to represent scalar formats usually contain a type name and size. The size represents the number of bytes needed to represent the given hardware type. Table 6.2 lists the basic type translations for standard C, Fortran, and Java compilers.

## Structured Data Formats

In addition to the basic types listed in Table 6.2, Maple also recognizes some compound types that can be derived from the basic types, such as arrays and pointers. These compound types are listed in Table 6.3 on page 393.

**Character String Data Formats** Strings are similar to both scalar and array data. A string in C is an array of characters, but it is often manipulated as if it were an object. A string in Maple is an atomic object, but it can be manipulated as if it were an array of characters.

Parameter *n* in *string[n]* indicates that the called function is expecting a fixed size string. Otherwise, a pointer to a character buffer (`char*`) is used.

Strings are implicitly passed by reference (only a pointer to the string is passed), but any changes made to the string are not copied back to Maple unless the string is declared with a size. Declaring a size on a string to be passed to a Java method has no effect. The string size will not be limited, and modifications are not copied back.

**Array Data Formats** An array of data is a homogeneous, n-rectangular structure matching the Maple `rtable` formats. Any `datatype` that is accepted by the Maple `Array`, `Matrix`, or `Vector` constructor are accepted.

The *options* are used to specify array conventions. They are the same optional arguments that can be passed to the `Array` constructor in Maple. The only significant difference is that indexing functions must be specified with `indfn=` (and are not allowed unless using custom wrapper external calling). These options override any defaults normally assumed by the `Array` constructor.

**datatype=...** Only hardware datatypes are allowed. This field is required, but the equation form of entry is not necessary. For example, simply specifying `integer[4]` is sufficient.

**order=...** This can be unspecified for vectors because Fortran and C representation is the same. Otherwise, this defaults to `Fortran_order` when calling a Fortran library and `C_order` when calling a C or Java library.

**storage=...** If this is not specified, the default is full rectangular storage

**subtype=...** This is optional and restricts the subtype to `Array`, `Matrix`, `Vector[row]`, or `Vector[column]`.

**indfn=(..., ...)** This specifies the indexing functions of the `Array`, `Matrix`, or `Vector`.

**Other Compound Types** There are other types, including records (structs), and procedures that are supported when using wrapper generated external linking. These data descriptors are described in **Method 2: Generating Wrappers** on page 338.

## Specifying Argument Passing Conventions

Different programming languages have different conventions for parameter passing. C always uses *pass-by-value*; *pass-by-reference* must be done explicitly by passing an address. Fortran uses pass-by-reference. Pascal uses either, depending on how the parameter was declared.

The Maple external calling mechanism currently supports C, Fortran, and Java calling conventions. Automatic wrapper generation is only supported for C. There is an external API for writing custom wrappers for C and Fortran but not Java. The default convention used is C. To use Fortran calling, specify the name `FORTRAN` as a parameter to `define_external`.

```
> f := define_external(`my_func`,`FORTRAN`, ...);
```

To use Java calling, specify the name `JAVA` as a parameter to `define_external`. Also, specify the `CLASSPATH=` option to point to classes used.

```
> f := define_external(`my_func`,`JAVA`, CLASSPATH="...", ...);
```

Some other compiler implementations (such as Pascal and C++) can work with C external calling by using the correct definitions and order of passed parameters.

## Method 2: Generating Wrappers

Some types in Maple are not suitable for automatic conversions. Two of these types are procedures (callbacks), and records (structs). Maple provides an alternate mechanism for handling this kind of data.

For a description of the steps required to use compiled code in Maple, see **Method 1: Calling External Functions** on page 332. The same three basic steps (DLL creation, function specification, and function invocation as described on pages 332-334) are used in this method. The information in this section extends the basic information by describing the use of wrappers.

Specifying the keyword `WRAPPER` in the call to `define_external` causes Maple to generate code for data translations. Maple compiles this code into a DLL and dynamically links to the new library. Subsequently invoking the procedure returned by `define_external` calls the newly generated conversion routine before calling the external function in the library you provided.

The C code generated by Maple wraps the Maple data structures by translating them to hardware equivalent types. Hence, the code file is called the *wrapper*, and the library generated by this code is called the *wrapper library*.

## Additional Types and Options

Generating a wrapper file allows Maple to translate more complicated types that are difficult to handle without compilation technology. It also allows greater flexibility when dealing with pointers and passed data that do not exactly match the required type.

Table 6.4 on page 394 lists additional types that are supported when the keyword `WRAPPER` is specified.

## Structured Data Formats

A structure is a non-homogeneous collection of members, corresponding to a *struct* in C, or a *record* in Pascal. A *union* is similar, except that all the members start at the same memory address.

Each *member :: descriptor* pair describes one member of the structure or union. The descriptor is any of the types described in this chapter.

The *options* are used to specify what kind of datatype the wrapper should expect for conversion purposes. The following two options are supported.

**TABLE** Tables are used as the corresponding Maple type. Using tables is the default behavior, and they are easier to use than lists. When tables are used, the *member* names correspond to table indices.

**LIST** Lists are used as the corresponding Maple type. Lists are primarily used in a read-only basis. Lists cannot be modified *in-place*, so making updates to a list structure in external code requires a copy to be made. When structures must be passed back to Maple, or if they contain pointer types, it is better to use tables.

Lists and tables cannot be used interchangeably. Once the wrapper has been generated, it accepts only the declared type, not both.

## Enumerated Types

The Maple external calling mechanism does not directly support enumerated types (such as *enum* in C). Instead, use the `integer[n]` type with `n` of an appropriate size to match the size of the enumerated type of the compiler with which the external function was compiled (usually this is the same size as the *int* type).

## Procedure Call Formats

Some languages, like C, support passing functions as arguments. A Maple procedure can be passed to an external function in the same way. The wrapper sets up a C style procedure to call Maple to execute the passed procedure with the given arguments. This C callback is given to the external call to be used like any other C function.

Each *member :: descriptor* pair describes one parameter of the procedure. The *descriptor* is any of the types described in this chapter.

It is not permitted to declare a procedure that itself takes a procedure parameter. In other words, a callback cannot itself call back to the external code.

## Call by Reference

Unless overridden, each argument is passed by value. The REF modifier can be used to override this.

```
argumentIdentifer :: REF( dataDescriptor, options )
```

The REF modifier can take the following options.

**ANYTHING** This option must be first in the list of options. Use this option to declare the equivalent of a C *void** parameter. The wrapper code attempts to convert passed arguments to simple types, (4-byte integer, 8-byte float, complex, or string), when encountered. If no conversion to one of these types is possible, NULL is passed to the external function.

**CALL_ONLY** This option specifies that although the object is to be passed by reference, any changes made by the external function are not written to the Maple symbol that was passed. This can be used both to protect the objects passed (see the following **Array Options** section), and to reduce overhead (as no translation back to Maple data structures need be made).

**RETURN_ONLY** This option specifies that no data is actually passed to the external function. Instead, only a reference to the allocated space is passed, and the external function is expected to fill the space with data. The result is converted into an appropriate Maple object.

## Array Options

If an ARRAY argument is declared as CALL_ONLY and an Array, Matrix, or Vector with proper settings is passed to the external function (so that no copying is required), `CALL_ONLY` has no effect and thus does not prevent the called function from overwriting the original array. To prevent this from occurring, include the option `COPY` in the `ARRAY` descriptor.

The `ARRAY` descriptor accepts extra options when used with wrapper generation. These options can be specified as follows.

```
ARRAY( dim1, ..., dimN, datatype=typename,
       order=..., ..., options )
```

The *dim1* through *dimN* parameters are integer ranges, specifying the range of each dimension of the array. Any of the upper or lower bounds may be the name of another argument, in which case the value of that argument specifies the corresponding array bound at run time.

The *options* are used to specify how an array is passed. The following are valid options.

**COPY** Do not operate *in-place* on the given array. That is, make a copy first, and use the copy for passing to and from the external function.

**NO_COPY** This ensures that a copy of the data is never made. Usually, when using a wrapper generated external call, if the `Array`, `Matrix`, or `Vector` is of the wrong type, (say the order is wrong), a copy is made with the correct properties before passing it to the external function. Using `NO_COPY` prevents this. Also, the returned array has the properties of the copy. If `NO_COPY` is specified, and an `Array`, `Matrix`, or `Vector` with incorrect options is passed, an exception is raised. Arrays are always passed by reference. If no options are given (via a `REF` descriptor), they are passed by using the `CALL_ONLY` behavior of `REF` with the noted exception described at the beginning of this section.

## Non-passed Arguments

Sometimes it is necessary to pass additional arguments to the Maple wrapper that should not be passed on to the external function. For example, consider the following hypothetical C function:

```
int sum( int *v1, int *v2 )
```

This function takes two integer vectors, `v1` and `v2`, and adds the elements of `v2` to `v1`, stopping when it finds an entry that is zero. The generated wrapper can be made to verify whether the vectors are the same size. The Maple definition for this function is as follows.

```
> Sum := define_external( 'sum',
>           v1 :: ARRAY(1..size,integer[4]),
>           v2 :: ARRAY(1..size,integer[4]),
>           size :: NO_PASS(integer[4]),
>           RETURN :: integer[4],
>           LIB="libsum.dll");
```

The NO_PASS modifier specifies that the size argument should not be passed to the external function. The Sum function is then called by the following statement,

```
> Sum(v1,v2,op(1,v1));
```

where v1 and v2 are vectors. Maple passes the vector data, or a copy of the vector data, to the external sum function. It does not pass the size element to the external function, but size is used for argument checking (because the NO_CHECK option was not specified).

Note that this option can only be used for top-level arguments. That is, it is *invalid* to declare a callback procedure's arguments as NO_PASS.

## Argument Checking and Efficiency Considerations

It is intended that the time and space costs of calling an external function not be any higher than the costs for calling an equivalent built-in function with the same degree of argument type checking. The amount of type checking done by a generated Maple language wrapper exceeds that done by most internal functions, so there is some additional overhead.

The define_external function has an option NO_CHECK which, if used, disables the type checking done by the Maple-language wrapper. For frequently called external functions that perform simple operations this can significantly improve performance. However, there is a risk associated with using the NO_CHECK option. If you pass an object of the wrong type, the generated C-language wrapper might misinterpret what it has received, resulting in erroneous translations to external types, and hence unpredictable behavior of the external function.

## Conversions

When the procedure returned by define_external is called, the Maple arguments that are passed are converted to the corresponding arguments of the external function. Likewise, the value returned from the external function is converted to the corresponding Maple type.

The following table describes the external types and the Maple types that can be converted. The first listed Maple type is the one to which a result of the corresponding external type is converted into.

| External Type | Allowed Maple Type(s) |
|---|---|
| boolean[n] | boolean |
| integer[n] | integer |
| float[n] | float, rational, integer, numeric |
| complex[n] | complex, numeric, float, rational, integer |
| char[n] | one-character string |
| string[n] | string, symbol, 0 |
| ARRAY() | Array, Vector, Matrix, name, 0 |
| STRUCT() | list, table |
| UNION() | table |
| PROC() | procedure |

For STRUCTs, either lists or tables are valid for a particular declaration. Once declared, only one of the types (a list or a table) is acceptable. They cannot be used interchangeably unless the wrapper is regenerated. For UNIONs, only tables are permitted, and the table must contain exactly one entry when passed (corresponding to one of the members of the union).

If an argument of an incompatible type is passed, an error occurs, and the external function is not called. Likewise, if a value is passed that is out of range for the specified type (for example, integer too large), an error occurs. When passing floating-point values, precision in excess of that supported by the external type is discarded, provided the magnitude of the value is within the range of the external type.

Arguments that were declared as REFerences, that is, passed by-reference, can be passed either a name, a zero, or the declared kind of Maple expression.

- If a name is passed, it is evaluated, and the value is passed by reference to the external function. After the external function returns, the revised value is converted back to the type specified for the argument and assigned back to the name.

- If the name passed has no value, then either NULL is passed, or a pointer to newly allocated space for the structure is passed. This behavior is determined by the presence or absence of ALLOC in the REF declaration.

- If a zero is passed, NULL is passed to the external function.

- If any other Maple expression is passed, its value is passed by reference, and the revised value is discarded.

## Compiler Options

To compile the wrapper library, Maple requires the use of a C compiler installed on the same machine that is running Maple. Maple generates a system command to call the compiler. The compiler must be recognized by the system. It should be in the system PATH and all associated environment variables must be set.

The compile and link commands are completely customizable provided that your compiler has a command-line interface. Default configurations are provided, which should make most cases work "out of the box." Maple is preprogrammed to use the vendor-supplied C compiler to compile wrappers on most platforms.[1]

All default compile and link options are stored in a module that can be obtained by using the command `define_external('COMPILE_OPTIONS')`. When the module returned by this command is modified, the modification affects all wrapper generation commands via `define_external` for the remainder of the session. Any of the names exported by the compile options module can also be specified as a parameter to `define_external`. When specified as a parameter, the effect lasts only for the duration of that call.

The compile and link commands are assembled by calling the `COMPILE_COMMAND` and `LINK_COMMAND` procedures defined in the compile options module. These procedures make use of the definitions in the compile options module to formulate a command string that is executed using `ssystem`.[2]

To customize the compile and link commands, you can modify the following options. All option values must be strings or `NULL`, except for `COMPILE_COMMAND` and `LINK_COMMAND`, which must be procedures or `NULL`.

**COMPILER** This specifies the name of the compiler executable.

**CFLAGS** This specifies miscellaneous flags passed to the compiler.

**COMPILE_ONLY_FLAG** This flag indicates that the file is only to be compiled. On most platforms it is "`-c`", which causes the compiler to generate an object file, but not link it to form any executable or library. A separate command performs the linking.

[1] In Microsoft Windows, Maple uses the Microsoft Visual C Compiler.

[2] If using the Microsoft C compiler, the `LINK_COMMAND` is set to `NULL` because the `COMPILE_COMMAND` does both the compiling and linking.

**COBJ_FLAG** This is the flag used by the compiler to specify the object filename. The compiler command uses `COBJ_FLAG || FILE || OBJ_EXT` to name the object file. On most platforms it is "-o".

**LOBJ_FLAG** This is the flag used by the linker to specify the target library name. The link command uses `LOBJ_FLAG || FILE || DLL_EXT` to name the shared library.

**FILE** This is the base name of the file to be compiled. The file extension must not be included in this name. For example, to compile "`foo.c`", set `FILE="foo"` and `FILE_EXT=".c"`. When `FILE` is set to `NULL` the system generates a file name based on the function name.

**FILE_EXT** This is the program file extension. If you want to compile "`foo.c`", set `FILE_EXT=".c"`, and `FILE="foo"`.

**OBJ_EXT** This is the object file extension. Common extensions are "`.o`" and "`.obj`".

**DLL_EXT** This is the dynamic library extension. Common extensions are "`.dll`" and "`.so`".

**INC_FLAG** This precedes directories in the `INC_PATH`. On most platforms it is "`-I`".

**INC_PATH** This specifies the directories to search for header files. Use an expression sequence to specify more than one directory, for example, `INC_PATH=("/usr/local/maple/extern/include", "/users/jdoe/include")`.

**COMPILE_COMMAND** This is set to the procedure that generates the compiler command. The procedure must return a string. In general, it is not necessary to change the default.

**LINKER** This specifies the name of the linker executable.

**LINK_FLAGS** This specifies miscellaneous flags passed to the linker, including those that cause the linker to build a dynamic (shared) library.

**LIB_FLAG** This precedes directories in the `LIB_PATH`. On most platforms it is "`-L`".

**LIB_PATH** This specifies the directories to search for libraries. Use an expression sequence to specify more than one directory, for example, `LIB_PATH=("/usr/local/maple/extern/lib","/users/jdoe/lib")`.

**LIB** This names the library which contains the external function to call. This option must be specified in every call to `define_external`.

**LIBS** This specifies other libraries that need to be linked with the wrapper library to resolve all external symbols. Use an expression sequence to specify more than one library, for example, `LIBS=("/usr/local/maple/extern/lib/libtest.so","/users/jdoe/libdoe.so")`.

**SYS_LIBS** This specifies system libraries to link with the wrapper library to resolve all external symbols. Use an expression sequence to specify more than one library, for example, `LIBS=("-lc","-lm")`.

**EXPORT_FLAG** This flag is used in combination with the `FUNCTION` option to name the function to be exported from the shared library. This is unassigned or set to `NULL` on platforms that export all symbols by default.

**FUNCTION** This is the name of the external function defined in the wrapper library. The system generates a `FUNCTION` name if this is left unassigned or set to `NULL`.

**LINK_COMMAND** This is set to the procedure that generates the linker command. The procedure must return a string. Set this to `NULL` if the compile command also does the linking.

A common use of these options as parameters to `define_external` with a standard compiler would be to specify the filename. For example, the following generates a wrapper file named "`foo.c`".

```
> f := define_external(‘myfunc‘,‘WRAPPER‘,‘FILE‘="foo",‘LIB‘=
>                       "mylib.dll"):
```

To use a non-standard compiler or to alter compile flags, assign directly to the compile options module.

**Example** The following example shows how to set up the GNU compiler on a machine running Solaris.

```
> p := define_external(‘COMPILE_OPTIONS‘):
> p:-COMPILER := "gcc";
> p:-COBJ_FLAG := "-o ":
> define_external(‘mat_mult‘,‘WRAPPER‘,‘LIB‘="libcexttest.so"):
```

The gcc requires a space between -o and the object name. Modifying the `COBJ_FLAG` allows this to be easily done. All other option default values are acceptable.

To view the executed commands, set the `infolevel` for `define_external` to 3 or higher. Repeating the previous example you might see the following.

```
> p := define_external('COMPILE_OPTIONS'):
> p:-COMPILER := "gcc";
> p:-COBJ_FLAG := "-o ":
> infolevel[define_external] := 3:
> define_external('mat_mult','WRAPPER','LIB'="libcexttest.so"):
```

```
"COMPILE_COMMAND"
"gcc  -g -c -I/user/local/maple/extern/include -o \
 mwrap_mat_mult.o mwrap_mat_mult.c"
"LINK_COMMAND"
"ld -znodefs -G -dy -Bdynamic
 -L/user/local/maple/bin/bin.SUN_SPARC_SOLARIS \
 -omwrap_mat_mult.so mwrap_mat_mult.o -lc -lmaplec"
```

Another way to view the compile and link commands is to call the command-builder procedures directly. Ensure to set or unassign the variables that will be assigned, otherwise they are blank.

```
> p := define_external('COMPILE_OPTIONS'):
> p:-COMPILER := "gcc";
> p:-COBJ_FLAG := "-o ":
> p:-COMPILE_COMMAND();
```

```
"gcc  -g -c -I/u/maple/extern/include -o .o .c"
```

```
> unassign('p:-FILE');
> p:-COMPILE_COMMAND();
```

```
"gcc  -g -c -I/u/maple/extern/include -o FILE.o FILE.c"
```

**Example** The following example shows two calls to `define_external` separated by the `restart` command. The first call does *not* use the `WRAPLIB` option and thus generates `quad.c` and compiles the wrapper library `quad.dll`. The second call uses the `WRAPLIB` option to reuse the existing `quad.dll`. No compilation or wrapper generation is done in the second call.

```
> quadruple_it := define_external('quadruple_it',
>                     WRAPPER,FILE="quad",
>                     x::float[4],
>                     RETURN::float[4],
>                     LIB="test.dll"):
> quadruple_it(2.2);
```

$$8.80000019073486328$$

```
> restart;
> quadruple_it := define_external('quadruple_it',
>                     WRAPPER,FILE="quad",
>                     x::float[4],
>                     RETURN::float[4],
>                     WRAPLIB="quad.dll",
>                     LIB="test.dll"):
> quadruple_it(2.2);
```

$$8.80000019073486328$$

When DLLs are created and compiled at runtime it is important *not* to duplicate the name of a previously generated DLL without restarting Maple (either by exiting Maple or issuing the `restart` command). Maple maintains an open connection with the first DLL opened with any given name. Attempting to create a new DLL of the same name without restarting can lead to unexpected results. The Maple command `dlclose` can be used to avoid restarting, but subsequently calling any external function in that closed DLL without reissuing the `define_external` command will likely crash Maple.

## Evaluation Rules

External functions follow normal Maple evaluation rules in that the arguments are evaluated during a function call. It therefore may be necessary to enclose assigned names in right single quotes when passing-by-reference. For example, consider the following function that multiplies a number by two in-place.

```
void double_it( int *i )
{
    if( i == NULL ) return;

    *i *= 2;
}
```

In Maple, the wrapperless definition of this function might appear as follows.

```
> double_it := define_external('double_it', i::REF(integer[4]),
>                              LIB="libtest.dll");
```

When executing this function, the argument 'i' is converted from the Maple internal representation of an integer to a 4-byte hardware integer. A pointer to the hardware integer is then passed to the external function, 'double_it'. Though 'i' is declared as a pointer to an integer, it is acceptable to call 'double_it' with non-pointer input.

```
> double_it(3);
```

In this case, a pointer to the hardware integer 3 is sent to 'double_it'. The modified value is not accessible from Maple. To access the modified value, the parameter must be named. The name must be enclosed in right single quotes to prevent evaluation.

```
> n:=3;
> double_it(n);  # n is evaluated first, so 3 is passed
> n;
```

3

```
> double_it('n');  # use unevaluation quotes to pass 'n'
> n;
```

6

For numeric data, the string "NULL" can be passed as a parameter to represent the address 0 (the C NULL). For strings, because "NULL" is a valid string, the integer 0 represents address 0.

```
> double_it("NULL");
>
> concat := define_external('concat',
>     RETURN::string, a::string, b::string,
>     LIB="libtest.dll"):
> concat("NULL","x");
```

"NULLx"

```
> concat(0,0);
```

0

In the concat example, the C code might look like the following. Note that this function does not clean memory as it should.

```
char * concat( char* a, char *b )
{
    char *r;

    if( !a || !b ) return( NULL );

    r = (char*)malloc((strlen(a)+strlen(b)+1)*sizeof(char));

    strcpy(r,a);
    strcat(r,b);

    return( r );
}
```

## Method 3: Customizing Wrappers

For complete control over data conversions, Maple allows modification of existing wrappers and creation of custom wrappers. There are numerous C and Fortran functions available for translating and manipulating Maple data structures.

To use this method, you must be familiar with the steps required to use compiled code in Maple, described in **Method 1: Calling External Functions** on page 332. For this method, you do *not* declare a function specification because Maple passes one data structure containing all the passed information. Therefore, there are only two basic steps (DLL creation and function invocation as described on pages 332-333) in addition to wrapper generation. Wrappers were introduced in **Method 2: Generating Wrappers** on page 338.

## External Function Entry Point

Maple finds the symbol name given as the first argument to define_external in the DLL specified in the LIB= argument. Maple also finds the MWRAP_symbolName in the wrapper library. This MWRAP_symbolName function prototype has the following format.

```
ALGEB MWRAP_quadruple_it(
```

```
    MKernelVector kv,
    FLOAT32 (*fn) ( FLOAT32 a1 ),
    ALGEB fn_args
);
```

This prototype is taken from the wrapper `quad.c` described in the previous section. The first argument `kv` is a handle to the Maple kernel function vector. The second argument `fn` is a function pointer assigned the symbol found in the external DLL. In this case, `fn` is assigned the `quadruple_it` external function. The last argument is a Maple expression sequence data structure containing all the arguments passed to the function during any given call to the Maple procedure generated by the `define_external` command.

The entry point is the format used when wrappers are automatically generated, and when `WRAPLIB` is specified. An alternate external entry point that excludes the function pointer is available when the parameter `MAPLE` is specified instead of `WRAPPER` or `WRAPLIB`.

```
ALGEB MWRAP_quadruple_it(
    MKernelVector kv,
    ALGEB fn_args
);
```

The API function prototypes for manipulating Maple data structures are in `$MAPLE/extern/include` where `$MAPLE` is the path of the Maple installation. The header file `maplec.h` should be included when writing custom C wrappers. One of the header files, `maplefortran.hf` or `maplefortran64bit.hf`, should be included when writing custom Fortran wrappers. Other header files, `mplshlib.h`, and `mpltable.h` contain macros, types, and data structures that are needed for direct manipulation of Maple data structures.

Maple uses directed acyclic graphs (dags) to represent all objects, such as integers, floating point numbers, sums, modules, or procedures. (For more information about Maple internal representation of objects, see Appendix A.) These dags have the type `ALGEB` in C wrappers, and `INTEGER` or `INTEGER*8` in Fortran wrappers. Fortran 77 has no user type definition semantics so `ALGEB` pointers must be "faked" by using machine word-sized integers. If the machine word size is 64-bit (for example, as on a DEC Alpha), the header `maplefortran64bit.hf` must be used and `INTEGER*8` must be used as the dag datatype. Execute the Maple command `kernelopts(wordsize)` to determine whether you need to use 32-bit or 64-bit integer-dag types in Fortran. When working with C, the datatype is `ALGEB` regardless of the machine word size.

You do not have to know the internal details of dags to manipulate and use them. The only exception is the argument sequence passed to the wrapper entry point. This is an expression seqence (EXPSEQ) dag, and can be treated as an array of dags starting at index 1 (not 0). Thus, fn_args[1] is the first parameter passed to the external function. Use MapleNumArgs to determine the number of arguments passed. Note that the Fortran API uses a slightly different naming convention. The equivalent Fortran call is maple_num_args. The C API names are used for the remainder of this chapter. To find equivalent Fortran names, refer to the API listing.

## Inspecting Automatically Generated Wrappers

The easiest way to start writing custom wrappers is to inspect automatically generated wrappers. Consider the add function that was introduced at the beginning of this chapter. Use the WRAPPER option to tell define_external to generate a wrapper. Also use the NO_COMPILE option with define_external so as not to compile the generated wrapper. The name of the generated file is returned.

```
> myAdd := define_external(
>     'add',
>     'WRAPPER',
>     'NO_COMPILE',
>     'num1'::integer[4],
>     'num2'::integer[4],
>     'RETURN'::integer[4]
> );
```

```
                    myAdd := "mwrap_add.c"
```

The file mwrap_add.c resembles the following.

```
/* MWRAP_add Wrapper
   Generated automatically by Maple
   Do not edit this file. */

#include <stdio.h>
#include <stdlib.h>
#include <string.h>
#include <mplshlib.h>
#include <maplec.h>

MKernelVector mapleKernelVec;
typedef void *MaplePointer;
```

```
ALGEB *args;

/* main - MWRAP_add */
ALGEB MWRAP_add( MKernelVector kv,
        INTEGER32 (*fn) ( INTEGER32 a1, INTEGER32 a2 ),
        ALGEB fn_args )
{
    INTEGER32 a1;
    INTEGER32 a2;
    INTEGER32 r;
    ALGEB mr;
    int i;
    mapleKernelVec = kv;
    args = (ALGEB*) fn_args;

    if( MapleNumArgs(mapleKernelVec,(ALGEB)args) != 2 )
        MapleRaiseError(mapleKernelVec,"Incorrect number
        of arguments");

    /* integer[4] */
    a1 = MapleToInteger32(mapleKernelVec,args[1]);

    /* integer[4] */
    a2 = MapleToInteger32(mapleKernelVec,args[2]);
    r = (*fn)(a1, a2);

    mr = ToMapleInteger(mapleKernelVec,(long) r);
    return( mr );
}
```

The generated wrapper is a good starting point for creating wrappers. There may be some extra variables and declarations used because the wrapper generation is generic. For example, the use of `args` rather than `fn_args` avoids the need for a cast with `args[1]`, but it also is a static global which is useful when working with callbacks that need access to the argument sequence outside the main entry point.

Remember that the `add` function simply added the arguments `a1` and `a2` and returned the result. This can be done directly in the wrapper. By removing the second argument `fn` so the `MAPLE` option can be used, plus inlining the `a1+a2` functionality and cleaning up the code, the wrapper resembles the following.

```
/* Program to add two numbers from Maple */

 #include <stdio.h>
 #include <stdlib.h>
 #include <maplec.h>

 /* main entry point - MWRAP_add */
 ALGEB myAdd( MKernelVector kv, ALGEB fn_args )
 {
     INTEGER32 a1;     /* INTEGER32 => int (defined in */
                       /* mpltable.h) */
     INTEGER32 a2;
     INTEGER32 r;

     if( MapleNumArgs(kv,fn_args) != 2 )
         MapleRaiseError(kv,"Incorrect number of arguments");

     /* convert from Maple integer to C int */
     a1 = MapleToInteger32(kv,((ALGEB*)fn_args)[1]);

     /* convert from Maple integer to C int */
     a2 = MapleToInteger32(kv,((ALGEB*)fn_args)[2]);

     r = a1 + a2;

     return( ToMapleInteger(kv,(long) r) );
 }
```

This program first verifies if the Maple function call passed exactly two arguments. It then converts the two arguments to hardware integers and adds them. The result is converted to a Maple integer and returned.

This program can be compiled into a DLL using your favorite C compiler. Ensure that you link with the Maple API shared library. The DLL can be placed into the Maple `bin.$SYSTEM` directory, or somewhere else in the PATH. When using DLLs outside of `bin.$SYSTEM` directory, you may need to specify the full path to the DLL in the `LIB` argument to `define_external`. UNIX developers may need to set their load-library-path.

Table 6.5 on page 395 lists the Maple API Libraries for C and Fortran.

After compiling the DLL, the function can be used in Maple. No type desciptors are needed in the `define_external` call because Maple does no conversion on arguments passed to the custom wrapper.

```
> myAdd := define_external('myAdd','MAPLE','LIB'=
>                          "myAdd.dll"):
> myAdd(2,3);
```

5

```
> myAdd(2.2,1);
```

```
Error, (in myAdd) integer expected for integer[4] parameter
```

```
> myAdd(2^80,2^70);
```

```
Error, (in myAdd) integer too large in context
```

The equivalent Fortran wrapper would look like the following.

```
Program to add two numbers from Maple


INTEGER FUNCTION myAdd(kv, args)

INCLUDE "maplefortran.hf"
INTEGER kv
INTEGER args

INTEGER arg
INTEGER a1, a2, r
CHARACTER ERRMSG*20
INTEGER ERRMSGLEN

ERRMSGLEN = 20

IF ( maple_num_args(kv, args) .NE. 2 ) THEN
     ERRMSG = 'Incorrect number of arguments'
     CALL maple_raise_error( kv, ERRMSG, ERRMSGLEN )
     myAdd = to_maple_null( kv )
     RETURN
ENDIF
```

```
arg = maple_extract_arg( kv, args, 1 )
a1 = maple_to_integer32(kv, arg)

arg = maple_extract_arg( kv, args, 2 )
a2 = maple_to_integer32(kv, arg)

r = a1 + a2

myAdd = to_maple_integer( kv, r )

END
```

Once compiled into a DLL, the same syntax can be used in Maple to access the function. The only difference is the additional keyword 'FORTRAN' in the define_external call.

```
> myAdd := define_external('myAdd','MAPLE','FORTRAN','LIB'=
>                          "myAdd.dll"):
> myAdd(2,3);
```

5

## External API

An external API is provided for users who want to augment existing wrappers or write their own custom wrappers. This section describes the functions available when linking with the Maple API library (see Table 6.5 on page 395) and including either maplec.h or maplefortran.hf.

**Argument Checking** The following C function can be used to query the number of arguments contained in the argument expression sequence passed as the last argument to the external function entry point. The expression sequence passed to this entry point can be queried directly (for example, ((ALGEB*)expr)[1]). If n = MapleNumArgs(kv,expr), the last argument is ((ALGEB*)expr[n].

```
M_INT MapleNumArgs( MKernelVector kv, ALGEB expr );
```

The arguments passed to the Fortran entry point cannot be queried directly. The maple_extract_arg function must be used to access the argument data (for example, arg1 = maple_extract_arg(kv,args,1)). If n = maple_num_args(kv,s), then the last argument is maple_extract_arg(kv,args,n).

```
INTEGER maple_num_args( kv, s )
INTEGER maple_extract_arg( kv, s, i )
```

The following functions indicate the type of the given Maple object.

```
M_BOOL IsMapleAssignedName( MKernelVector kv, ALGEB s );
M_BOOL IsMapleComplexNumeric( MKernelVector kv, ALGEB s );
M_BOOL IsMapleNumeric( MKernelVector kv, ALGEB s );
M_BOOL IsMapleInteger( MKernelVector kv, ALGEB s );
M_BOOL IsMapleInteger8( MKernelVector kv, ALGEB s );
M_BOOL IsMapleInteger16( MKernelVector kv, ALGEB s );
M_BOOL IsMapleInteger32( MKernelVector kv, ALGEB s );
M_BOOL IsMapleInteger64( MKernelVector kv, ALGEB s );
M_BOOL IsMapleName( MKernelVector kv, ALGEB s );
M_BOOL IsMapleNULL( MKernelVector kv, ALGEB s );
M_BOOL IsMaplePointer( MKernelVector kv, ALGEB s );
M_BOOL IsMaplePointerNULL( MKernelVector kv, ALGEB s );
M_BOOL IsMapleProcedure( MKernelVector kv, ALGEB s );
M_BOOL IsMapleRTable( MKernelVector kv, ALGEB s );
M_BOOL IsMapleString( MKernelVector kv, ALGEB s );
M_BOOL IsMapleTable( MKernelVector kv, ALGEB s );
M_BOOL IsMapleUnassignedName( MKernelVector kv, ALGEB s );
M_BOOL IsMapleUnnamedZero( MKernelVector kv, ALGEB s );
```

Equivalent Fortran functions are as follows. The C functions, `IsMaplePointer`, `IsMaplePointerNULL`, and `IsMapleUnnamedZero` are not available in the Fortran API.

```
INTEGER is_maple_assigned_name( kv, s )
INTEGER is_maple_complex_numeric( kv, s )
INTEGER is_maple_numeric( kv, s )
INTEGER is_maple_integer( kv, s )
INTEGER is_maple_integer8( kv, s )
INTEGER is_maple_integer16( kv, s )
INTEGER is_maple_integer32( kv, s )
INTEGER is_maple_integer64( kv, s )
INTEGER is_maple_name( kv, s )
INTEGER is_maple_null( kv, s )
INTEGER is_maple_procedure( kv, s )
INTEGER is_maple_rtable( kv, s )
INTEGER is_maple_string( kv, s )
INTEGER is_maple_table( kv, s )
INTEGER is_maple_unassigned_name( kv, s )
```

These functions all return `TRUE (1)` when the Maple dag `s` fits the description given by the function name. If `s` is not of the correct type, `FALSE (0)` is returned. The Maple `NULL` is not the same as a C *Pointer-NULL*. The former is the empty expression sequence in the Maple language. The latter is a pointer variable set to the address zero. Since there is no concept of real pointers in the Maple Language, the idea of *Pointer-NULL* in this context means the Maple integer zero, or an unassigned Maple name. The `IsMaple...Numeric` routines use the Maple type `numeric` definition. All other checks use the dag type definition. For example, `type(t[1],name)` returns `true` in Maple, but `IsMapleName` checks for a `NAME` dag and returns `FALSE` because `t[1]` is internally represented as a `TABLEREF` dag. Integer query routines with the bit size specified in the name check to ensure the given Maple object `s` is a Maple integer and also that it could fit into the specified number of bits if converted to a hardware integer.

**Conversions From Maple Objects** The following functions return the specified type when given a dag `s` that can be converted to that type.

```
COMPLEXF32 MapleToComplexFloat32( MKernelVector kv, ALGEB s );
COMPLEXF64 MapleToComplexFloat64( MKernelVector kv, ALGEB s );
CXDAG MapleToComplexFloatDAG( MKernelVector kv, ALGEB s );
FLOAT32 MapleToFloat32( MKernelVector kv, ALGEB s );
FLOAT64 MapleToFloat64( MKernelVector kv, ALGEB s );
INTEGER8 MapleToInteger8( MKernelVector kv, ALGEB s );
INTEGER16 MapleToInteger16( MKernelVector kv, ALGEB s );
INTEGER32 MapleToInteger32( MKernelVector kv, ALGEB s );
INTEGER64 MapleToInteger64( MKernelVector kv, ALGEB s );
M_BOOL MapleToM_BOOL( MKernelVector kv, ALGEB s );
M_INT MapleToM_INT( MKernelVector kv, ALGEB s );
void* MapleToPointer( MKernelVector kv, ALGEB s );
char* MapleToString( MKernelVector kv, ALGEB s );
```

The following are the equivalent Fortran routines. Note that complex and string conversion are done by reference. That is, the third argument passed to the function is set to the converted value rather than the function returning the value. Equivalent functions for `MapleToComplexFloatDAG` and `MapleToPointer` are not available.

```
SUBROUTINE maple_to_complex_float32( kv, s, c )
SUBROUTINE maple_to_complex_float64( kv, s, c )
REAL maple_to_float32( kv, s )
DOUBLEPRECISION maple_to_float64( kv, s )
```

```
INTEGER maple_to_integer8( kv, s )
INTEGER maple_to_integer16( kv, s )
INTEGER maple_to_integer32( kv, s )
INTEGER*8 maple_to_integer64( kv, s )
INTEGER maple_to_m_bool( kv, s )
INTEGER maple_to_m_int( kv, s )
INTEGER maple_to_string( kv, s, string )
```

Floating Point numbers may lose precision during the conversion to hardware size data.

Conversion from a `STRING` dag to an integer returns the ASCII value of the first character in that string. Conversion from a Maple `Boolean` to an integer returns `1` for `true` or `0` for `false`.

Conversions from a `STRING` dag to a string should not be modified in-place. A copy should be made if any modifications are necessary.

The `MapleToPointer` conversion returns the pointer value stored in a Maple `BINARY` dag.

**Conversions To Maple Objects** The following functions return a dag of the specified dag type when given a dag the corresponding hardware data.

```
ALGEB ToMapleBoolean( MKernelVector kv, long b );
ALGEB ToMapleChar( MKernelVector kv, long c );
ALGEB ToMapleComplex( MKernelVector kv, double re,
        double im );
ALGEB ToMapleComplexFloat( MKernelVector kv, ALGEB re,
        ALGEB im );
ALGEB ToMapleExpressionSequence( MKernelVector kv, int
        nargs, /* ALGEB arg1, ALGEB arg2, */ ... );
ALGEB ToMapleInteger( MKernelVector kv, long i );
ALGEB ToMapleInteger64( MKernelVector kv, INTEGER64 i );
ALGEB ToMapleFloat( MKernelVector kv, double f );
ALGEB ToMapleName( MKernelVector kv, char *n, M_BOOL
        is_global );
ALGEB ToMapleNULL( MKernelVector kv );
ALGEB ToMapleNULLPointer( MKernelVector kv );
ALGEB ToMaplePointer( MKernelVector kv, void *v, M_INT
        type );
ALGEB ToMapleRelation( MKernelVector kv, const char *rel,
        ALGEB lhs, ALGEB rhs );
ALGEB ToMapleString( MKernelVector kv, char *s );
```

```
ALGEB ToMapleUneval( MKernelVector kv, ALGEB s );
```

The equivalent Fortran routines are as follows. The Fortran API does not support ToMapleExpressionSequence, ToMapleNULLPointer, ToMaplePointer, ToMapleRelation, or ToMapleUneval.

```
to_maple_boolean( kv, b )
to_maple_char( kv, c )
to_maple_complex( kv, re, im )
to_maple_complex_float( kv, re, im )
to_maple_integer( kv, i )
to_maple_integer64( kv, i )
to_maple_float( kv, f )
to_maple_name( kv, s, s_len )
to_maple_null( kv )
to_maple_string( kv, s, s_len )
```

ToMapleBoolean is three valued. When b is zero, it returns the Maple false dag. If n is -1, the Maple FAIL dag is returned. If n is non-zero (and not -1), the Maple true dag is returned.

ToMapleChar returns a single character Maple string dag.

ToMapleComplex converts the pair of doubles, re and im, to the Maple expression re + I*im, and returns this dag.

ToMapleComplexFloat converts a pair of FLOAT dags to the Maple expression re + I*im, and returns this dag.

ToMapleExpressionSequence create and returns a Maple expression sequence and fills it with the N algebraics, arg1, arg2, ..., argN.

ToMapleName returns a Maple NAME dag with the name n. If is_global is set to TRUE, the name is global in the Maple name space. Otherwise, if is_global is FALSE, the name is a unique exported local.

ToMapleNULL returns the Maple NULL dag (an empty EXPSEQ).

ToMapleNULLPointer returns the Maple zero dag. This is the wrapper representation of a NULL pointer passed to a procedure. Do not confuse this with the value returned by ToMapleNULL.

ToMapleString copies the character string s to a Maple STRING dag and returns it. When using the Fortran API, the length of the given string must also be passed.

**Rectangular Table (Vector, Matrix, Array) Manipulation** *Rtables*[3] are the container class of Vector, Matrix, and Array data structures in Maple. The basic access functions are as follows.

[3]For information on rtables, refer to ?rtable.

```
ALGEB RTableCreate( MKernelVector kv, RTableSettings *s,
        void *pdata, M_INT *bounds );
void* RTableDataBlock( MKernelVector kv, ALGEB rt );
M_INT RTableNumElements( MKernelVector kv, ALGEB rt );
M_INT RTableNumDimensions( MKernelVector kv, ALGEB rt );
M_INT RTableLowerBound( MKernelVector kv, ALGEB rt,
        M_INT dim );
M_INT RTableUpperBound( MKernelVector kv, ALGEB rt,
        M_INT dim );
M_BOOL RTableIsReal( MKernelVector kv, ALGEB rt );
```

The Fortran API contains the following functions.

```
SUBROUTINE copy_to_array( kv, rt, a, num_rdims,
             rbounds, num_fdims, fbounds, data_type )
SUBROUTINE copy_to_rtable( kv, a, rt, num_fdims,
             fbounds, num_rdims, rbounds, data_type )
INTEGER convert_to_rtable( kv, a, num_rdims,
             rbounds, num_fdims, fbounds, data_type )
INTEGER rtable_num_elements( kv, s )
INTEGER rtable_num_dimensions( kv, s )
INTEGER rtable_lower_bound( kv, s, dim )
INTEGER rtable_upper_bound( kv, s, dim )
INTEGER rtable_is_real( kv, s )
```

RtableDataBlock returns a pointer to the data block of a given rtable. The returned value should be casted to the known data type of the rtable. The data block can be manipulated directly instead of using RtableAssign or RtableSelect. Users who directly manipulate the data block must be aware of the storage type, order, data type, and presence of indexing functions to do this properly.

In Fortran, there is no way to return an ARRAY pointer. To work with an array created in Maple, the data-block must be copied to a pre-allocated Fortran data block using the copy_to_array function. It copies the contents of the rtable rt to the ARRAY, a. For a complete explanation of the parameters that are passed, refer to the maplefortran.hf file. To copy an array back to Maple, the copy_to_rtable function can be used.

RtableCreate returns a newly created RTABLE as specified by:

1. The definitions given in the RtableSettings structure s.

2. A pointer to an existing block of data. If pdata is NULL, a data-block is allocated and initialized to s->fill. When providing an already

created block of data, it is important that s->foreign is set to TRUE. Size, storage, data type, order, and indexing functions should all be considered when managing your data block. Generally, let Maple create the data-block, then use RtableDataBlock to gain access to it.

3. The bounds array, bounds. An m x n matrix must have bounds = 1,m,1,n (that is, both the upper and lower bounds must be specified).

The Fortran equivalent function is convert_to_rtable. It creates an rtable from an existing Fortran array. The data is not copied into the table. Instead, the rtable maintains a pointer to the external data.

RtableNumElements returns the number of elements in a given rtable. This may be different in sparse versus dense rtables.

1. For dense rtables, return the number of elements of storage allocated for this rtable.

2. If rt is in NAG-sparse format, then this returns the number of elements in the data vector specified for the rtable, (which is the same as the length of each index vector). Note that the number returned here represents the number of data elements that are actually filled in, not the number of elements allocated. Some of the elements may have the value zero.

3. For Maple-sparse rtables, this always returns zero.

RtableNumDimensions returns the number of dimensions in a given rtable.

RtableUpperBound and RtableLowerBound give the upper and lower bound of the *dim*th dimension of the RTABLE, rt. For a 2 x 3 matrix, RtableLowerBound(rt,1) returns 1 because the first dimension bounds are 1..2, and the lower bound is 1.

RtableIsReal checks the elements of the RTABLE rt to verify whether they are all real. If datatype=complex, it returns FALSE. If datatype is a hardware type with no indexing function, for example, float[8], it returns TRUE. Otherwise, it scans the rtable and returns FALSE when the first complex entry is found or TRUE if no complex entries are found.

In addition to the above functions, there is an extensive C API for working with rtable data types.

```
void RTableAppendAttribute( MKernelVector kv, RTableSettings
       *s, char *name );
void RTableAppendIndFn( MKernelVector kv, RTableSettings
```

```
        *s, ALGEB indfn );
void RTableGetDefaults( MKernelVector kv, RTableSettings
        *s );
void RTableGetSettings( MKernelVector kv, RTableSettings
        *s, ALGEB rt );
M_INT RTableIndFn( MKernelVector kv, ALGEB rt, M_INT num );
ALGEB RTableIndFnArgs( MKernelVector kv, ALGEB rt, M_INT num );
void RTableSetAttribute( MKernelVector kv, RTableSettings
        *s, char *name );
void RTableSetIndFn( MKernelVector kv, RTableSettings *s,
        ALGEB indfn );
void RTableSetType( MKernelVector kv, RTableSettings *s,
        M_INT id, char *name );
RTableData RTableSelect( MKernelVector kv, ALGEB rt, M_INT
        *index );
RTableData RTableAssign( MKernelVector kv, ALGEB rt, M_INT
        *index, RTableData val );
void RTableSparseCompact( MKernelVector kv, ALGEB rt );
NAG_INT* RTableSparseIndexRow( MKernelVector kv, ALGEB rt,
        M_INT dim );
ALGEB RTableSparseIndexSort( MKernelVector kv, ALGEB rt,
        M_INT by_dim );
void RTableSparseSetNumElems( MKernelVector kv, ALGEB rt,
        M_INT num );
M_INT RTableSparseSize( MKernelVector kv, ALGEB rt );

ALGEB RTableCopy( MKernelVector kv, RTableSettings *s,
        ALGEB rt);
ALGEB RTableCopyImPart( MKernelVector kv, RTableSettings
        *s, ALGEB rt );
ALGEB RTableCopyRealPart( MKernelVector kv, RTableSettings
        *s, ALGEB rt );
ALGEB RTableZipReIm( MKernelVector kv, RTableSettings *s,
        ALGEB rt_re, ALGEB rt_im );
```

Most Rtable access functions use the RtableSettings structure defined in mpltable.h. This struct corresponds directly to the options available to the rtable constructor in Maple.

RtableAppendAttribute appends the name attribute to the list of attributes in the RtableSettings structure.

RtableAppendIndFn appends the indexing function, infn to the list of indexing functions in the RtableSettings structure. Note that infn must be a valid Maple name or table reference. For example,

```
RTableAppendIndFn(kv,&settings,ToMapleName(kv,"symmetric",
    TRUE));
RTableAppendIndFn(kv,&settings,EvalMapleStatement(kv,
    "triangular[upper]"));
```

RtableGetDefaults fills the RtableSettings structure s with standard default values. These defaults are as follows.

```
data_type = RTABLE_DAG
maple_type = 'anything' (Maple name 'anything')
subtype = RTABLE_ARRAY
storage = RTABLE_RECT
p1 = -1, p2 = -1
order = RTABLE_FORTRAN
read_only = FALSE
foreign = FALSE
num_dimensions = -1
index_functions = 'NULL' (Maple NULL)
attributes = 'NULL' (Maple NULL)
transpose = FALSE
fill = 0
```

RtableGetSettings fills the RtableSettings structure s with the settings held by the RTABLE, rt.

RtableIndFn returns the *i*th indexing function code. The indexing codes are defined in mpltable.h in the form RTABLE_INDEX_XXXX. If there are no indexing functions, this gives an error for any value of i. If there is one indexing function, then rtableIndFun(rt,1) returns the code for the only indexing function. Use MapleNumArgs to determine the number of indexing functions.

RtableIndFnArgs returns the argument expression sequence for indexing function 'num' in rtable 'rt'. If there are no arguments, Maple 'NULL' is returned. The result can be further converted to a hardware type using the MapleToXXX function(s). The number of arguments returned can be determined using MapleNumArgs. Note that some knowledge about the indexing functions is required to convert the return value to the appropriate hardware type. For example, RTableIndFnArgs(kv,rt,1) of a band[b1,b2] rtable returns the b1 part of the expression sequence (b1,b2). The user must know that b1 and b2 are always integers. Conversely, c in constant[c] is always the same type as the rtable's datatype. Thus for float[8] rtables, to convert to a hardware type use MapleToFloat64.

RtableSetAttribute sets all the attributes of the RtableSettings structure s to the single NAME attribute, name.

RtableSetIndFn sets all the indexing functions of the RtableSettings structure s and resets it to the single indexing function infn.

RtableSetType sets the data_type field in the given RtableSettings structure s to id, and when id=RTABLE_DAG, sets the maple_type to name. For example, to set the data type to float[8], RTableSetType(kv,&s, RTABLE_FLOAT,NULL) is called. To set the type to numeric, RTableSetType(kv,&s,RTABLE_DAG,"numeric") is called. Basic type ids are defined in mpltable.h. To set compound types, the RtableSettings data structure can be manipulated directly as follows.

```
settings.data_type = RTABLE_DAG;
settings.maple_type = EvalMapleStatement(kv,
                          "complex(numeric)");
```

RtableSelect returns the value rt[index], where rt is an RTABLE, and index is an integer array.

RtableAssign assigns the value val to rt[index]. This function must be used instead of assigning directly to the rtable data-block whenever the given rtable has an indexing function or unusual storage format (for example, sparse). The index is an integer array. For example, the following code assigns the value 3.14 to the [2,1] element of the given datatype=float[8] rtable.

```
RTableData val;
M_INT *index;

index[0] = 2;
index[1] = 1;
val.float64 = 3.14;

RTableAssign(kv,rt,index,val);
```

RtableSparseCompact removes any zeros in the sparse rtable data block. This should be called after an external routine that modifies the sparse data block directly.

RtableSparseIndexRow returns the vector of indices for the $i$th dimension of rt. The rt must be a NAG sparse rtable.

RtableSparseIndexSort sorts the $N$th index vector for the NAG sparse rtable rt. This is done in-place, and the other index vectors are adjusted accordingly so that the index/value mapping is preserved.

RtableSparseSetNumElems sets the number of non-zero entries in the NAG sparse rtable rt to N. This should be done only if the number of elements has changed.

RtableSparseSize returns the number of entries allocated to store data in the NAG sparse rtable rt. This is not necessarily the same as RtableNumElems.

RtableCopy returns a copy of the rtable rt with new settings as given by the RtableSettings structure s.

RtableCopyImPart returns a copy of the imaginary part of the rtable rt with new settings as given by the RtableSettings structure s. The copy returned is purely real, but contains only the imaginary parts of the given rtable.

RtableCopyRealPart returns a copy of the real part of the rtable rt with new settings as given by the RtableSettings structure s.

RtableZipReIm combines two real RTABLEs, rt_re and rt_im, into a complex rtable of the form rt_re + I*rt_im. The settings of the new rtable that is returned are determined by the RtableSettings structure s.

**List Manipulation** To work with Maple lists, the following API functions can be used. These functions are only available using the C API.

```
ALGEB MapleListAlloc( MKernelVector kv, M_INT num_members );
void MapleListAssign( MKernelVector kv, ALGEB list,
        M_INT i, ALGEB val );
ALGEB MapleListSelect( MKernelVector kv, ALGEB list,
        M_INT i );
```

MapleListAlloc creates a LIST dag with space for num_members elements. This list must be filled before it can be passed to Maple.

MapleListAssign sets the $i$th element of the given list to the value val. That is, list[i] := val.

MapleListSelect returns the $i$th element of the given list.

**Table Manipulation** To use Maple tables, the following API functions can be used. These functions are only available using the C API.

```
ALGEB MapleTableAlloc( MKernelVector kv );
void MapleTableAssign( MKernelVector kv, ALGEB table,
        ALGEB ind, ALGEB val );
```

```
ALGEB MapleTableSelect( MKernelVector kv, ALGEB table,
        ALGEB ind );
void MapleTableDelete( MKernelVector kv, ALGEB table,
        ALGEB ind );
M_BOOL MapleTableHasEntry( MKernelVector kv, ALGEB table,
        ALGEB ind );
```

`MapleTableAlloc` creates a `TABLE` dag. The table is initially empty.

`MapleTableAssign` sets the `ind` element of the given `table` to the value `val`. That is, `table[ind] := val`, where `ind` can be a `NAME` or an expression sequence of numbers, or any other valid index into a Maple table.

`MapleTableSelect` returns the `ind` element of the given `table`.

`MapleTableDelete` removes the `ind` element from the `table`.

`MapleTableHasEntry` queries the `table` to determine whether it contains an element at index `ind`. If it does, `TRUE` is returned; otherwise, `FALSE` is returned.

**Data Selection** The following functions are available when using the C API only and deal with selecting from various kinds of Maple data structures.

```
ALGEB MapleSelectImaginaryPart( MKernelVector kv, ALGEB s );
ALGEB MapleSelectRealPart( MKernelVector kv, ALGEB s );
ALGEB MapleSelectIndexed( MKernelVector kv, ALGEB s, M_INT
        dim, M_INT *ind );
```

`MapleSelectImaginaryPart` and `MapleSelectRealPart` return the imaginary and real parts of a complex number dag, respectively.

`MapleSelectIndexed` returns a value from any indexable object in Maple, such as `list`, `array`, or `set`. The index is specified by filling the `ind` array with the desired index. The second parameter `dim` is the number of dimensions in the array `s` (also the number of elements in `ind`).

For example, to lookup `a[1,2,3]`, the following code could be used (assuming `arg1` points to the array `a`).

```
ALGEB val;
M_INT ind[3];

ind[0] = 1;
ind[1] = 2;
ind[2] = 3;
```

```
val = k->selectIndexed(arg1, 3, ind);
```

**Unique Data** The following function is available only in the C API.

```
ALGEB MapleUnique( MKernelVector kv, ALGEB s );
```

This function processes the given Maple expression `s`, and returns the unique copy of that expression from the Maple simpl table. For example, if you create the number `num = one-billion`, then you compute the number `val = 2*500-million`. An address comparison of `num` and `val` does not indicate equality. After calling simplify as in `num = MapleUnique(kv,num)`, both `num` and `val` point to the same memory.

**Error Handling** The following functions raise a Maple software-style error message.

```
void MapleRaiseError( MKernelVector kv, char *msg );
void MapleRaiseError1( MKernelVector kv, char *msg,
        ALGEB arg1 );
void MapleRaiseError2( MKernelVector kv, char *msg,
        ALGEB arg1, ALGEB arg2 );
```

The Fortran equivalent is:

```
SUBROUTINE maple_raise_error( kv, msg, len )
```

These functions display the message `msg`, stop execution, and return to the Maple input loop. A call to `MapleRaiseError` does not return.

The character string `msg` can contain wildcards of the form `%N`, where `N` is a non-zero integer. These wildcards are replaced by the extra argument, `arg1` or `arg2`, before displaying the message. If `%-N` is specified, then the optional argument is displayed with `st`, `nd`, `rd`, or `th` appended to it. For example:

```
MapleRaiseError2(kv, "the %-1 argument, '%2', is not valid",
                 ToMapleInteger(i), args[i]);
```

This, if invoked, raises the error, *"the 4th argument, 'foo', is not valid"*, assuming `i=4`, and `args[i]` is set to the Maple name `foo`.[4]

The only option not allowed is `%0` because the function cannot determine the number of unparsed optional arguments.

The C API also provides a mechanism for trapping errors raised by Maple.

[4]For more information, refer to `?error`.

```
void* MapleTrapError( MKernelVector kv, void *(*proc)
        P(( void *data )), void *data, M_BOOL *errorflag );
```

MapleTrapError executes the C function proc, passing it the data, data. If an error occurs, errorflag is set to TRUE and traperror returns immediately. If no error occurs, the result of proc(data) is returned and errorflag is FALSE.

For example, the following code attempts to execute a Maple procedure. If an error occurs, a separate branch of code is taken.

```
typedef struct {
   MKernelVector k;
   ALGEB fn, arg1, arg2;
} CallbackArgs;

void *tryCallback( void *data )
{
 /* calls the maple procedure 'fn' with arguments 'arg1' */
 /* and 'arg2' */
 return (void*)
     EvalMapleProc( ((CallbackArgs*)data)->k,
       ((CallbackArgs*)data)->fn, 2,
       ((CallbackArgs*)data)->arg1,
       ((CallbackArgs*)data)->arg2);
}

void MainProc( MKernelVector k, ALGEB fn )
{
 M_BOOL errorflag;
 ALGEB result;
 CallbackArgs a;

 a.k = k;
 a.fn = fn;
 a.arg1 = ToMapleFloat(k,3.14);
 a.arg2 = ToMapleInteger(k,44);

 result = (ALGEB)MapleTrapError(k,tryCallback,&a,&errorflag);
 if( errorflag ) {
     /* do something */
 }
 else {
```

```
      /* do something else */
    }
  }
```

**Hardware Float Evaluation** The following procedures evaluate a Maple procedure or statement using hardware floats.

```
double MapleEvalhf( MKernelVector kv, ALGEB s );
double EvalhfMapleProc( MKernelVector kv, ALGEB fn,
                        int nargs, double *args );
```

The equivalent Fortran functions are as follows.

```
DOUBLEPRECISION maple_evalhf( kv, s)
DOUBLEPRECISION evalhf_maple_proc( kv, fn, nargs, args )
```

`MapleEvalhf` applies `evalhf` to the given dag `s`. Then `evalhf` either evaluates an expression, using hardware floats to produce a hardware float result, or returns the handle to an `evalhfable` rtable that can be used as a parameter to `EvalhfMapleProc`.

`EvalhfMapleProc` calls the `evalhf` computation engine directly to evaluate the given procedure `fn` without converting the hardware float parameters to software floats. The procedure `fn` is a valid Maple `PROC` dag, `nargs` is the number of parameters to pass to `fn`, and `args` is the list of parameters. Note that `args` starts at `1`; `args[1]` is the first parameter, `args[nargs]` is the last, and `args[0]` is not used.

Setting up a callback may require static local variables in the wrapper module so that the callback has access to the kernel vector (unless it is passed via a `data` parameter that the callback receives). The following is an example of a wrapper that uses `EvalhfMapleProc` to evaluate a function that takes an `hfarray` and some numeric values.

```
#include "maplec.h"

static MKernelVector kv;                     /* kernel vector */
static ALGEB fn;                           /* function handle */
static double hfparams[HF_MAX_PARAMS+1]; /* parameters */

void callback( int N, double X, double Y[] )
{
 hfparams[1] = (double)N;
 hfparams[2] = X;
 /* hfparams[3] is already set */
```

```
 EvalhfMapleProc(kv,fn,3,hfparams);
}

/* main wrapper function called from Maple */
ALGEB test( MKernelVector k, ALGEB args )
{
 /* skip arg checking for the sake of brevity */

 kv = k;                            /* save kernel vector */
 /* get the hfarray handle */
 hfparams[3] = MapleEvalhf(DAG(args[1]));
 fn = DAG(args[2]);            /* save the function handle */

 do_stuff(callback);           /* start the routine that */
                               /* calls callback() */
 return( k->toMapleNULL() );
}
```

In Maple, the external routine is accessed like any other, except an error is raised if the given procedure is not able to use evalhf.

```
> f := proc(n,x,y) y[1] := n*sin(x); end:
> y := Vector([1,2],datatype=float[8]):

> p := define_external('test',MAPLE,LIB="libtest.so"):
> p(y,f):
```

**General Evaluation** The following procedures evaluate Maple procedures or statements. These routines are not available in the Fortran API.

```
ALGEB MapleEval( MKernelVector kv, ALGEB s );
ALGEB EvalMapleProc( MKernelVector kv, ALGEB fn, int nargs,
          /* ALGEB arg1, ALGEB arg2, */ ... );
ALGEB EvalMapleStatement( MKernelVector kv, char *statement );
```

`EvalMapleProc` is a callback to Maple. The first argument `fn` is a Maple `PROC` or `FUNCTION` dag, which is evaluated with the arguments, `arg1 .. argN`. For example, consider the following Maple function.

```
> f := proc(x) x^2; end:
```

If this function is passed to the external function as `args[1]`, the following code executes the given function at `x := 3.14`.

```
ALGEB a1, MapleResult;
double CResult;

a1 = ToMapleFloat(kv,3.14);
MapleResult = EvalMapleProc(kv,args[1],1,a1);
CResult = MapleToFloat64(kv,MapleResult);
```

EvalMapleStatement enables you to enter a single parsable Maple statement and evaluate it. For example, the following call evaluates the integral of $x^3$ in the range `x = 0..1`.

```
ALGEB MapleResult;
double CResult;

MapleResult = EvalMapleStatement(kv,"int(x^3,x=0..1)");
CResult = mapleToFloat64(kv,MapleResult);
```

MapleEval evaluates a Maple expression. It is especially useful for determining the value of an assigned name.

**Assignment to Maple Variables** The following assignment functions are available only when using the C API.

```
ALGEB MapleAssign( MKernelVector kv, ALGEB lhs, ALGEB rhs );
ALGEB MapleAssignIndexed( MKernelVector kv, ALGEB lhs,
                M_INT dim, M_INT *ind, ALGEB rhs );
```

MapleAssign sets the value dag rhs to the name dag lhs. This is equivalent to the Maple statement

```
> lhs := rhs;
```

MapleAssignIndexed sets the value rhs to the indexed variable lhs. The second parameter dim indicates the number of dimensions in the array (or 1 if lhs is a table). The third parameter ind is a hardware array of indices.

For example, to make the assignment `a[1][2][3] = 3.14`, the following code could be used (assuming arg1 points to the array a).

```
ALGEB rhs;
M_INT ind[3];

ind[0] = 1;
ind[1] = 2;
```

```
ind[3] = 3;

rhs = ToMapleFloat(kv,3.14);
MapleAssignIndexed(kv,arg1,3,ind,rhs);
```

**User Information** The MapleUserInfo command displays "msg" when infolevel['name'] is set to level. This command is only available in the C API.

```
void MapleUserInfo( MKernelVector kv, int level, char
        *name, char *msg );
```

**Memory Management** The following functions are available only when using the C API.

```
void* MapleAlloc( MKernelVector kv, M_INT nbytes );
void MapleDispose( MKernelVector kv, ALGEB s );
void MapleGcAllow( MKernelVector kv, ALGEB a );
void MapleGcProtect( MKernelVector kv, ALGEB a );
```

MapleAlloc allocates nbytes bytes of memory and returns a pointer to it. Garbage collection of this memory is handled by Maple. Note that to allocate this memory, a new BINARY dag structure is created, and a pointer to the data part of the dag is returned.

The following code snapshot might be seen in a wrapper that converts an integer reference (a name) in Maple to C.

```
ALGEB arg1;
INTEGER32 *i;

i = MapleAlloc(kv,sizeof(INTEGER32));
*i = MapleToInteger32(kv,arg1);
```

MapleDispose frees the memory allocated to the structure s. This should only be used on data structures created using MapleAlloc, or those that were created externally and are guaranteed not to be pointed to by any other Maple structure. The Maple garbage collector reclaims any memory not pointed to by any other data structure, so in typical cases it is not necessary to use MapleDispose.

MapleGcProtect prevents the algebraic a from being collected by the Maple garbage collector. The memory pointed to (by a) is not freed until Maple exits, or a call to MapleGcAllow is issued. Any dags that must persist between external function invocations must be protected. This includes any external global or static ALGEB variables that will be referred to in a later external call. Failure to protect such a persistent variable leads to unexpected results if the Maple garbage collector removes it between function calls.

MapleGcAllow allows the algebraic structure a to be collected by the Maple garbage collector. Any algebraic structure that is not referenced by another algebraic structure is automatically destroyed and its memory reclaimed. Algebraics are protected from garbage collection if they are used somewhere (that is, the value of a global name or part of an array's data). The normal state of an algebraic is to have garbage collection enabled on it.

### System Integrity

The Maple kernel has no control over the quality or reliability of external functions. If an external function performs an illegal operation, such as accessing memory outside of its address space, that operation can result in a segmentation fault or system error. The external routine crashes, causing Maple to crash too.

If an external routine accesses memory outside of its address space but inside the Maple address space, the external routine will likely *not* crash, but Maple will become corrupted, resulting in inexplicable behavior or a crash later in the Maple session. Similarly, an external routine that deals directly with Maple data structures can corrupt Maple by misusing the data structure manipulation facilities.

Therefore, use external calling at your own risk. Whether an external routine is one that you have written, or is one supplied by a third party to which you have declared an interface (via define_external), Maple must rely on the integrity of the external routine when it is called.

## 6.3 OpenMaple: Using Maple in Compiled Code

This section describes the Application Programming Interface (API) to the OpenMaple kernel. OpenMaple is a suite of functions that allows you to access Maple algorithms and data structures in your compiled C or C++ program. To run your application, Maple 9 must be installed. You can distribute your application to any licensed Maple 9 user.

The information in this document is hardware independent. Unless otherwise noted, the information is also operating system architecture independent.

## Interface Overview

The programming interface (API) is built on the existing *external calling* mechanism. Using OpenMaple provides direct access to many of the Maple internal data types. This is similar to the access `define_external` provides to the author of an external wrapper. For more information on external calling, see **6.2 External Calling: Using Compiled Code in Maple** or refer to `?external_calling` and `?CustomWrapper`.

OpenMaple provides the ability to start the Maple kernel and control output. By default, output is sent to *stdout*. Setting up call-back functions allows you to direct output to, for example, a text box or a string. For more information on call-back functions, see **Call-back Functions** on page 380.

**Data Types** Maple defines a few low-level data types to improve portability between architectures. Some types are used as parameters or return values for OpenMaple API functions.

`M_INT` An integer that is the same size as a pointer on the architecture. On most architectures, for example, Windows, this is equivalent to `int`. On some architectures, this is equivalent to `long int`.

`M_BOOL` An integer that can take one of two values, `TRUE` or `FALSE`. The size of this type is the same as `M_INT`.

`ALGEB` A Maple expression in native internal format. The format is not documented, but some functions (such as `MapleEval`) use such an expression for further processing by other API functions. The data type definitions are in `mplshlib.h` and `mpltable.h`.

`INTEGER8, INTEGER16, INTEGER32, INTEGER64, FLOAT32, FLOAT64` These macros aid in developing platform-independent code. The macro resolves to the correct byte-sized integer type recognized by the underlying compiler.

All API functions are declared with the modifier `M_DECL` and `EXT_DECL`. When using Microsoft Visual C/C++ (MSVC), `M_DECL` is defined using `#define` as `__stdcall` and `EXT_DECL` is defined using `#define` as `__declspec(dllimport)` (to specify calling conventions and `dll` symbol exports). For other compilers, these are defined using `#define` as nothing. When **not** using MSVC on Windows, ensure that you define them appropriately.

**Basic API Functions** The OpenMaple API consists of all the standard functions available in the external call API, plus StartMaple, StopMaple, and RestartMaple functions. For more information on external calling, see **6.2 External Calling: Using Compiled Code in Maple** or refer to ?external_calling.

The sequence for calling the basic API functions is as follows.

1. Call StartMaple. For more information, see the following **Initializing Maple** subsection.

2. Execute a string command in Maple by calling EvalMapleStatement or use any of the other functions listed in maplec.h. For more information, see **Evaluating Maple Input** on page 377.

3. Reset Maple by calling RestartMaple (if necessary). To execute additional commands in this session, return to step 2. For more information on restarting Maple, see **Reinitializing Maple** on page 379.

4. Call StopMaple. Once you stop the Maple kernel, you cannot restart it. For more information on stopping Maple, see **Terminating Maple** on page 379.

The call-back functions are declared in maplec.h and defined in the following subsections.

**Initializing Maple** The StartMaple function:

- Creates a Maple kernel
- Passes command-line parameters to this kernel (a subset of those that can be passed to the stand-alone version of Maple)
- Prepares the kernel for computation

The calling sequence is as follows.

```
MKernelVector StartMaple( int argc, char *argv[],
    MCallBackVector cb, void *user_data, void *info,
    char *errstr );
```

- The argc parameter indicates the number of command-line arguments passed in argv.

- The `argv` parameter is an array of string pointers giving the command-line parameters. This array must have at least `argc` + 1 elements, the first of which (`argv[0]`) must be the name of the application or the string **"maple"**. If `argv` is `NULL`, `argc` and `argv` are ignored.

  The OpenMaple kernel supports a subset of the command-line options supported by the command-line version of Maple. Options that take arguments (such as "`-b`") can be passed as either:

  – A single parameter, in which the argument immediately follows the option with no intervening space, for example, "`-b/usr/maple/lib`"

  – A pair of parameters, for example, "`-b`" and "`/usr/maple/lib`"

  Options that are **not** supported include preprocessor directives (-D, -I, -U) and filter modes (-F, -l, -P). Options specific to only the graphical interface are also **not** supported.

- The `cb` parameter specifies a collection of functions that Maple uses to return results to your application. For more information on call-back functions, see **Call-back Functions** on page 380.

- The `user_data` parameter is an arbitrary user-supplied value. It is the first argument passed to the call-back functions.

- The `info` parameter is currently used only for internal purposes. It must be set to `NULL`.

- The `errstr` parameter is a preallocated string buffer. The error parameter points to a memory area where an error is written if initialization fails. The error message will not exceed 2048 characters (including the nul terminator).

The `StartMaple` function returns a Maple kernel handle if successful. This handle is needed as an argument to all other functions listed in `maplec.h`. If `MapleInitialize` fails (for example, if incorrect arguments are passed), it returns a zero and an error message is written in the memory pointed to by the `errstr` parameter. Currently, multiple kernels are **not** supported.

**Evaluating Maple Input** The most general evaluation function, `EvalMapleStatement` takes an input string, parses it, and then executes it as if it were entered in stand-alone Maple. The result and intermediate output can be displayed using the call-back functions supplied to `StartMaple`.

The structure representing the final result is also returned and can be manipulated by other functions that work with ALGEB types.

The EvalMapleStatement function is defined as follows.

```
ALGEB M_DECL EvalMapleStatement( MKernelVector kv, char
    *statement );
```

- The kv parameter specifies the handle to the Maple kernel. This is the handle returned by StartMaple.
- The statement parameter specifies the statement to be evaluated, expressed in Maple syntax. If the expression contains a syntax error, EvalMapleStatement calls the errorCallBack with two parameters: a syntax error message and the offset into statement at which the error occurred. For more information on the errorCallBack function, see **Error Call-back Function** on page 382. As in stand-alone Maple, statements ending in a colon (:) do not generate output. Output caused by print or lprint commands, by errors, or by help requests is always displayed.

**Raising a Maple Exception** The MapleRaiseError function can be called from any call-back function to cause a Maple error, as if the Maple error statement had been called. If a Maple try-catch[5] is in effect, it catches the error, and Maple code continues to execute after the try-catch call. Otherwise, computation stops, and a Maple error message is generated and sent to errorCallBack function. For more information on the errorCallBack function, see **Error Call-back Function** on page 382.

The MapleRaiseError family of functions is defined as follows.

```
void MapleRaiseError( MKernelVector kv, char *msg );
void MapleRaiseError1( MKernelVector kv, char *msg,
    ALGEB arg1 );
void MapleRaiseError2( MKernelVector kv, char *msg,
    ALGEB arg1, ALGEB arg2 );
```

- The kv parameter specifies the handle to the Maple kernel.
- The msg parameter is the text of the error message to produce (unless the exception is caught).

[5]For more information on the try-catch statement, refer to chapter 6 of the *Introductory Programming Guide* or ?try.

- The `arg` parameters are one or more arbitrary Maple objects that are substituted into numbered parameter locations in the `msg` string when the exception is displayed. For information on using optional arguments, refer to `?error`.

**Reinitializing Maple** The `RestartMaple` function can be called any time to reinitialize the state of a Maple kernel. Reinitializing the kernel is equivalent to restarting the application, except that any existing allocated memory is allocated to the kernel internal free storage lists; the memory is not returned to the operating system. Calling `RestartMaple` when no computation is active is equivalent to sending the statement "`restart;`" to the `EvalMapleStatement` function.

The `RestartMaple` function is defined as follows.

```
M_BOOL RestartMaple( MKernelVector kv, char *errstr );
```

- The `kv` parameter specifies the handle to the Maple kernel to be restarted.

- The `errstr` parameter is a preallocated string buffer. The error parameter points to a memory area where an error is written if reinitialization fails. The error message will not exceed 2048 characters, including the nul terminator.

- If an error occurs when the `RestartMaple` function is called and no computation is active, `RestartMaple` returns `FALSE`, and an error message is written in the memory pointed to by the `errstr` parameter. If no error occurs, it returns `TRUE`.

**Terminating Maple** To terminate the Maple kernel (for example, prior to exiting your application), call the `StopMaple` function to free memory that has been allocated by Maple. The `StopMaple` function also closes open files and performs other cleanup operations.

The `StopMaple` function is defined as follows.

```
void StopMaple( MKernelVector kv );
```

The `kv` parameter specifies the handle to the Maple kernel to terminate.

**Note:** After calling the `StopMaple` function, you cannot call OpenMaple API functions (**including** `StartMaple`).

## Call-back Functions

Results are returned from a Maple computation using your call-back functions. The output is passed to a call-back function. Otherwise, the results go to standard output, stdout.

You must pass the call-back functions to the StartMaple function in a structure of type MCallBackVector. The MCallBackVector type is defined as follows.

```
typedef struct {
     void (M_DECL *textCallBack)( void *data, int tag,
          char *output );
     void (M_DECL *errorCallBack)( void *data, M_INT
          offset, char *msg );
     void (M_DECL *statusCallBack)( void *data, long
          kilobytesUsed, long kilobytesAlloc, double
          cpuTime );
     char * (M_DECL *readLineCallBack)( void *data,
          M_BOOL debug );
     M_BOOL (M_DECL *redirectCallBack)( void *data, char
          *name, char *mode );
     char * (M_DECL *streamCallBack)( void *data, char
          *name, M_INT nargs, char **args );
     M_BOOL (M_DECL *queryInterrupt)( void *data );
     char * (M_DECL *callBackCallBack)( void *data, char
          *output );
} MCallBackVector, *MCallBack;
```

Each function takes one or more parameters. All take a generic data parameter. The data parameter is passed the value of the data parameter of the StartMaple function.

If a call-back function needs the MKernelVector of the kernel from which it was called, your application can use the data parameter to pass this information. For example, the data parameter can pass a pointer to an object or structure containing the MKernelVector.

**Note:** All the API functions, including the call-back functions, are declared with the M_DECL modifier. The functions assigned to the call-back vector must also be declared with the M_DECL modifier.

The call-back functions are defined in maplec.h and described in the following subsections.

**Text Call-back Function** It is recommended that you specify a `textCallBack` function.

The `textCallBack` function is called with typical (non-exceptional) Maple output. The output that Maple generates, for example, an intermediate result or the output from a `printf` statement, is passed to the `textCallBack` function.

```
void (M_DECL *textCallBack)( void *data, int tag, char
    *output )
```

- The `tag` parameter indicates the type of Maple output. The `tag` parameter can take one of the following values (as defined in `moemapi.h`).

  **MAPLE_TEXT_OUTPUT** A line-printed (1-D) Maple expression or statement.

  **MAPLE_TEXT_DIAG** Diagnostic output (high `printlevel` or `trace` output).

  **MAPLE_TEXT_MISC** Miscellaneous output, for example, from the Maple `printf` function.

  **MAPLE_TEXT_HELP** Text help output. This is generated in response to a help request. For a more comprehensive help facility, see **6.3 Maple Online Help Database**.

  **MAPLE_TEXT_QUIT** Response to a Maple `quit`, `done`, or `stop` command.

  **MAPLE_TEXT_WARNING** A warning message generated during a computation.

  **MAPLE_TEXT_ERROR** An error message generated during parsing or processing. This is generated only if you do **not** specify an `errorCallBack` function. For more information on the `errorCallBack` function, see the following **Error Call-back Function** subsection.

  **MAPLE_TEXT_STATUS** Kernel resource usage status (a "`bytes used`" message). This is generated only if you do **not** specify a `statusCallBack` function. For more information on the `statusCallBack` function, see the following **Status Call-back Function** subsection.

  **MAPLE_TEXT_DEBUG** Output from the Maple debugger.

- The `output` parameter contains the output of the type indicated by the `tag` parameter. Each output string can be arbitrarily long.

**Error Call-back Function** The errorCallBack function is called when an error occurs during parsing or processing.

```
void (M_DECL *errorCallBack)( void *data, M_INT offset,
    char *msg )
```

- The offset parameter indicates the location of a parsing error.
  - If offset $\geq 0$, the error was detected at the specified offset in the string passed to EvalMapleStatement.
  - If offset $< 0$, the error is **not** a parsing error; it is a computation error.
- The msg parameter contains the text of the error message.

If an errorCallBack function is **not** specified, error messages are sent to the textCallBack function, with the MAPLE_TEXT_ERROR tag. For more information on the textCallBack function, see the previous subsection **Text Call-back Function.**

**Status Call-back Function** The statusCallBack function is called when Maple reports resource usage information (equivalent to the "bytes used" messages in stand-alone Maple).

```
void (M_DECL *statusCallBack)( void *data, long
    kilobytesUsed, long kilobytesAlloc, double
    cpuTime )
```

- The cpuTime parameter is the number of seconds of CPU time consumed since the Maple kernel was started. This includes time spent in any call-back functions.
- The bytesUsed parameter indicates how many bytes of storage have been allocated by the Maple internal storage manager.
- The bytesAlloc parameter indicates how many bytes of storage have been allocated by the operating system by the Maple internal storage manager.

If **no** statusCallBack function is specified, status information is sent to the textCallBack function in the form "bytes used=%ld, alloc=%ld, time=%1.2f", with the MAPLE_TEXT_STATUS tag. For more information on the textCallBack function, see **Text Call-back Function** on page 380.

**Read Line Call-back Function** The readLineCallBack function is called when the kernel executes the Maple readline[6] function (which is also used by readstat and history) to obtain a line of input from the user. In most applications, this is not used.

```
char * (M_DECL *readLineCallBack)( void *data, M_BOOL
    debug )
```

- The debug parameter indicates that the call to readline was made by the Maple debugger (the Maple debugger uses readline to get debugger commands from the user).
  - If debug is TRUE, the readline call is from the debugger.
  - If debug is FALSE, the readline call is from history, readstat, or another non-debugger call.

If **no** readLineCallBack function is provided, any attempt to execute the Maple readline function produces an error (reported using the errorCallBack or textCallBack function). For more information on the errorCallBack function, see **Error Call-back Function** on page 382. For more information on the textCallBack function, see **Text Call-back Function** on page 380.

**Redirect Call-back Function** The redirectCallBack function is called when the kernel executes the Maple writeto[7] or appendto function. The intent is to redirect subsequent output.

```
M_BOOL (M_DECL *redirectCallBack)( void *data, char *name,
    char *mode )
```

- The name parameter specifies the name of the file to which output is appended.
- The mode parameter specifies the file access mode to use: "wt" for write or "at" for append.

The name and mode parameters are compatible with the C library function fopen.

[6]For more information on the readline function, refer to chapter 7 of the *Introductory Programming Guide* or ?readline.

[7]For more information on the writeto and appendto functions, see **Redirecting the default Output Stream** on page 217.

If the name parameter is NULL (in which case the parameters are not compatible with fopen), Maple is signalling that redirection is terminated. Subsequent output is sent to the main output stream. Again, this is user-dependent.

If no redirectCallBack function is provided, any attempt to execute the Maple writeto function or appendto function produces an error (reported using the errorCallBack function or textCallBack function).

**Call Back Call-back Function** The callBackCallBack function is called when Maple code calls the Maple callback function.

```
char * (M_DECL *callBackCallBack)( void *data, char
     *output )
```

- The output parameter contains the text version of the parameters passed to the Maple callback function.

On return, the callBackCallBack function returns either a NULL pointer or a string containing a valid Maple expression.

- If the Maple callback function returns nothing, the callbackCallBack function returns NULL.
- If a Maple expression is returned, it is parsed, and the Maple callback function returns the (unevaluated) expression, or the callbackCallBack function returns a parsed Maple expression.

This function can be used to explicitly pass intermediate values of a computation to your code and to return a value to Maple.

If no callBackCallBack function is provided, any attempt to execute the Maple callback function produces an error (reported using the errorCallBack function or textCallBack function).

**Query Interrupt Call-back Function** The queryInterrupt call-back function is called to allow the user to halt the computation. This function is called before each Maple statement is executed. In general, this occurs hundreds of times per second. For some operations (notably large integer manipulations), the queryInterrupt function is called every few seconds.

```
M_BOOL (M_DECL *queryInterrupt)( void *data )
```

To halt the computation, the function must return TRUE. To continue the computation, the function must return FALSE.

If **no** `queryInterrupt` function is provided, computations cannot be interrupted.

**Stream Call-back Function** The Maple math engine and the OpenMaple API communicate using logical *streams.* The Maple engine interprets a stream as an unevaluated call to a function with a name that begins with "`INTERFACE_`". Data is sent on a stream either implicitly by various operations (for example, the Maple `print` function sends its data on the `INTERFACE_PRINT` stream), or explicitly by a call to the Maple `streamcall` function. There are several predefined streams. In OpenMaple, most streams map to one of the call-back functions described in this subsection.

Streams are usually used to output information (as is done by the `INTERFACE_PRINT` stream), but some streams can be used to request information as well. For example, the `INTERFACE_READLINE` stream is used to request user input during execution of a Maple procedure. In OpenMaple, `INTERFACE_READLINE` is mapped to the `readLineCallBack`.

In addition to the predefined streams, a Maple user, or an OpenMaple developer, can create streams by passing a Maple expression of the form,

```
INTERFACE_streamName(arguments)
```

to the `streamcall` function. If the stream returns a result, the `streamcall` function returns that result. (You can also send to a stream by passing such an expression to the Maple `print` function, or by allowing such an expression to be the result of a computation, but in that case, no result can be passed on the stream back to Maple).

The `streamCallBack` function is called when Maple sends output as a stream that is not explicitly handled by the OpenMaple API.

```
char * (M_DECL *streamCallBack)( void *data, char *name,
     M_INT nargs, char **args )
```

- The `name` parameter specifies the name of the stream without the "`INTERFACE_`" prefix.

- The `nargs` parameter indicates the number of arguments passed. If no arguments are passed, `nargs` is zero.

- The `args` parameter points to an array of string pointers, one for each argument passed. Each string is a line-printed (1-D) Maple expression corresponding to that argument.

The `streamCallBack` function must return a string in valid Maple syntax. If no result is to be returned, it must return the `NULL` pointer.

User-defined streams are an alternative to using the `callBackCallBack` function. For more information on the `callBackCallBack` function, see **Call Back Call-back Function** on page 384. Streams have several advantages:

- The stream name is passed. You can use multiple streams in Maple code, and quickly determine which operation to perform by examining the stream name in the `streamCallBack` function.
- Multiple arguments are passed as separate strings, unlike the `callBackCallBack` function to which multiple arguments are passed as a single comma-separated string. This reduces parsing requirements in the OpenMaple application.
- The number of arguments is passed, making it easier to check that the *correct* arguments are passed.

If **no** `streamCallBack` function is specified and output is sent to an unknown stream, the arguments to the stream are sent to the call-back function to which Maple results are sent, that is, the `textCallBack` function.

## Maple Online Help Database

The Maple online help system is also available to your application. Although help output can be generated by passing a Maple `help` command to a kernel (in which case the output is returned to the `textCallBack` function with a `MAPLE_TEXT_HELP` tag), such output does not reflect any markup in the help file. By calling the help system directly, formatted help pages can be retrieved.

**Setting the Help Database Search Path** The help system is accessed using the `MapleHelp` function. As with stand-alone Maple, the help search path is defined by the value of `libname`[8]. The `MapleLibName` function can be used to query or change this path. For more information on the `MapleLibName` function, refer to `maplec.h`.

**Retrieving a Help Page** To retrieve and display a help page, use the `MapleHelp` function.

The following figure illustrates text mode help output.

[8]For more information on `libname`, refer to `?libname`.

```
int or Int - Definite and Indefinite Integration

Calling Sequences:
 int(expr, x)
 int(expr, x=a..b, ...)

Parameters:
 expr - an algebraic expression, the integrand
 x    - a name
 a, b - interval on which integral is taken
 ...  - options

Description:
- The function int computes an indefinite or definite
integral of the expression expr with respect to the
variable x. The name integrate is a synonym for int.

- Indefinite integration is performed if the second argument
x is a name. Note that no constant of integration appears
in the result. Definite integration is performed if the
second argument is of the form x=a..b where a and b are the
endpoints of the interval of integration.

- For numerical integration, see int[numerical].

Examples:
> int( sin(x), x );
                                        -cos(x)
See Also:
diff, evalf, series, limit
```

The `MapleHelp` function retrieves and displays a help page, or a section of a help page, based on the specified topic. The results are passed as a stream of characters and attributes to the specified call-back functions.

```
char * M_DECL MapleHelp(
     MKernelVector kv,
     char *topic,
     char *section,
     M_BOOL (M_DECL *writeChar)( void *data, int c ),
     M_BOOL (M_DECL *writeAttrib)( void *data, int a ),
     int width,
     void *data
)
```

- The `kv` parameter specifies the handle to the Maple kernel. This handle is returned by `StartMaple`.
- The `topic` parameter specifies the help page. The topic is generally a Maple keyword, function name, symbol, or a combination thereof separated by commas. For example, to refer to a function in a package, use "*package_name*, *function_name*".

- The `section` parameter indicates which section of the page to display. If this is passed as "" or `NULL`, the entire page is displayed. To restrict display to a particular section of the page, pass one of the following values.

  **"usage"** Displays the function name (one-line description) and calling sequence

  **"description"** Displays the detailed description of the function

  **"examples"** Displays examples of the function usage

  **"seealso"** Displays a list of related topics

- The `writeChar` parameter defines a call-back function to which the characters are passed. The characters are all printable. Leading spaces are added to achieve the appropriate alignment. No trailing spaces are generated. A newline ('**\n**') character is sent at the end of each line. The `writeChar` function terminates rendering by returning `TRUE`.

- The `writeAttrib` parameter defines a call-back function to which attribute information is passed. The attribute passed to `writeAttrib` applies to all characters passed to `writeChar` until another attribute is passed to `writeAttrib`. The possible attribute values are:

  **FN_NORMAL** Normal text mode.

  **FN_BOLD Boldfaced text mode.** This can be used for key words in Maple procedures in example output and for section headings.

  **FN_ITAL** *Italic text mode.* This can be used for calling sequence parameter names.

  **FN_UNDER** Underlined text mode. This is used for links to other topics. The format of this text is "*linkReference##linkText*", where *linkReference* is the topic to which the link refers and *linkText* is the link text displayed in the help page. It is equivalent to the HTML code:

  **<A HREF=**"*linkReference*">*linkText* </**A**>

  The `writeAttrib` function can be omitted by passing `NULL` for the `writeAttrib` parameter.

- The `width` parameter indicates the width, in characters, to which the help information is formatted.

- The `data` parameter is an arbitrary user-supplied value. It is the first argument passed to the call-back functions.

The `MapleHelp` function returns `NULL` if successful, or it returns a pointer to an error message if unsuccessful. It may return the same pointer in all cases of failure. To save the message, make a copy of it immediately.

## Technical Issues

This subsection discusses technical issues related to using OpenMaple.

**Memory Usage** Maple allocates memory from the operating system (through the C `malloc` function on most architectures) in large chunks (64KB on most architectures). This memory is not returned to the operating system (that is, by `free`) until Maple terminates. When Maple no longer requires a piece of memory, the memory is added to one of the Maple internal free storage lists. Maple maintains several storage lists, for different sizes of memory blocks, so it can quickly find blocks of the required size. For example, Maple makes extensive use of three-word blocks, so it maintains a list of free blocks of that size. Maple allocates additional memory from the operating system only when it is **unable** to satisfy a request using its storage lists.

Maple *appears* to leak memory because the amount of memory allocated to Maple only increases. The more memory Maple is allocated by the operating system, the less it is allocated in future because it reuses memory. For most applications, 4MB of memory must be available for Maple to allocate.

Under Microsoft Windows, the Maple kernel is compiled using 4-byte structure alignment. Your application must be compiled this way. This is a general requirement for Windows applications.

## File Structure

Off the main Maple installation path, the following subdirectories contain files related to OpenMaple.

**bin.$SYS** Location of `maplec.dll` and `maplec.lib`. Also holds various dynamic libraries used by the OpenMaple kernel. To determine `$SYS` for your platform, see Table 6.5 on page 395.

**samples/OpenMaple** Location of the C/C++ `#include` files for use with external calling and OpenMaple.

**lib** Location of the Maple math libraries and help database.

**extern/examples** Location of platform-independent sample code.

The OpenMaple files installed are platform dependent.[9]

**UNIX** On UNIX platforms, the OpenMaple engine consists of a shared object library (`libmaplec.so`, `libmaplec.sl` (HP), or `libmaplec.a` (AIX)) which exports the functions described in this document.

**Microsoft Windows** Under Microsoft Windows, the OpenMaple engine consists of a DLL (`maplec.dll`) which exports the functions described in this document.

An import library is also provided. The file `maplec.lib` in the `bin.$SYS` directory is an import library in COFF format.

**Mac OS X** Under Mac OS X, the OpenMaple engine consists of two dynamic libraries (`libmaplec.dylib` and `libmaple.dylib`), which export the functions described in this document.

## Building the Sample Program

The code for one simple example of how to use OpenMaple is in the file `samples/OpenMaple/cmaple/omexample.c`. The example program illustrates how to evaluate expressions, access help, and interrupt computations.

The following assumes the current directory is the root of the Maple installation, and that the compiler is set up to work in command-line mode, that is, it is in the `PATH` and relevant environment variables are set up.

### AIX

```
setenv LIBPATH bin.IBM\_RISC\_UNIX
cc samples/OpenMaple/cmaple/omexample.c -o
     bin.IBM\_RISC\_UNIX/omexample -Lbin.IBM\_RISC\_UNIX
     -Iinclude -lmaplec
bin.IBM\_RISC\_UNIX/omexample
```

### Digital UNIX / Compaq Tru64

```
setenv LD\_LIBRARY\_PATH bin.DEC\_ALPHA\_UNIX
cc samples/OpenMaple/cmaple/omexample.c -o
     bin.DEC\_ALPHA\_UNIX/omexample -Lbin.DEC\_ALPHA\_UNIX
     -Iinclude -lmaplec
bin.DEC\_ALPHA\_UNIX/omexample
```

[9] For a list of currently supported operating system versions, refer to the installation instructions.

### HP-UX

```
setenv SHLIB\_PATH bin.HP\_RISC\_UNIX
cc samples/OpenMaple/cmaple/omexample.c -o
     bin.HP\_RISC\_UNIX/omexample -Lbin.HP\_RISC\_UNIX
     -Iinclude -lmaplec -lCsup
bin.HP\_RISC\_UNIX/omexample
```

### IRIX

```
setenv LD\_LIBRARY\_PATH bin.SGI\_MIPS\_UNIX
cc samples/OpenMaple/cmaple/omexample.c -o
     bin.SGI\_MIPS\_UNIX/omexample -Lbin.SGI\_MIPS\_UNIX
     -Iinclude -lmaplec
bin.SGI\_MIPS\_UNIX/omexample
```

### Linux

```
setenv LD\_LIBRARY\_PATH bin.IBM\_INTEL\_LINUX
gcc samples/OpenMaple/cmaple/omexample.c -o
     bin.IBM\_INTEL\_LINUX/omexample
     -Lbin.IBM\_INTEL\_LINUX -Iinclude -lmaplec
bin.IBM\_INTEL\_LINUX/omexample
```

### Mac OS X

```
setenv DYLD\_LIBRARY\_PATH bin.APPLE\_PPC\_OSX
gcc samples/OpenMaple/cmaple/omexample.c -o
     bin.APPLE\_PPC\_OSX/omexample -Lbin.APPLE\_PPC\_OSX
     -Iinclude -lmaplec -lmaple
bin.APPLE\_PPC\_OSX/omexample
```

### Microsoft Windows with Microsoft Visual C/C++ (MSVC)

```
cd bin.IBM\_INTEL\_NT
cl -Gz ../samples/OpenMaple/cmaple/omexample.c -I../include
     maplec.lib
omexample
```

### Solaris

```
setenv LD\_LIBRARY\_PATH bin.SUN\_SPARC\_SOLARIS
cc samples/OpenMaple/cmaple/omexample.c -o
     bin.SUN\_SPARC\_SOLARIS/omexample
     -Lbin.SUN\_SPARC\_SOLARIS -Iinclude -lmaplec
bin.SUN\_SPARC\_SOLARIS/omexample
```

## 6.4 Conclusion

This chapter outlined how the `CodeGeneration` package provides utilities for translating Maple code to other programming languages. Additionally, this chapter discussed how the Maple kernel can be extended by integrating compiled code using the `ExternalCalling` package and how Maple can be used by compiled code using `OpenMaple`.

**Table 6.3** Compound Types

| Maple Data Descriptor | C Type | Fortran Type | Java Type |
|---|---|---|---|
| ARRAY(datatype=typename, order=..., etc. ) | type *A | type *A | type[] A |
| string[n] | char x[n] | CHARACTER*2 | string |
| complex[4] | struct { float r, i; } | COMPLEX COMPLEX*8 | NA |
| complex[8] | struct { double r, i; } | DOUBLE COMPLEX COMPLEX*16 | NA |
| REF(typename) | TYPENAME* | NA | NA |

**Table 6.4** Wrapper Compound Types

| Maple Data Descriptor | C Type | Fortran Type | Java Type |
|---|---|---|---|
| `STRUCT( member1 :: descriptor1, ..., memberN :: descriptorN, options )` | `struct { type1 member1; ..., typeN memberN; }` | NA | NA |
| `UNION( member1 :: descriptor1, ..., memberN :: descriptorN, options )` | `union { type1 member1; ..., typeN memberN; }` | NA | NA |
| `PROC( member1 :: descriptor1, ..., memberN :: descriptorN, RETURN :: descriptorR )` | `typeR (*proc) (type1 member1, ..., typeN, memberN );` | NA | NA |

**Table 6.5** Maple API Libraries for C and Fortran

| *Operating System* | *Binary Directory* | *Load Library Environment Variable* | *C Maple API Library* | *Fortran Maple API Library* |
|---|---|---|---|---|
| Microsoft Windows | bin.wXX[1] | PATH | maplec.lib (maplec.dll) | maplefortran.lib (maplefortran.dll) |
| Mac OS X | NA | DYLD_LIBRARY_PATH | maplec.dylib | maplefortran.dylib |
| Solaris | bin.SUN_SPARC_SOLARIS | LD_LIBRARY_PATH | libmaplec.so | libmaplefortran.so |
| HP-UX | bin.HP_RISC_UNIX | SHLIB_PATH | libmaplec.sl | libmaplefortran.sl |
| IRIX | bin.SGI_MIPS_UNIX | LD_LIBRARY_PATH | libmaplec.so | libmaplefortran.so |
| AIX | bin.IBM_RISC_UNIX | LIBPATH | libmaplec.a | libmaplefortran.a |
| OSF1/True64 | bin.DEC_ALPHA_UNIX | LD_LIBRARY_PATH | libmaplec.so | libmaplefortran.so |
| Linux | bin.IBM_INTEL_LINUX | LD_LIBRARY_PATH | libmaplec.so | libmaplefortran.so |

[1] For Microsoft Windows, the binary directory name depends on the platform. It is one of: `bin.w9x` (Windows 98), `bin.wnt` (Windows NT), and `bin.win` (other Windows platforms).

**Table A.1** Maple Structures

| | | | | |
|---|---|---|---|---|
| AND | ASSIGN | BINARY | BREAK | CATENATE |
| COMPLEX | CONTROL | DCOLON | DEBUG | EQUATION |
| ERROR | EXPSEQ | FLOAT | FOR | FOREIGN |
| FUNCTION | GARBAGE | HASH | HASHTAB | HFLOAT |
| IF | IMPLIES | INEQUAT | INTNEG | INTPOS |
| LESSEQ | LESSTHAN | LEXICAL | LIST | LOCAL |
| MEMBER | MODDEF | MODULE | NAME | NEXT |
| NOT | OR | PARAM | POWER | PROC |
| PROD | RANGE | RATIONAL | READ | RETURN |
| RTABLE | SAVE | SERIES | SET | STATSEQ |
| STOP | STRING | SUM | TABLE | TABLEREF |
| TRY | UNEVAL | USE | XOR | ZPPOLY |

# A Internal Representation and Manipulation

Table A.1 lists the structures currently implemented in Maple.

Each of structure, along with the constraints on its length and contents, is described in the following sections.

## A.1 Internal Organization

Maple appears to the user as an interactive calculator. The user interface reads input, parses it, and then calls the math engine for each complete statement encountered. Maple can read and evaluate an unlimited number of statements until a `quit` statement is evaluated, or the user interface is shut down.

## Components

Maple consists of three main components: a kernel, a library, and a user interface. The kernel and library together are known as the math engine.

**Kernel** The kernel is written in the C language and is responsible for low-level operations such as arbitrary precision arithmetic, file I/O, execution of the Maple language, and the performance of simple mathematical operations such as differentiation of polynomials.

**Library** Most of the Maple mathematical functionality is in the Maple library, which is written in the Maple language. The library is stored in an archive, and pieces of it are loaded and interpreted by the kernel on demand.

**User Interface** The user interface is the part of Maple that the user sees, and is conceptually separate from the math engine. The same math engine can be used with different user interfaces. Usually, Maple is provided with a graphical user interface (GUI) and a command-line interface. The GUI is more useful for interactive use, especially when working with plots or large matrices. The command-line interface is practical for batch processing, or solving large problems where you want to devote all the resources of your computer to computation.

Maplet applications provide an alternate user interface, which is built from a description generated in the Math Engine by a series of user commands. For more information on the `Maplets` package, refer to the *Introductory Programming Guide.*

## Internal Functions

The internal functions in Maple are divided into five distinct groups:

1. **Evaluators** The evaluators are the main functions responsible for evaluation. There are six types of evaluations: statements, algebraic expressions, boolean expressions, name forming, arbitrary precision floating-point arithmetic, and hardware floating-point arithmetic. The user interface calls only the statement evaluator, but thereafter, there are many interactions between evaluators. For example, the statement,

   ```
   if a > 0 then b||i := 3.14/a end if
   ```

   is first analyzed by the statement evaluator, which calls the Boolean evaluator to resolve the `if` condition. Once completed (for example, with a `true` result), the statement evaluator is invoked again to do the assignment, for which the name-forming evaluator is invoked with the left side of the assignment, and the expression evaluator with the right side. Since the right side involves floating-point values, the expression evaluator calls the arbitrary precision floating-point evaluator.

Normally, the user does not specifically invoke any of the evaluators, but in some circumstances, when a non-default type of evaluation is needed, the user can directly call `evalb` (the Boolean evaluator), `evaln` (the name-forming evaluator), `evalf` (the arbitrary precision floating-point evaluator), or `evalhf` (the hardware floating-point evaluator).

2. **Algebraic Functions** These are commonly called basic functions. Some examples are: taking derivatives (`diff`), dividing polynomials (`divide`), finding coefficients of polynomials (`coeff`), computing series (`series`), mapping a function (`map`), expanding expressions (`expand`), and finding indeterminates (`indets`).

3. **Algebraic Service Functions** These functions are algebraic in nature, but serve as subordinates of the functions in the previous group. In most cases, these functions cannot be explicitly called by the user. Examples of such functions are the internal arithmetic packages, the basic simplifier, and retrieval of library functions.

4. **Data Structure Manipulation Functions** These are like the algebraic functions, but instead of working on mathematical objects, such as polynomials or sets, they work on data structures, such as expression sequences, sums, products, or lists. Examples of such functions are operand selection (`op`), operand substitution (`subsop`), searching (`has`), and length determination (`length`),

5. **General Service Functions** Functions in this group are at the lowest hierarchical level. That is, they may be called by any other function in the system. They are general purpose, and not necessarily specific to symbolic or numeric computation. Some examples are: storage allocation and garbage collection, table manipulation, internal I/O, and exception handling.

## Flow of Control

The flow of control need not remain internal to the Maple kernel. In many cases, where appropriate, a decision is made to call functions written in Maple and residing in the library. For example, many uses of the `expand` function are handled in the kernel. However, if an expansion of a sum to a large power is required, then the internal `expand` calls the external Maple library function `'expand/bigpow'` to resolve it. Functions such as `diff`, `evalf`, `series`, and `type` make extensive use of this feature.

Thus, for example, the basic function `diff` cannot differentiate any function. All of that functionality resides in the Maple library in procedures named `'diff/`*`functionName`*`'`. This is a fundamental feature of Maple since it permits:

- Flexibility (changing the library)
- Personal tailoring (by defining your refined handling functions)
- Readability (much of the Maple functionality is visible at the user level)

Maple allows the kernel to remain small by unloading non-essential functions to the library.

## A.2 Internal Representations of Data Types

The parser and some internal functions are responsible for building all the data structures used internally by Maple. All the internal data structures have the same general format:

| Header | $Data_1$ | ... | $Data_n$ |
|---|---|---|---|

The header field, stored in one or more machine words, encodes the length of the structure and its type. Additional bits are used to record simplification status, garbage collection information, persistent store status, and various information about specific data structures (for example, whether or not a `for` loop contains a `break` or `next`).

The length is encoded in 26 bits on 32-bit architectures, resulting in a maximum single object size of $67,108,863$ words ($268,435,452$ bytes, or 256 megabytes). On 64-bit architectures, the length is stored in 32 bits, for a maximum object size of $4,294,967,295$ words ($34,359,738,360$ bytes, or 32 gigabytes).

Every structure is created with its own length, and that length does not change during the existence of the structure. Furthermore, the contents of most data structures are never changed during execution, because it is unpredictable how many other data structures may be referring to it, and relying on it not to change. The normal procedure to modify a structure is to copy it, and then to modify the copy. Structures that are no longer used are eventually reclaimed by the garbage collector.

The following figures describe each of the 60 structures currently implemented in Maple, along with the constraints on their length and contents. The 6-bit numeric value identifying the type of structure is of little interest, so symbolic names will be used.

## Logical AND

| AND | $^{\wedge}expr1$ | $^{\wedge}expr2$ |
|---|---|---|

Maple syntax: `expr1 and expr2`
Length: 3

## Assignment Statement

| ASSIGN | $^{\wedge}name - seq$ | $^{\wedge}expr - seq$ |
|---|---|---|

Maple syntax: `name1, name2, ... := expr1, expr2, ...`
Length: 3

The left-hand side *name* entries must evaluate to assignable objects: `NAME`, `FUNCTION`, or `TABLEREF` structures. The right-hand side must be an expression sequence of the same length as the left-hand side.

## Binary Object

| BINARY | data | ... |
|---|---|---|

Maple syntax: none
Length: arbitrary

The `BINARY` structure can hold any arbitrary data. It is not used directly as a Maple object, but is used as storage for large blocks of data inside other Maple objects (currently only `RTABLE`s). It is also sometimes used as temporary storage space during various kernel operations.

## Break Statement

| BREAK |
|---|

Maple syntax: `break`
Length: 1

## Name Concatenation

| CATENATE | $^{\wedge}name$ | $^{\wedge}expr$ |
|---|---|---|

Maple syntax: `name || expr`
Length: 3

- If the *name* entry is one of NAME, CATENATE, LOCAL, or PARAM, and if the *expr* entry evaluates to an integer, NAME, or STRING, then the result is a NAME.
- If the *name* entry is a STRING or CATENATE that resolves to a STRING, and if the *expr* entry evaluates to an integer, NAME, or STRING, then the result is a STRING.
- If *expr* is a RANGE, then the result is to generate an EXPSEQ of NAMEs or STRINGs.

## Complex Value

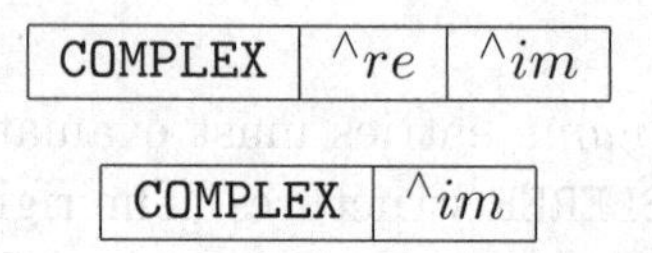

Maple syntax: `Complex(re,im)` or `re + im * I`
Length: 2 or 3

The *re* and *im* fields must point to INTPOS, INTNEG, RATIONAL, or FLOAT structures, one of the NAMEs `infinity` or `undefined`, or a SUM structure representing `-infinity`. In the length 3 case, if either *re* or *im* is a FLOAT, the other must be a FLOAT as well.

## Communications Control Structure

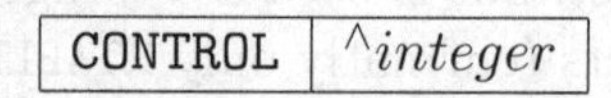

Maple syntax: none
Length: 2

This is an internal structure used in kernel to user-interface communication. Such a structure never reaches the user level, or even the mathematical parts of the kernel.

## Type Specification or Test

| DCOLON | $\wedge$*expr* | $\wedge$*type* − *expr* |
|---|---|---|

Maple syntax: `expr :: typeExpr`
Length: 3

This structure has three interpretations depending on the context in which it is used. When it appears in the header of a procedure definition, it is a typed parameter declaration. When it appears in the **local** section of a procedure or on the left side of an assignment, it is a type assertion. When it appears elsewhere (specifically in a conditional expression), it is a type test.

## Debug

| DEBUG | $\wedge$*expr1* | $\wedge$*expr2* | ... |
|---|---|---|---|

Maple syntax: none
Length: 2 or more

This is another internal-only structure. It is used by the kernel when printing error traceback information to transmit that information up the call stack.

## Equation or Test for Equality

| EQUATION | $\wedge$*expr1* | $\wedge$*expr2* |
|---|---|---|

Maple syntax: `expr1 = expr2`
Length: 3

This structure has two interpretations depending on the context in which it is used. It can be either a test for equality, or a statement of equality (not to be confused with an assignment).

## Error Statement

| ERROR | $\wedge$*expr* |
|---|---|

Maple syntax: `error "msg", arg, ...arg`
Length: 2

This represents the Maple `error` statement. The *expr* is either a single expression (if only a message was specified in the `error` statement), or an expression sequence (if arguments were also specified). The actual internal tag used for the `ERROR` structure is `MERROR`, to prevent collision with a macro defined by some C compilers.

## Expression Sequence

| EXPSEQ | ^*expr*1 | ^*expr*2 | ... |
|---|---|---|---|

Maple syntax: `expr1, expr2, ...`
Length: 1 or more

Expression sequences are available to the user as a data structure, and are also used to pass arguments to procedures. Effectively, procedures take a single argument that is an expression sequence. An expression sequence may be of length 1 (that is, an empty sequence), which is represented by the Maple symbol `NULL`, or in some contexts (such as parameters to a function call) as nothing at all.

## Floating-Point Number

| FLOAT | ^*integer*1 | ^*integer*2 | ^*attrib* − *expr* |
|---|---|---|---|

Maple syntax: `1.2`, `1.2e3`, `Float(12,34)`, `Float(infinity)`
Length: 2 (or 3 with attributes)

A floating-point number is interpreted as $integer1 * 10^{integer2}$. A floating-point number may optionally have attributes, in which case the length of the structure is 3, and the third word points to a Maple expression. This suggests that several floating-point numbers with the same value but different attributes can exist simultaneously.

The *integer2* field can optionally be one of the names `undefined` or `infinity`, in which case the `FLOAT` structure represents an undefined floating-point value (not-a-number, or NaN, in IEEE terminology), or a floating-point infinity. When *integer2* is `undefined`, *integer1* can take on different small integer values, allowing the existence of different NaNs. When *integer2* is `infinity`, *integer1* must be 1 or −1.

## For/While Loop Statement

| FOR | ^*name* | ^*from*−*expr* | ^*by*−*expr* | ^*to*−*expr* | ^*cond*−*expr* | ^*stat*−*seq* |
|---|---|---|---|---|---|---|

| FOR | $^\wedge name$ | $^\wedge in - expr$ | $^\wedge cond - expr$ | $^\wedge stat - seq$ |
|---|---|---|---|---|

Maple syntax:

```
for name from fromExpr by byExpr to toExpr
    while condExpr do
        statSeq
    end do
```

Maple syntax:

```
for name in inExpr
    while condExpr do
        statSeq
    end do
```

Length: 7 or 5

The *name* follows the same rules as in ASSIGN, except that it can also be the empty expression sequence (NULL), indicating that there is no controlling variable for the loop.

The *from-expr*, *by-expr*, *to-expr*, and *cond-expr* entries are general expressions. All are optional in the syntax of for loops and can thus be filled in with default values (1, 1, NULL, and true respectively) by the parser.

The *stat-seq* entry can be a single Maple statement or expression, a STATSEQ structure, or NULL indicating an empty loop body. An additional bit in the FOR structure's header is used to indicate whether the *stat-seq* contains any break or next statements.

## Foreign Data

| FOREIGN | ... |
|---|---|

Maple syntax: none
Length: 1 or more

This is similar to the BINARY structure, except that it is for use by components of Maple outside the kernel, such as the user interface. A FOREIGN structure is exempt from garbage collection, and it is the responsibility of the external component to free it when it is finished using it.

FOREIGN data structures can be created and managed in external code via the MaplePointer API functions. For more information, refer to ?MaplePointer.

## Function Call

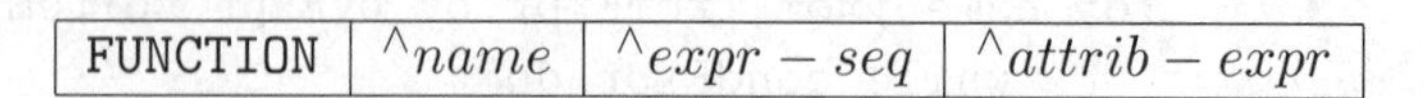


Maple syntax: name( exprSeq )
Length: 2 (or 3 with attributes)

This structure represents a function invocation (as distinct from a procedure definition that is represented by the PROC structure). The *name* entry follows the same rules as in ASSIGN, or it may be a PROC structure. The *expr-seq* entry gives the list of actual parameters, and is always an expression sequence (possibly of length 1, indicating no parameters).

## Garbage

| GARBAGE | ... |
|---|---|

Maple syntax: none
Length: 1 or more

This structure is used internally by the Maple garbage collector as a temporary object type for free space.

## Hardware Float

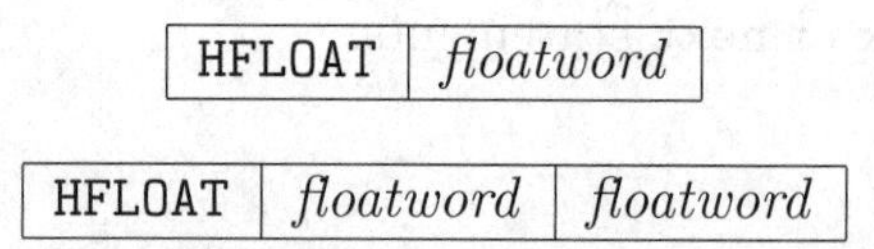


Maple syntax: none
Length: 2 on 64-bit architectures, 3 on 32-bit architectures

This structure is used to hold a hardware floating-point value. The one or two words (always 8 bytes) after the header hold the actual double-precision floating-point value. HFLOAT objects are currently not available directly to the user, but they are used internally to more efficiently transfer hardware floating-point values between RTABLEs of such values, and the Maple I/O facilities (for example, the printf and scanf families of functions).

## If Statement

| IF | ^cond–expr1 | ^stat–seq1 | ^cond–expr2 | ^stat–seq2 | ... ... | ... ... | ^stat–seqN |
|---|---|---|---|---|---|---|---|

Maple syntax:

```
if condExpr1 then
     statSeq1
elif condExpr2 then
     statSeq2
...
else statSeqN
end if
```

Length: 3 or more

This structure represents the `if ... then ... elif ... else ... end if` statement in Maple. If the length is even, the last entry is the body of an `else` clause. The remaining entries are interpreted in pairs, where each pair is a condition of the `if` or `elif` clause, followed by the associated body.

## Logical IMPLIES

| IMPLIES | ^expr1 | ^expr2 |
|---|---|---|

Maple syntax: `expr1 implies expr2`
Length: 3

## Not Equal or Test for Inequality

| INEQUAT | ^expr1 | ^expr2 |
|---|---|---|

Maple syntax: `expr1 < > expr2`
Length: 3

This structure has two interpretations, depending on the context in which it is used. It can be either a test for inequality or an inequality statement (not to be confused with an assignment).

## Negative Integer

| INTNEG | integer | integer | ... |
|---|---|---|---|

Maple syntax: $-123$
Length: 2 or more

This data structure represents a negative integer of arbitrary precision. For positive integer representation information, see the following section.

## Positive Integer

| INTPOS | *integer* | *integer* | ... |
|---|---|---|---|

Maple syntax: 123
Length: 2 or more

This data structure represents a positive integer of arbitrary precision. Integers greater than or equal to the threshold $10^{kernelopts(gmpthreshold)}$ are represented internally in a base equal to the full word size of the host machine. On 32-bit architectures, this base is $2^{32}$. On 64-bit architectures, the base is $2^{64}$. Integers in this range use the GNU Multiple Precision Arithmetic (GMP) library for integer arithmetic.

Integers less than the threshold $10^{kernelopts(gmpthreshold)}$ are represented internally in a smaller base that is also dependent on the host machine. On 32-bit architectures, this base is $10,000$. On 64-bit architectures, the base is $1,000,000,000$. The base is chosen such that the square of the base is still representable in a machine integer. Each *integer* field represents either 4 or 9 digits. The least significant digits are represented first. For example, on a 32-bit platform, the integer $123,456,789,638,747$ is represented as:

| INTPOS | 8747 | 8963 | 4567 | 123 |
|---|---|---|---|---|

Small integers are not represented by data structures at all. Instead of a pointer to an INTPOS or INTNEG structure, a small integer is represented by the bits of what would normally be a pointer. The least significant bit is 1, which makes the value an invalid pointer (since pointers must be word-aligned). Such an integer is called an *immediate integer*.

The range of integers representable in this way is $-1,073,741,823$ to $1,073,741,823$ (that is, about $\pm 10^9$) on 32-bit architectures, and $-4,611,686,018,427,387,903$ to $4,611,686,018,427,387,903$ (that is, about $\pm 4 * 10^{18}$) on 64-bit architectures. (These numbers may not seem small, but consider that the Maple maximum integer magnitude is about $2^{2,147,483,488}$ on 32-bit architectures and $2^{274,877,906,688}$ on 64-bit architectures.)

## Less Than or Equal

| LESSEQ | $^\wedge expr1$ | $^\wedge expr2$ |
|---|---|---|

Maple syntax: `expr1 <= expr2, expr2 >= expr1`
Length: 3

This structure has two interpretations, depending on the context. It can be interpreted as a relation (that is, an inequation), or as a comparison (for example, in the condition of an `if` statement, or the argument to a call to `evalb`). Maple does not have a greater-than-or-equal structure. Any input of that form is stored as a `LESSEQ` structure.

## Less Than

| LESSTHAN | $^\wedge expr1$ | $^\wedge expr2$ |
|---|---|---|

Maple syntax: `expr1 < expr2, expr2 > expr1`
Length: 3

Like the `LESSEQ` structure above, this structure has two interpretations, depending on the context. It can be interpreted as a relation (that is, an inequation), or as a comparison (for example, in the condition of an `if` statement, or the argument to a call to `evalb`).

Maple does not have a greater-than structure. Any input of that form is stored as a `LESS` structure.

## Lexically Scoped Variable within an Expression

| LEXICAL | *integer* |
|---|---|

Maple syntax: `name`
Length: 2

This represents an identifier within an expression in a procedure or module that is not local to that procedure, but is instead declared in a surrounding procedure or module scope. The *integer* field identifies which lexically scoped variable of the current procedure is being referred to. The *integer*, multiplied by 2, is an index into the *lexical-seq* structure referred to by the `PROC` DAG of the procedure. Specifically, `|integer| * 2 - 1` is the index to the `NAME` of the identifier, and `|integer| * 2` is the index to a description (`LOCAL`, `PARAM`, or `LEXICAL`) relative to the surrounding scope. The value of *integer* can be positive or negative. If positive, the original identifier is a local variable of a surrounding procedure; if negative, it is a parameter of a surrounding procedure.

## List

| LIST | ^*expr − seq* | ^*attrib − expr* |
|---|---|---|

Maple syntax: `[ expr, expr, ... ]`
Length: 2 (or 3 with attributes)

The elements of the *expr-seq* are the elements of the list. The list can optionally have attributes.

## Local Variable within an Expression

| LOCAL | *integer* |
|---|---|

Maple syntax: `name`
Length: 2

This indicates a local variable when it appears within an expression in a procedure or module. The *integer* is an index into the procedure *local-seq*. At procedure execution time, it is also an index into the internal data structure holding the active locals on the procedure activation stack, and holds private copies of the `NAME`s of the local variables (private copies in the sense that these `NAME`s are not the same as the global `NAME`s of the same name).

## Member

| MEMBER | ^*module* | ^*name* |
|---|---|---|

Maple syntax: `module :- name`
Length: 3

This structure represents a module member access in an expression. `MEMBER` objects typically do not persist when a statement is simplified. Instead, they are replaced by the actual member that they refer to (an instance of a `NAME`).

## Module Definition

| MODDEF | *param-seq* | *local-seq* | *option-seq* | *export-seq* | *stat-seq* | *desc-seq* | ... |
|---|---|---|---|---|---|---|---|

| *global-seq* | *lexical-seq* | *mod-name* |
|---|---|---|

Maple syntax:

**module** modName ( )
  **description** descSeq;
  **local** localSeq;
  **export** exportSeq;
  **global** globalSeq;
  **option** optionSeq;
  statSeq
**end module**

Length: 10

The *param-seq* points to an expression sequence describing the formal parameters of the module. Currently, Maple does not support parameterized modules, so this field always points to the sequence containing just an instance of the name `thismodule`.

The *local-seq* points to an expression sequence listing the explicitly and implicitly declared local variables. Each entry is a `NAME`. The explicitly declared variables appear first. Within the module, locals are referred to by `LOCAL` structures, the local variable number being the index into the *local-seq*.

The *export-seq* points to an expression sequence listing the exported module members. Each entry is a `NAME`. Within the module, exports are referred to by `LOCAL` structures, the local variable number being the number of elements in the *local-seq*, plus the index into the *export-seq*.

The *option-seq* points to an expression sequence of options to the module (for modules, options are the same thing as attributes). Each entry is a `NAME` or `EQUATION` specifying an option. Typical options are `load=` ... and `unload=` ...

The *stat-seq* field points to a single statement or a statement sequence (`STATSEQ`). If the module has an empty body, this is a pointer to `NULL` instead.

The *desc-seq* field points to an expression sequence of `NAME`s or `STRING`s. These are meant to provide a brief description of what the Module does, and are displayed even when `interface(verboseproc)` is less than 2.

The *global-seq* field points to a list of the explicitly declared global variables in the module (those that appeared in the `global` statement). This information is never used at run time, but it is used when simplifying nested modules and procedures to determine the binding of lexically scoped identifiers (for example, an identifier on the left side of an assignment in a nested procedure can be global if it appears in the `global` statement of a surrounding context). This information is also used at printing time, so that the `global` statement contains exactly the global identifiers that were declared in the first place.

The *lexical-seq* field points to an expression sequence of links to identifiers in the surrounding scope, if any. The sequence consists of pairs of pointers. The first pointer of each pair is to the globally unique `NAME` of the identifier; this is needed at simplification and printing time. The second pointer is a pointer to a `LOCAL`, `PARAM`, or `LEXICAL` structure which is understood to be relative to the surrounding scope. When a module definition is evaluated, the *lexical-seq* is updated by replacing each of the second pointers with a pointer to the actual object represented. The name pointers are not touched, so that the actual identifier names are still available. The *lexical-seq* for a module contains entries for any surrounding-scope identifiers used by that module or by any procedures or modules contained within it.

The *mod-name* field points to the optional name of the module. If a module name was specified when the module was declared, the name will appear there. If no module name was specified, this field will contain `NULL`.

## Module Instance

| MODULE | ^*export – seq* | ^*mod – def* | ^*local – seq* |
|---|---|---|---|

Maple syntax: none
Length: 4

Executing a module definition (`MODDEF`) results in a module instance. Each local or exported member of the module is instantiated and belongs to that instance of the module. The *export-seq* field points to an expression sequence of names of the instantiated exports (as opposed to the global names, as stored in the module definition). The *mod-def* field points back to the original module definition. The *local-seq* field points to an expression sequence of names of the instantiated local variables of the module.

## Identifier

| NAME | ^*assigned–expr* | ^*attrib–expr* | *characters* | *characters* | ... |
|---|---|---|---|---|---|

Maple syntax: name
Length: 4 or more

The *assigned-expr* field points to the assigned value of the name. If the name has no assigned value, this field is a null pointer (not a pointer to NULL). The next field points to an expression sequence of attributes of the name. If there are no attributes, this field points to the empty expression sequence (NULL). The remaining fields contain the characters making up the name, stored 4 or 8 per machine word (for 32-bit and 64-bit architectures respectively). The last character is followed by a zero-byte. Any unused bytes in the last machine word are also zero. The maximum length of a name is 268,435,447 characters on 32-bit architectures and 34,359,738,351 characters on 64-bit architectures.

## Next Statement

| NEXT |
|---|

Maple syntax: `next`
Length: 1

## Logical NOT

| NOT | ^*expr* |
|---|---|

Maple syntax: **not** `expr`
Length: 2

## Logical OR

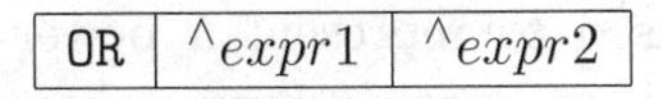


Maple syntax: `expr1` **or** `expr2`
Length: 3

## Procedure Parameter within an Expression

| PARAM | *integer* |
|---|---|

Maple syntax: `name`
Length: 2

This indicates a parameter when it appears within a procedure. The *integer* is an index into the procedure *param-seq*. Several special `PARAM` structures exist:

| PARAM | 0 |
|---|---|

This represents the Maple symbol `nargs`, the number of arguments passed when the procedure was called.

| PARAM | −1 |
|---|---|

This represents the Maple symbol `args`, the entire sequence of arguments passed when the procedure was called.

| PARAM | −2 |
|---|---|

This represents the Maple symbol `procname`, referring to the currently active procedure.

At procedure execution time, the *integer* (if positive) is used as an index into the internal data structure `Actvparams` which is part of the Maple procedure activation stack, and holds pointers to the values (which are also Maple structures, of course) of the actual parameters passed to the procedure.

## Power

| POWER | ^*expr*1 | ^*expr*2 |
|---|---|---|

Maple syntax: *expr*1^*expr*2
Length: 3

This structure is used to represent a power when the exponent is not an integer, rational, or floating-point value. When the exponent is numeric, the `POWER` structure is converted to a length 3 `PROD` structure.

## Procedure Definition

| PROC | ^*param–seq* | ^*local–seq* | ^*option–seq* | ^*rem–table* | ^*stat–seq* | ^*desc–seq* | ... |
|---|---|---|---|---|---|---|---|

| ^*global–seq* | ^*lexical–seq* |
|---|---|

Maple syntax:

**proc** ( paramSeq )
    **description** descSeq;

```
        local localSeq;
        export exportSeq;
        global globalSeq;
        option optionSeq;
        statSeq
    end proc
```

Length: 9

The *param-seq* points to an expression sequence describing the formal parameters of the procedure. Each entry is either a `NAME` or a `DCOLON` (which in turn contains a `NAME` and an expression specifying a type). Within the procedure, parameters are referred to by `PARAM` structures, the parameter number being the index into the *param-seq*.

The *local-seq* points to an expression sequence listing the explicitly and implicitly declared local variables. Each entry is a `NAME`. The explicitly declared variables appear first. Within the procedure, locals are referred to by `LOCAL` structures, the local variable number being the index into the *local-seq*.

The *option-seq* field points to an expression sequence of options to the procedure (for procedures, options are the same thing as attributes). Each entry is a `NAME` or `EQUATION` specifying an option. Typical options are `remember`, `operator`, and `‘Copyright ...‘`.

The *rem-table* field points to a hash table containing remembered values of the procedure. Entries in the table are indexed by the procedure arguments, and contain the resulting value. If there is no remember table, this field contains a pointer to `NULL`, the empty expression sequence.

The *stat-seq* field points to a single statement or a statement sequence (`STATSEQ`). If the procedure has an empty body, this is a pointer to `NULL` instead. For each procedure that is built into the kernel, there is a wrapper `PROC` that has the option `builtin` in its *option-seq*, and a single Maple integer pointed to by its *stat-seq*. The integer gives the built-in function number.

The *desc-seq* field points to an expression sequence of `NAME`s or `STRING`s. These are meant to provide a brief description of what the procedure does, and are displayed even when `interface(verboseproc)` is less than 2.

The *global-seq* field points to a list of the explicitly declared global variables in the procedure (those that appeared in the global statement). This information is never used at run time, but it is used when simplifying nested procedures to determine the binding of lexically scoped identifiers. For example, an identifier on the left side of an assignment in a nested procedure can be global if it appears in the global statement of a surrounding procedure. This information is also used at procedure printing time, so that the `global` statement will contain exactly the same global identifiers that were declared in the first place.

The *lexical-seq* field points to an expression sequence of links to identifiers in the surrounding scope, if any. The sequence consists of pairs of pointers. The first pointer of each pair is to the globally unique `NAME` of the identifier; this is needed at simplification and printing time. The second pointer is a pointer to a `LOCAL`, `PARAM`, or `LEXICAL` structure which is understood to be relative to the surrounding scope. When a procedure is evaluated (not necessarily called), the *lexical-seq* is updated by replacing each of the second pointers with a pointer to the actual object represented. The name pointers are not touched, so that the actual identifier names are still available. The *lexical-seq* for a procedure contains entries for any surrounding-scope identifiers used by that procedure or by any procedures contained within it.

## Product, Quotient, Power

| PROD | ^*expr1* | ^*expon1* | ^*expr2* | ^*expon2* | ... | ... |
|---|---|---|---|---|---|---|

Maple syntax: `expr1 ^ expon1 * expr2 ^ expon2 ...`
Length: $2n+1$

This structure is interpreted as pairs of factors and their numeric exponents. Rational or integer expressions to an integer power are expanded. If there is a rational constant in the product, this constant is moved to the first entry by the simplifier. A simple power, such as `a^2`, is represented as a `PROD` structure. More complex powers involving non-numeric exponents are represented as `POWER` structures.

## Range

| RANGE | ^*expr1* | ^*expr2* |
|---|---|---|

Maple syntax: `expr1 .. expr2`
Length: 3

## Rational

| RATIONAL | ^*integer* | ^*pos − integer* |
|---|---|---|

Maple syntax: `1/2`
Length: 3

This structure is one of the basic numeric objects in Maple. Note that this is not a division operation, but only a representation for rational numbers. Both fields must be integers (`INTPOS`, `INTNEG`, or an immediate integer) and the second must be positive.

## Read Statement

| READ | ^*expr* |
|---|---|

Maple syntax: `read expr`
Length: 2

The Maple `read` statement. The expression must evaluate to either a string or symbol (`STRING` or `NAME` structure), and specifies the name of the file to read.

## Return Statement

| RETURN | ^*expr − seq* |
|---|---|

Maple syntax: `return expr1, expr2, ...`
Length: 2

The Maple `return` statement. The expression sequence is evaluated, giving the value(s) to return.

## Rectangular Table

| RTABLE | ^*data* | ^*maple−type* | ^*ind−fn* | ^*attrib* | *flags* | *num-elems* | ... |
|---|---|---|---|---|---|---|---|

| $L_1$ | $U_1$ | ... | ... | $L_N$ | $U_N$ | $P_1$ | $P_2$ |
|---|---|---|---|---|---|---|---|

Maple syntax: `rtable(...)`
Length: `2n + p` where `n` is the number of dimensions (0 to 63), and `p` is 0, 1, or 2, depending on the number of $P_i$ parameters.

The *data* field points to either a block of memory (for dense and NAG-sparse `RTABLE`s), or to a `HASHTAB` structure (for Maple-sparse `RTABLE`s). The data block is either an object of type `BINARY`, or memory allocated directly from the operating system's storage manager when the block would be too large to be allocated as a Maple data structure. If the data block is a `BINARY` object, the *data* pointer points to the first data word, not to the object header.

The *maple-type* field points to a Maple structure specifying the data type of the elements of an `RTABLE` of Maple objects. If the `RTABLE` contains hardware objects, the *maple-type* field points to the Maple `NAME` `anything`.

The *ind-fn* pointer points to either an empty expression sequence (`NULL`), or an expression sequence containing at least one indexing function and a pointer to a copy of the `RTABLE` structure. The copy of the `RTABLE` is identical to the original, except that its *ind-fn* field refers to one less indexing function (either `NULL`, or another expression sequence containing at least one indexing function and a pointer to another copy of the `RTABLE` with one less indexing function again).

The *attrib* pointer points to an expression sequence of zero or more arbitrary attributes, which can be set by the `setattribute` function, and queried by `attributes`.

The *flags* field is a bit field containing the following subfields.

- data type - 5 bits - indicates one of several hardware datatypes or that a Maple data type (as specified by *maple-type*) is being used.
- subtype - 2 bits - indicates if the `RTABLE` is an Array, Matrix, or Vector.
- storage - 4 bits - describes the storage layout (e.g. sparse, upper triangular, etc.)
- order - 1 bit - indicates C or Fortran ordering of `RTABLE` elements.
- read only - 1 bit - indicates the `RTABLE` is to be read-only once created.
- foreign - 1 bit - indicates that the space pointed to by the *data* field does not belong to Maple, so Maple should not garbage collect it.
- eval - 1 bit - indicates if full evaluation should occur on lookup. For more information, refer to `?rtable_eval`.
- literal - 1 bit - optimization for internal type checking of data contained in an `RTABLE`.
- number of dimensions - 6 bits - the number of dimensions of the `RTABLE`, from 0 to 63.

The *num-elems* field indicates the total number of elements of storage allocated for the data. For a Maple-sparse RTABLE, *num-elems* is not used. For a NAG-sparse RTABLE, *num-elems* specifies the number of elements currently allocated, some of which might not be in use.

The remaining fields specify the upper and lower bounds of each dimension, and are stored directly as signed machine integers. The limits on bounds are $-2,147,483,648$ to $2,147,483,647$ for 32-bit architectures and $-9,223,372,036,854,775,808$ to $9,223,372,036,854,775,807$ for 64-bit architectures. The total number of elements cannot exceed the upper limit numbers either.

## Save Statement

| SAVE | $\wedge expr - seq$ |
|---|---|

Maple syntax: `save expr, expr, ...`
Length: 2

The Maple `save` statement. The expression sequence gives a list of names of objects to save, and either a file name or repository name in which to save them. The file or repository name can be specified as a NAME or STRING.

## Series

| SERIES | $\wedge expr1$ | $\wedge expr2$ | *integer* | $\wedge expr3$ | *integer* | ... | ... |
|---|---|---|---|---|---|---|---|

Maple syntax: none
Length: $2n + 2$

This is the internal representation of a series in Maple. There is no input syntax for a series; one can only arise from a computation. The first expression has the general form `x-a`, where `x` denotes the variable of the series used to do that expansion, and `a` denotes the point of expansion. The remaining entries are interpreted as pairs of coefficients and exponents. The exponents are integers, *not* pointers to integers or immediate integers. The exponents appear in increasing order. A coefficient `O(1)` (a function call to the function `O`, with parameter 1) is interpreted specially by Maple as an order term.

## Set

| SET | $\wedge expr - seq$ | $\wedge attrib - expr$ |
|---|---|---|

Maple syntax: $\{expr, expr, ...\}$
Length: 2 (or 3 with attributes)

The entries in the set's expression sequence are sorted in order of increasing memory address. This is an arbitrary but consistent order, necessary for efficiently working with sets.

## Statement Sequence

| STATSEQ | ^*stat1* | ^*stat2* | ... |
|---|---|---|---|

Maple syntax: `stat1; stat2; ...`
Length: 3 or more

This structure represents a sequence of two or more statements, and can be used wherever a single statement (for example, ASSIGN, IF, FOR) can appear. A statement sequence, containing only a single statement, is replaced by that statement. A statement sequence containing no statements is replaced by the empty expression sequence (NULL). Nested STATSEQ structures are flattened. All of the above transformations are made by the simplifier.

## Stop Maple

| STOP |
|---|

Maple syntax: `quit`, `done`, or `stop`
Length: 1

## String

| STRING | *reserved* | ^*attrib* − *expr* | *characters* | *characters* | ... |
|---|---|---|---|---|---|

Maple syntax: `"This is a string"`
Length: 4 or more

A Maple string is structurally similar to a NAME, except that it has no *assigned-value* field. The *attrib-expr* field points to an expression sequence of attributes of the string. If there are no attributes, this field points to the empty expression sequence (NULL). The remaining fields contain the characters making up the string, stored 4 or 8 per machine word (for 32-bit and 64-bit architectures respectively). The last character is followed by a zero-byte. Any unused bytes in the last machine word are also zero.

The maximum length of a string is 268, 435, 447 characters on 32-bit architectures and 34, 359, 738, 351 characters on 64-bit architectures.

## Sum, Difference

| SUM | $^\wedge expr1$ | $^\wedge factor1$ | $^\wedge expr2$ | $^\wedge factor2$ | ... | ... |
|---|---|---|---|---|---|---|

Maple syntax: `expr1 * factor1 + expr2 * factor2 ...`
Length: $2n + 1$

This structure is interpreted as pairs of expressions and their numeric factors. Rational or integer expressions with an integer factor are expanded and the factor replaced with 1. If there is a rational constant in the sum, this constant is moved to the first entry by the simplifier. Simple products, such as `a*2`, are represented as `SUM`s. More complex products involving non-numeric factors are represented as `PROD` structures.

## Table

| TABLE | $^\wedge index - func$ | $^\wedge array - bounds$ | $^\wedge hash - tab$ |
|---|---|---|---|

Maple syntax: N/A
Length: 4

This is a general table type, as created by the `table` and `array` functions in Maple. The *index-func* will point to either a `NAME` or a `PROC`. For general tables, the *array-bounds* field points to the empty expression sequence (`NULL`). For `arrays` (not to be confused with `Arrays`, which are implemented as `RTABLE`s), the *array-bounds* field refers to an expression sequence of `RANGE`s of integers. The *hash-tab* field points to a `HASHTAB` structure containing the elements.

## Table Reference

| TABLEREF | $^\wedge name$ | $^\wedge expr - seq$ | $^\wedge attrib - expr$ |
|---|---|---|---|

Maple syntax: `name [ expr ]`
Length: 3 (or 4 with attributes)

This data structure represents a table reference, or indexed name. The *name* entry follows the same rules as for `ASSIGN`, or it may be a `TABLE` or `MODULE` structure. (The parser will not generate a `TABLEREF` with a `TABLE` structure for the *name* entry, but this can arise internally.) The expression sequence contains the indices.

## Try Statement

| TRY | ^*try–stat–seq* | ^*catch––str* | ^*catch–stat–seq* | ... | ... | ^*final–stat–seq* |
|---|---|---|---|---|---|---|

Maple syntax:

**try** tryStat
  **catch** "catchStr": catchStat
  ...
  **finally** finalStat;
**end try**

Length: 3 or more

This structure represents a `try` statement, and can have an arbitrary length, depending on how many `catch` blocks there are within it, and whether or not it has a `finally` block. The *catch-strs* point to the catch string of the corresponding `catch` block. If no catch string was specified, the *catch-str* points to `NULL`. Empty *catch-stat-seqs* are also represented by pointers to `NULL`, as is an empty (but present) `finally` block.

The actual internal tag used for the `TRY` structure is `MTRY`, to prevent collision with a macro defined by some C exception handling libraries.

## Unevaluated Expression

| UNEVAL | ^*expr* |
|---|---|

Maple syntax: ' `expr` '
Length: 2

## Use Statement

| USE | ^*bindings* | ^*statseq* |
|---|---|---|

Maple Syntax:

**use** bindings in
  statseq
**end use**

Length: 3

The *bindings* component points to an expression sequence of equations whose left sides are symbols, and the *statseq* component points to a sequence of statements that form the body of the `use` statement. The right sides of the binding equations can be arbitary expressions.

The `use` statement introduces a new binding contour and binds the names that appear on the left side of the equations in *bindings*. For convenience, on input, a module `'m'` can appear among the *bindings*, and is treated as if it were the sequence `e1 = m:-e1, e2 = m:-e2, ...`, where the `ei` are the exports of `'m'`. Within the sequence *statseq* of statements, the symbols appearing on the left side of the equations in *bindings* are bound to the corresponding right sides. The previous bindings of those symbols are restored upon exit from the `use` statement. Bindings are resolved during automatic simplification.

## Logical XOR

| XOR | ^*expr1* | ^*expr2* |
|---|---|---|

Maple syntax: `expr1 xor expr2`
Length: 3

## Polynomials with Integer Coefficients modulo $n$

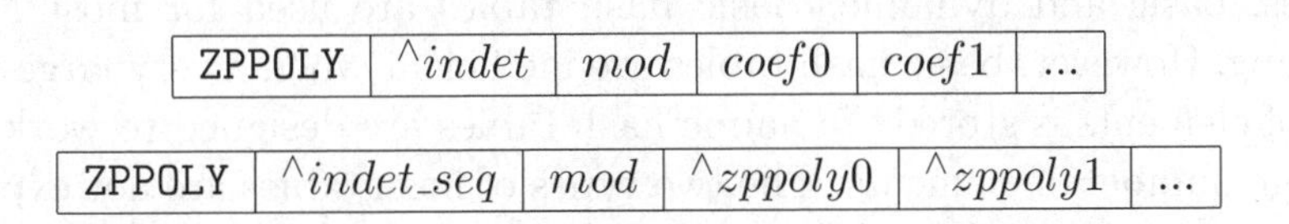

Maple Syntax: `modp1( ConvertIn( expr, indet ), n );`
Maple Syntax: `modp2( ConvertIn( expr, indet1, indet2 ), n );`

Length: `degree(zppoly)` +2 (for the zero polynomial)
Length: `degree(zppoly)` +3 (otherwise)

This is the internal representation of univariate and bivariate polynomials modulo some integer. The `modp1()` and `modp2()` front ends provide a suite of functions to work on this data structure operating in the domain of polynomials in one or two variables with integer coefficients modulo $n$, written $Z_n[x]$ or $Z_n[x, y]$, respectively. *indet_seq* is an expression sequence of the indeterminates of the polynomial (x), or (x,y). *mod* is the integer modulus of the integer domain. In a univariate polynomial the coefficients are stored in the following order.

```
(coef0*indet^0 + coef1*indet^1 + ... + coefi*indet^i) mod n
```

A bivariate polynomial contains pointers to univariate ZPPOLY structures representing the coefficients of the first indeterminate.

```
(coef0(indet2)*indet1^0 + coef1(indet2)*indet1^1 + ...) mod n
```

where each `coefi` is a univariate polynomial in `indet1` mod $n$.

All coefficients are stored including zero coefficients. The leading coefficient is always non-zero.

## A.3 The Use of Hashing in Maple

An important factor in achieving the overall efficient performance of Maple is the use of hash-table-based algorithms for critical functions. Tables are used in both simplification and evaluation, as well as for less critical functions. For simplification, Maple keeps a single copy of each expression, or subexpression, during a session. This is done by keeping all objects in a table. In procedures, the `remember` option specifies that the result of each computation of the procedure is to be stored in a *remember table* associated with the procedure. Finally, tables are available to the user as one of the Maple data types.

All table searching is done by hashing. The are two types of hash tables, basic and dynamic. Basic hash tables are used for most Maple hashing. However, basic hash tables are inefficient when a very large number of elements is stored. Dynamic hash tables are designed to work with a large number of elements. The two types of hash tables are not exposed. When a basic hash table becomes full, it is automatically converted to a dynamic hash table.

### Basic Hash Tables

The algorithm used for the basic hash tables is direct chaining, except that the chains are dynamic vectors instead of the typical linked lists. The two data structures used to implement hash tables are `HASHTAB` and `HASH`.

#### Hash Table

| HASHTAB | $\wedge hash-chain1$ | $\wedge hash-chain2$ | ... |
|---|---|---|---|

Maple syntax: none
Length: $2^n + 1$

This is an internal data structure with no Maple syntax equivalent. It is used in the representation of tables within Maple. Each entry points to a hash chain (a `HASH` structure), or is a null pointer if no entry has been created in that bucket yet. The size of a `HASHTAB` structure depends on the type of table and the platform, but is always a power of 2 plus one.

### Hash Chain

| HASH | *key* | ^*expr1* | *key* | ^*expr2* | ... | ... |
|---|---|---|---|---|---|---|

Maple syntax: none
Length: $2n + 1$

Each table element is stored as a pair of consecutive entries in a hash bucket vector. The first entry of this pair is the hash key, and the second is a pointer to a stored value. In some cases (for example, procedure remember tables, user defined tables), the key is also a pointer. In other cases, the key is a hashed value (for example, the simplification table, the symbol table). The key cannot have the value zero (or the null pointer) since this is used to indicate the bottom of the bucket.

## Dynamic Hash Tables

The Maple dynamic hash table is a complex data structure. A complete description of the algorithms is not given. The following is a brief description of the structure.

Instead of using a flat, fixed length directory, Maple dynamic hash tables use a tree structure with contiguous bits from the hash key to select a child. A child of a directory can be a subdirectory or a hash chain. For example, a top-level directory may use the first 10 bits to index 1024 children. One of its children may be a directory that uses, say, the next 8 bits of the key to index 256 children.

A hash chain in a dynamic table stores elements using key value pairs (in the same way that a hash chain does in a basic hash table). The first n bits of the keys in a hash chain are identical, where n is the number of bits required to locate the hash chain. The remaining bits are arbitrary. Using the example in the previous paragraph, the elements of a hash chain that is a child of the directory with 256 children have hash keys that are identical in the first 18 bits.

When a hash chain with unused bits overflows, it is split into two. This may require creating a subdirectory with two children or doubling the size of the hash chain's parent directory. In either case, another bit from the hash key is introduced for indexing. This bit is used to divide the elements of the old chain into the two new chains. If the hash chain has no unused bits for indexing, the chain grows as needed. This growth occurs only if many elements are inserted with identical hash keys.

## The Simplification Table

By far, the most important table maintained by the Maple kernel is the *simplification table*. All simplified expressions and subexpressions are stored in the simplification table. The main purpose of this table is to ensure that simplified expressions have a unique instance in memory. Every expression, which is entered into Maple or generated internally, is checked against the simplification table and, if found, the new expression is discarded and the old one is used. This task is done by the simplifier which recursively simplifies (applies all the basic simplification rules) and checks against the table. Garbage collection deletes the entries in the simplification table that cannot be reached from a global name or from a live local variable.

The task of checking for equivalent expressions within thousands of subexpressions would not be feasible if it were not done with the aid of hashing. Every expression is entered in the simplification table using its signature as a key. The signature of an expression is a hashing function itself, with one very important attribute: signatures of trivially equivalent expressions are equal. For example, the signatures of the expressions $a + b + c$ and $c + a + b$ are identical; the signatures of $a * b$ and $b * a$ are also identical. If two expressions' signatures disagree then the expressions cannot be equal at the basic level of simplification.

Searching for an expression in the simplification table is done by:

- Simplifying recursively all of its components
- Applying the basic simplification rules
- Computing its signature and searching for this signature in the table

If the signature is found, then a full comparison is performed (taking into account that additions and multiplications are commutative) to verify that it is the same expression. If the expression is found, the one in the table is used and the searched one is discarded. A full comparison of expressions has to be performed only when there is a collision of signatures.

Since simplified expressions are guaranteed to have a unique occurrence, it is possible to test for equality of simplified expressions using a single pointer comparison. Unique representation of identical expressions is a crucial ingredient to the efficiency of tables, hence also the `remember` option. Also, since the relative order of objects is preserved during garbage collection, this means that sequences of objects can be ordered by machine address. For example, sets in Maple are represented this way. The set operations, such as union or intersection, can be done in linear time by merging sorted sequences. Sorting by machine address is also available to the user with the `sort` command.

## The Name Table

The simplest use of hashing in the Maple kernel is the *name table*. This is a symbol table for all global names. Each key is computed from the name's character string and the entry is a pointer to the data structure for the name. The name table is used to locate global names formed by the lexical scanner or by name concatenation. It is also used by functions that perform operations on all global names. These operations include:

1. Marking for garbage collection
2. Saving a Maple session environment in a file
3. Maple functions `anames` and `unames` which return all assigned and unassigned global names, respectively

## Remember Tables

A remember table is a hash table in which the argument(s) to a procedure call are stored as the table index, and the result of the procedure call is stored as the table value. Because a simplified expression in Maple has a unique instance in memory, the address of the arguments can be used as the hash function. Hence, searching a remember table is very fast.

There are several kernel functions which use remember tables including, `evalf`, `series`, `divide`, `normal`, `expand`, `diff`, `readlib`, and `frontend`. The functions `evalf`, `series`, and `divide` are handled internally in a special way for the following reasons:

- `evalf` and `series` need to store some additional environment information (`'Digits'` for evalf and `'Order'` for series). Consequently, the entries for these are extended with the precision information. If a result is requested with the same or less precision than what is stored in the table, it is retrieved and rounded. If a result is produced with more precision than what is stored, it is replaced in the table.
- `evalf` remembers only function calls (this includes named constants); it does not remember the results of arithmetic operations.

- If a division operation succeeds and the divisor is a nontrivial polynomial, the divide function stores the quotient in its remember table. Otherwise nothing is stored in the remember table.

If `option remember` is specified together with `option system`, at garbage collection time the remember table entries which refer to expressions no longer in use elsewhere in the system are removed. This provides a relatively efficient use of remembering that does not waste storage for expressions that have disappeared from the expression space.

## Maple Language Arrays and Tables

Tables and arrays are provided as data types in the Maple language via the `table` and `array`[1] functions. An array is a table for which the component indices must be integers lying within specified bounds. Tables and arrays are implemented using the Maple internal hash tables. Because of this, sparse arrays are equally as efficient as dense arrays. A table object consists of the following.

1. Index bounds (for arrays only)
2. A hash table of components
3. An indexing function

The components of a table `T` are accessed using a subscript syntax (for example, `T[a,b*cos(x)]`). Since a simplified expression is guaranteed to have a unique instance in memory, the address of the simplified index is used as the hash key for a component. If no component exists for a given index, then the indexed expression is returned.

The semantics of indexing into a table are described by its indexing function. Aside from the default, general indexing, some indexing functions are provided by the Maple kernel. Other indexing functions are loaded from the library or are supplied by the user.

## Maple Language Rectangular Tables

Rectangular tables (as implemented by the `RTABLE` structure), can use a variety of storage formats. One format, Maple-sparse, is identical to that used in tables and arrays, namely a hash table. There is another sparse format, NAG-sparse, which uses one vector for each dimension to record

[1]**Note:** Unlike the `array` command, the `Array` command creates a rectangular table, which is described in the following subsection.

**Table A.2** Select Supported Maple Platforms

| Hardware | Operating System |
|---|---|
| Intel Pentium Based PC | Microsoft Windows |
| | Linux |
| Apple Power Macintosh | Mac OS |
| Sun SPARC | Sun OS/Solaris |
| Silicon Graphics Iris | IRIX |
| Hewlett Packard PA-RISC | HP-UX |
| IBM RS/6000 | AIX |
| DEC Alpha | Digital UNIX/Compaq Tru64 |

indices, and a third vector to record the values of the entries. The majority of `RTABLE` storage formats are dense, the simplest being the rectangular. Other dense formats include upper-triangular and band, where storage is allocated only for the upper triangle or a band of elements respectively. To the user, rectangular tables manifest themselves as objects of type `Array`, `Matrix`, `Vector[row]`, and `Vector[column]`. Note that an `Array` is not the same thing as an `array`. For definitions, refer to `?Array` and `?array`.

## A.4 Portability

The Maple kernel and the command-line interface are not tied to any one operating system or hardware architecture. The Maple kernel is designed to be portable to any system which supports a C compiler, a flat address space, and a 32-bit or 64-bit word size. Table A.2 lists some platforms on which Maple is supported (refer to the installation instructions for a list of currently supported operating system versions).

The majority of the source code comprising the kernel is the same across all platforms. Extensive use of macros and conditional compilation take care of platform dependencies, such as word size, byte ordering, storage alignment requirements, differences in hardware floating point support, and sometimes, C compiler bugs.

The Maple library is interpreted by the Maple kernel. Therefore, other than issues such as maximum object size, it is completely independent of the underlying architecture.

The Maple graphical user interface has two versions, the standard worksheet and the classic worksheet (not available on Macintosh). The standard worksheet is implemented in Java, which is platform independent. The classic worksheet is implemented in C and $C$++, and makes use of a platform independent user interface class library to achieve portability. The Maplet User Interface Customization System (available in both worksheet versions) is written in Java with some native libraries. The Java portion is identical on all platforms.

# Index


%, 204
&, 33

accuracy, 223, 225, 229, 297
algebraic functions, 399
anames, 427
and, 401
AND internal data structure, 401
animations, 301
  data structures of, 301
  static form of, 302
  with backdrops, 304
  with display, 303, 306
appendto, 217, 383, 384
args, 18, 48
arguments, 251
  not passed, 341
  sequence of, 18
Array, 234
array, 428
Arrays, 232
arrays, 22, 214, 232
  and hardware floats, 232
  hardware floating-point, 234
  initializing, 23
  sorting, 8
assign, 20
ASSIGN internal data structure, 401
assignment
  multiple, 288
assignment statements, 401
assume, 21, 37
assumptions, 21
atomic, 60
audience, 1
automatic simplification, 20

backdrops, 304
BesselJ, 232
Beta, 226
binary, 401
BINARY internal data structure, 401
binding list, 105
break, 48, 401
BREAK internal data structure, 401
buffered files, 190
  flushing, 216

C
  notes, 220
call by reference, 340
  ANYTHING, 340
  CALL_ONLY, 340
  RETURN_ONLY, 340
callback function, 384
Cartesian product
  sequence of sets, 22
CATENATE internal data structure, 402
classic worksheet, 2
close, 194
CodeGeneration, 319–330
  calling functions, 320
  Define command, 327
  extensibility, 324–330
  intermediate code, 323
  intermediate form, 324
  language definition, 327
  language definition model, 329
  Printer module, 325
  translation process, 321
  using a new language, 330

coeff, 399
COLOR, 308
  HUE, 259
  POLYGONS, 308
  RGB, 262
color, 255, 308
  adding, 312, 315
color tables, 309, 310
  gray scale, 311
  HUE, 310
columns
  printing, 187, 214
  reading, 204
command-line version, 2
commands
  long names of, 252
compiled code
  using in Maple, 330–374
  using Maple in, 374–391
Complex, 402
COMPLEX internal data structure, 402
complex numbers, 236
  imaginary unit, 35
computing
  areas, 95
  circumferences, 95
concatenation, 70, 402
constants
  defining numeric, 238
constructors, 108
CONTROL internal data structure, 402
control, flow of, 399
conversions, 342
converting
  expressions to strings, 275, 310
  grids to polygons, 315
  integers to string, 217
  meshes to polygons, 273, 284, 315
  strings to bytes, 217
  strings to expressions, 30, 218
  to formatted strings, 219
  to PLOToptions, 267, 286
CopyFile, 198, 210
Copyright, 57
coverage, 87
customer feedback, 3

data
  from other applications, 185
  reading from files, 187
  saving to file, 186
data structures, 39
  for animations, 301
  for plotting, 254–256, 262
  internal, *see* internal data structures
  manipulation, 399
DCOLON internal data structure, 403
DEBUG internal data structure, 403
debugopts, 87
define_external, 334
description, 50
diff, 70, 399
  extending, 39
Digits, 12, 224, 235, 237
  evalhf, 228
digits, number of, 224
display
  insequence, 303
divide, 399
done, 381, 420
dsolve, 14

efficiency, 22, 223, 229, 234, 239, 297, 298

embedding 2-D graphics in 3-D, 268, 269, 277
encapsulation, 43, 66
`end`, 47
`end module`, 47
enumerated types, 339
equality, 403
EQUATION internal data structure, 403
`error`, 403
ERROR internal data structure, 403
errors
  catastrophic cancellation, 238, 241
  roundoff, 236
`eval`, 16, 31
`evalb`, 20, 399
`evalf`, 12, 224, 227, 399, 427
  extending, 238
  new constants, 238
  new functions, 240
`evalhf`, 227, 399
  arrays, 232–234
  `Digits`, 228
  structured objects, 232, 233
  `var`, 234
`evaln`, 399
evaluating
  parsed strings, 218
evaluation
  full, 16
  numerical, 224
  using hardware floats, 227
  using software floats, 224
evaluators, 398
event, numeric, 236
`expand`, 399, 400
`export`, 44, 52
exported local variables, 45, 52
exported variables
  vs. local variables, 118
exports, 52
expressions
  converting from strings, 30
  reading from terminal, 28
EXPSEQ internal data structure, 404
extending
  commands, 39
  `convert`, 289
  `diff`, 39
  `evalf`, 238
  `simplify`, 40
  `type`, 31
extensibility, 66
extension mechanism, 70
external calling, 330–374
  argument passing conventions, 338
  array data formats, 337
  custom wrapper, 331, 350
  direct calling, 331, 332
  Maple-generated wrapper, 331, 338
  other data formats, 337
  scalar data formats, 336
  string data formats, 337
  structured data formats, 336
  types, 335

`fclose`, 194
`feof`, 195
`fflush`, 216
file descriptors, 192, 194
`filepos`, 194
files, 190
  appending to, 193
  binary, 190
  buffered, 190, 216
  closing, 187, 194
  creating, 187, 193

current position in, 194
default, 191, 197
deleting, 196
descriptors of, 192, 194
detecting end of, 195
flushing, 216
length of, 195
opening, 187, 192, 193
printing bytes to, 210
printing columns to, 187, 214
printing formatted, 186, 210
printing strings to, 210
RAW, 190
READ, 191
reading bytes from, 197
reading columns from, 189, 204
reading formatted, 189
reading lines from, 197
reading remainder of, 198
redirecting default, 217
removing, 196
scanning, 189, 198
status of, 195
STREAM, 190
terminal, 191
text, 190
truncating, 193
unbuffered, 190
WRITE, 191
FLOAT internal data structure, 404
floating-point numbers, 223, 404
$n$-digit machine, 224
accuracy of, 225
and new constants, 238
and new functions, 240
bases of, 225
digits of, 224, 225
hardware, 227, 236, 297
hardware or software, 229
limitations, 235
models of, 235
precision, 235
representation of zero, 236
roundoff errors, 236
software, 224, 235, 297
zero, 236
flow of control, 399
fopen, 193
fopen C function, 383, 384
for loop, 405
FOR internal data structure, 405
foreign data, 405
FOREIGN internal data structure, 405
format strings, 187, 189, 199, 211
fprintf, 186, 210
free, 389
fremove, 196
fscanf, 189, 198
function call, 406
FUNCTION internal data structure, 406
function table, 65
functions
algebraic, 399
defining numeric, 240
numeric and symbolic, 242
garbage collection, 401, 405, 406, 426, 428
GARBAGE internal data structure, 406
generic programming, 117, 124, 125, 129
generic programs, 44
*Getting Started Guide*, 2
global, 51
global options, 258, 272
global variables, 21
interactive session, 20

referencing, 51
graphical interface
versions, 2
graphics, programming with, 245
`GRID`, 255
converting to polygons, 273
gridpoints, 291, 296
`group`, 78

Hamiltonians, 34, 35, 40
associativity of, 40
inverse of, 37
hardware float, 406
hardware floating-point numbers, 227, 235, 236, 297
and arrays, 232
and structured objects, 232
base of, 228
digits of, 228, 232
`has`, 399
HASH internal data structure, 425
hash tables, 424
basic, 424
dynamic, 425
hashing, 427
HASHTAB internal data structure, 424
`help`, 386
`hfarray`, 214
structured objects, 232
HFLOAT internal data structure, 406
histograms, 258, 263
`history`, 383

`I`, 35
IEEE standard, 224, 236
`if`, 407
IF internal data structure, 407
imaginary part
sign preservation, 236
immediate integer, 408
immutable state, 110
implementations
vs. interfaces, 118
implicit scoping rules, 58
`implies`, 407
IMPLIES internal data structure, 407
`indets`, 399
inequality, 407
INEQUAT internal data structure, 407
infinite recursion, 35
`infinity`, 236
infix, 34
`infolevel`
`all`, 41
`simplify`, 41
input
formatted, 198
from a file, 27
from the terminal, 27, 28
interactive, 27
prompting for, 27
`Int`, 227
`int`, 227
integers, 408
immediate, 408
negative, 408
positive, 408
integration
numerical, 225, 227
interactive
input, 27
session, 20
`interface`, 35, 205
`indentamount`, 208
`labelling`, 208
`labelwidth`, 208
`prettyprint`, 207

screenwidth, 206, 208
verboseproc, 208
interfaces, 118
manipulation, 119
vs. implementations, 118
internal data structures, 400
AND, 401
ASSIGN, 401
BINARY, 401
BREAK, 401
CATENATE, 402
COMPLEX, 402
CONTROL, 402
DCOLON, 403
DEBUG, 403
EQUATION, 403
ERROR, 403
EXPSEQ, 404
FLOAT, 404
FOR, 405
FOREIGN, 405
FUNCTION, 406
GARBAGE, 406
HASH, 425
HASHTAB, 424
HFLOAT, 406
IF, 407
IMPLIES, 407
INEQUAT, 407
INTNEG, 408
INTPOS, 408
length, 400
LESSEQ, 409
LESSTHAN, 409
LEXICAL, 409
LIST, 410
LOCAL, 410
MEMBER, 410
MODDEF, 410
MODULE, 412
NAME, 412
NEXT, 413
NOT, 413
OR, 413
PARAM, 413
POWER, 414
PROC, 414
PROD, 416
RANGE, 416
RATIONAL, 416
READ, 417
RETURN, 417
RTABLE, 417, 428
SAVE, 419
SERIES, 419
SET, 420
STATSEQ, 420
STOP, 420
STRING, 420
SUM, 421
TABLE, 421, 428
TABLEREF, 421
TRY, 422
UNEVAL, 422
USE, 422
XOR, 423
ZPPOLY, 423
internal functions, 398
internal organization, 397
internal representations of data types, 400
INTNEG internal data structure, 408
INTPOS internal data structure, 408
*Introductory Programming Guide*, 2
iostatus, 195

kernel, 398
supported platforms, 429
Klein bottle, 284

`last_name_eval`, 60
*Learning Guide*, 2
`length`, 399
LESSEQ internal data structure, 409
LESSTHAN internal data structure, 409
LEXICAL internal data structure, 409
lexical scoping, 6
  rules, 7, 58
lexically scoped variable, 409
`libmaple.dylib` file, 390
`libmaplec.a` file, 390
`libmaplec.dylib` file, 390
`libmaplec.sl` file, 390
`libmaplec.so` file, 390
`libname`, 386
library, 398
`Limit`, 227
`limit`, 227
limits
  numerical, 227
`LinearAlgebra`, 78
`LinkedList`, 80
LIST internal data structure, 410
lists, 410
  appending elements to, 250
`load`, 57
`local`, 52
LOCAL internal data structure, 410
local options, 258, 271, 286
local variables, 26, 410
  escaped, 19
  exported, 45, 52
  invoking procedures, 19
  outside their procedure, 19
  referencing, 52
  returning, 22
  vs. exported variables, 118
logical AND, 401
logical IMPLIES, 407
logical XOR, 423
`lprint`, 206

`MakeIteration`, 15
`MakeZn`, 59
`malloc` C function, 389
Mandelbrot set, 248
manual
  audience, 1
  conventions, 3
  set, 2
`map`, 399
  in procedures, 6
Maple
  using Compiled Code in, 330–374
  using in compiled code, 374–391
*Maple Getting Started Guide*, 2
*Maple Introductory Programming Guide*, 2
*Maple Learning Guide*, 2
`Maple_floats`, 236
`maplec.dll` file, 389, 390
`maplec.h` file, 376, 377, 380, 386
`maplec.lib` file, 389, 390
Maplet
  applications, 2
  User Interface Customization System, 2, 430
`Maplets` package, 398
math engine, 398
MATLAB, 243
Matrices, 214
  reading, 215
  writing, 215
`member`, 56, 100
MEMBER internal data structure, 410

MEMBER objects, 410
memory usage, 389
`MESH`, 256
  converting to polygons, 273
messages, 110
microwave circuit analysis, 280
MODDEF internal data structure, 410
modeling objects, 108
`module`, 44, 47, 60, 410
MODULE internal data structure, 412
`moduledefinition`, 60
modules, 43
  and types, 60
  declarations, 50
  definition, 44, 47, 51
  definition syntax, 47
  description, 50
  error reporting, 50
  exports, 110
  implicit scoping rules, 58
  lexical scoping rules, 58
  manipulation, 87
  members of, 52
  membership tests, 56
  named, 49
  nested, 58
  options, 57
  parameterized, 59
  referencing global variables, 51
  referencing local variables, 52
  referring to, 48
  types of variables in, 118
  use for new packages, 78
  versus procedures, 44–46
`moemapi.h` file, 381
`mplshlib.h` file, 375
`mpltable.h` file, 375
multiple assignments, 288

`name`, 413
NAME internal data structure, 412
name table, 427
named modules, 49
names
  with a tilde, 21
`nargs`, 48
negative integer, 408
nested modules, 58
nested procedures, 5, 17
neutral operators, 33
  defining, 34
  infix, 34
newline character, 190
Newton's method, 14, 230
`next`, 48, 413
NEXT internal data structure, 413
`nops`, 23
`not`, 413
NOT internal data structure, 413
numeric estimate, 14
numeric event, 236
numerical integration, 225, 227
numerical limits, 227
numerical programming, 223
numerical sums, 227
numerics, 236

objects, 44, 108
  modeling, 108
`omexample.c` file, 390
`op`, 399
`open`, 193
OpenMaple, 374–391
  `ALGEB` data type, 375, 378
  basic API functions, 376–379
  call-back functions, 380–386
  `callBackCallBack` function, 380, 384, 386

data types, 375
errorCallBack function, 378, 380–384
EvalMapleStatement API function, 376, 377, 379, 382
EXT_DECL modifier, 375
file structure, 389–390
Mac OS X, 390
UNIX, 390
Windows, 390
FLOAT32 data type, 375
FLOAT64 data type, 375
help database, 386–389
retrieving a help page, 386
setting the path, 386
INTEGER16 data type, 375
INTEGER32 data type, 375
INTEGER64 data type, 375
INTEGER8 data type, 375
interface overview, 375
M_BOOL data type, 375
M_DECL modifier, 375, 380
M_INT data type, 375
MapleHelp function, 386, 389
MapleLibName function, 386
MapleRaiseError API function, 378
MCallBack function, 380
MCallBackVector function, 380
MKernelVector, 380
queryInterrupt function, 380, 384
readLineCallBack function, 380, 383, 385
redirectCallBack function, 380, 383
RestartMaple API function, 376, 379
sample program, 390–391
StartMaple API function, 376, 377, 379, 380, 387
statusCallBack function, 380–382
StopMaple API function, 376, 379
streamCallBack function, 380, 385
streams, 384–387
advantages, 386
technical issues, 389
textCallBack function, 380, 382–384, 386
using Microsoft Visual C/CC++, 375
operator rebinding, 106
operators, 33
*, 35
custom, 33
neutral, 33
options
converting to PLOToptions, 267, 286
global, 258, 272
local, 258, 271, 286
processing, 252
type equals numeric, 14
or, 413
OR internal data structure, 413
organization
internal, 397
output
controlling, 205
rounding, 187

package, 57
packages, 43, 78
exports, 78
in the standard library, 78
table-based, 78
use modules for, 78
using interactively, 79

PARAM internal data structure, 413
parameters
  sequence of, 18
  within procedures, 413
`parse`, 30, 218
partition, 27
partitioning, 8
pipes, 192
plot drivers, 256
plotting, 246, 249
  animations, 301
  `AXESSTYLE`, 262
  `COLOR`, 258
  colors, 275
  `CURVES`, 257, 258, 262
  data structures, 254–256, 259, 262
  formulæ, 246, 252
  functions, 247, 252, 288
  `GRID`, 264
  `MESH`, 265
  non-numeric values, 257, 287, 291, 297
  numerical approximations, 224
  options, 248, 249
  `POINTS`, 258
  `POLYGONS`, 258, 262, 269
  `SCALING`, 269
  `STYLE`, 263
  `TEXT`, 258, 275
  undefined values, 287, 291, 297
  with `plottools`, 273
polygon meshes, 272, 281
  cutting faces of, 281
  stellating, 283
`POLYGONS`
  `COLOR`, 308
  converting from grids or meshes, 273
  convex, 269, 287
portablility, 429
positive integer, 408
POWER internal data structure, 414
powers, 414, 416
precision, 238
  floating-point numbers, 235
preface, 1
`print`, 207, 232, 385
`printf`, 210, 381, 385
printing, 206, 207
  bytes, 210
  columns, 214
  formatted, 186, 187, 210
  strange expressions, 19
  strings, 210
  to files, 186
`printlevel`, 381
priority queue, 111
`proc`, 44
PROC internal data structure, 414
procedures
  as returned objects, 22
  call formats, 340
  defining, 414
  dispatching, 99
  execution details, 41
  nested, 5, 9, 17
  parameters within, 413
  passing information, 22
  passing input to, 27
  that return procedures, 14
processing options, 252
`procname`, 48
PROD internal data structure, 416
products, 416
programming

generic, 44, 117, 124, 125, 129
numerical, 223
with color, 308
with graphics, 245
with plot structures, 266

Quaternions, 34, 35, 40
associativity of, 40
inverse of, 37
quaternions, 75
quick-sort algorithm, 8
`quit`, 381, 397, 420
quotient field, 129
quotients, 416

`rand`, 11, 14
random floating point numbers, 11
random distribution, 11
random numbers
generating, 11
range, 416
RANGE internal data structure, 416
rational, 416
RATIONAL internal data structure, 416
`read`, 417
READ internal data structure, 417
readability
of code, 6
`readbytes`, 197
`readdata`, 189, 204
reading
bytes from files, 197
columns, 204
data, 187
expressions from terminal, 28
from `default`, 197
lines from files, 197
remainder of file, 198
statements, 204
strings from terminal, 27
`readline`, 27, 195, 197, 383
`ReadRows`, 203
`readstat`, 28, 219, 383
advantages, 28
`record`, 57
records, 72
instantiating, 72
representing quaternions, 75
types, 74
rectangular tables, 428
`REF`, 343
reference
call by, 340
remember tables, 36, 240, 427
`return` statement, 48, 417
RETURN internal data structure, 417
`RGB`, 255
root finding, 14
rotating plots, 274
rounding, 225
roundoff errors, 236, 237
catastrophic cancellation, 238, 241
IEEE standard, 237
increasing precision, 238
similar magnitudes, 237
`rtable`, 417, 428
RTABLE internal data structure, 417, 428
rtables, 211, 214, 215, 232

`samples` directory, 46
`save`, 419
SAVE internal data structure, 419
`protect`, 198
scanning

files, 189, 198
strings, 219
scoping rules, 6
searching, 426
selection operation, 18
sequence of sets
Cartesian product, 22
sequences
of arguments, 251
of statements, 420
`series`, 399, 427
SERIES internal data structure, 419
SET internal data structure, 420
sets, 19
shadows, 276
`Shapes`, 58, 94
object-oriented approach, 115
`shift`
multivariate function, 18
univariate function, 17
sign
of zero, 236
simplification table, 426
`simplify`
extending, 40
Smith charts, 280
software floating-point numbers, 224, 235, 297
accuracy of, 225
base of, 225
digits of, 224, 225
solutions
analytical, 224
numerical, 224
`sort`, 427
sorting, 8
`sprintf`, 219
`sscanf`, 219
standard worksheet, 2
STATSEQ internal data structure, 420
`stop`, 381, 420
STOP internal data structure, 420
`streamcall`, 385
STRING internal data structure, 420
strings, 420
converting to expressions, 30
parsing, 30
reading from terminal, 27
submodules, 58
`subsop`, 399
`Sum`, 227
`sum`, 227
SUM internal data structure, 421
sums, 421
numerical, 227
suppressing
symbolic evaluation, 227
system
integrity, 374

`table`, 428
TABLE internal data structure, 421, 428
table references, 421
TABLEREF internal data structure, 421
tables, 421
terminators, 28, 218
`thismodule`, 48
tilde, 21
tilings, 278
Truchet, 279
`trace`, 57, 381
transforming plots, 281
Truchet tilings, 279
`try`, 232, 422
TRY internal data structure, 422
type

record, 74
`type`, 400
extending, 31
`typematch`, 40
types
and modules, 60
checking, 27, 32, 250
defining new, 31, 35
enumerated, 339
matching, 259
structured, 32

`unapply`, 15
unbuffered files, 190
`undefined`, 236
UNEVAL internal data structure, 422
unevaluated expressions, 229, 422
uniform distribution, 11
uniform random number generator, 11
`unload`, 57
`use`, 46, 103, 422
USE internal data structure, 422
user input, 27, 30
user interface, 398
`userinfo`, 41

variables
exported vs. local, 118
global, 20, 21
identifying, 20
lexically scoped, 409
local, 19, 26, 410
scope of, 6
unassigning, 21
undeclared, 7
vector fields, 286
Vectors, 214, 215
read, 215
write, 215
version
classic worksheet, 2
command-line, 2
standard worksheet, 2

worksheet
classic, 2
graphical interface, 2
standard, 2
versions, 2
wrapper, 331
custom, 331, 350
Maple-generated, 331, 338
`writebytes`, 210
`writedata`, 187, 214
`writeline`, 210
`writeto`, 217, 383, 384

`xor`, 423
XOR internal data structure, 423

zero
floating-point representation, 236
sign of, 236
ZPPOLY internal data structure, 423